LIFE SCIENCE

All Creatures Great And Small

Michael J. Spear
Science Department
LOVE Christian Academy
Nanuet, New York

LIFE SCIENCE

ALL CREATURES GREAT AND SMALL

Published by:

Spear Printing Company
15 Goshen Avenue
Washingtonville, New York 10992
914-496-3611   FAX: 914-496-1715

ABOUT THE AUTHOR

Michael J. Spear instructing students in outdoor living and the natural sciences at a summer camp, Chenango County, in central New York State.

The author is a native of Washingtonville where his interest in nature grew from the farms, ponds and fields of Orange County, New York. Mr. Spear has helped guide the interests of young boys and girls for more than two decades at science and outdoor living camps in New York State.

Saint Thomas of Canterbury Elementary School in Cornwall-on-Hudson and John S. Burke Catholic High School in Goshen, N.Y., provided the foundation and motivation for college studies. Mr. Spear's Bachelor's Degree in Forest Biology was earned at the College of Environmental Sciences and Forestry in Syracuse, New York. He has a concurrent degree in Biology awarded by Syracuse University. His Master's Degree was earned through private and public colleges in the Hudson River valley.

Mr. Spear is married and has seven children. He and his family reside at 72 Goshen Avenue in the Village of Washingtonville, NY, 10992.

Seton Home Study School Edition

SPECIAL THANKS TO

Daniel
Elena
Emily
Gabriele
Jane
John
Rachel
Mr. and Mrs. Elmer J. Spear
Mr. and Mrs. John M. Spear
Mrs. Lynn Harter
Brigette Olejniczak
Spear Printing Company, Inc.
Washingtonville Pediatrics

PREFACE

TO THE STUDENT

The vocabulary in <u>LIFE SCIENCE All Creatures Great And Small</u> has not been filtered to remove words you might not know and understand. As you read, many words take on meaning from their use in the text. Do not skip words you do not know. Look up words new to you and learn them! If the scientific names are difficult, you can get friendly and just use their initials. Study hard, work harder and learn plenty. It is my hope that you will keep this book and use it again and again.

TO THE PARENT

The text of <u>LIFE SCIENCE All Creatures Great And Small</u> is written with the idea that your child will learn what is expected of him or her. Plenty is expected and plenty can be learned. The text covers only the basic ideas of most topics. It does so clearly with ample review questions to reinforce the essential material. Difficult vocabulary is not to be avoided but learned. Scientific names can be easily handled by reading only their initials when the common name is also in the sentence.

TO THE TEACHER

Your students will be best served by <u>LIFE SCIENCE All Creatures Great And Small</u> if you use my two T's, M's and E's:

Teach the Top - Measure the Middle - Emphasize the Essentials.

Teach the top means to teach the very highest levels possible with your students, and then go just a little higher. Expect the very most in class. Measure the middle reminds you to test and evaluate the students based on the information that appears most often and is given clear emphasis. Require responses for information that will appear most often in later courses and in life. Don't quiz students on minute details of fact on one hand; on the other, don't expect them to present essays on the great ideas of life science. Emphasize the essentials requires memorization and practice, lots of vocabulary and more review than usual. Buttress the basics so that your students will <u>never</u> loose them.

Scientific names can be easily handled by reading only their initials when the common name is also in the sentence. It is important that students not get bogged down by the scientific terms. They should practice them orally and in writing, so they become confident in using them.

Many of the review questions instruct the student to write out the complete sentence or statement. Do not cut corners. Each statement is designed to reinforce a piece of information. Permanent learning requires more than A, B, C or 1, 2, 3 answers. Full sentences and complete ideas are remembered better when they are written out completely and neatly.

LIFE SCIENCE
All Creatures Great And Small

TABLE OF CONTENTS

CHAPTER 1 - INTRODUCTION

LIFE SCIENCE

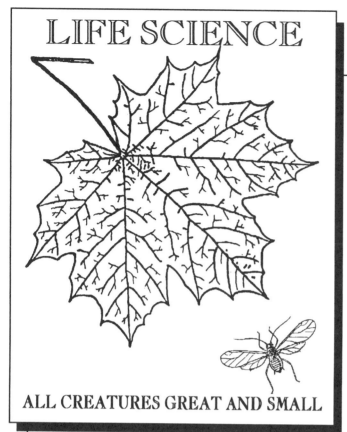

ALL CREATURES GREAT AND SMALL

DOWN

1. Any living thing.

2. Increase in size and number.

3. All the life functions together.

4. The breaking down of food.

6. Getting and using food.

8. The taking in of food.

9. The study of living things.

11. Producing more of one's own kind

12. Making useful chemicals.

Introduction Crossword Puzzle

Use the keywords from this chapter to fill in the puzzle.
See how many you know before reading the chapter!
Complete the puzzle after completing this chapter.

ACROSS

5. Eliminating waste products.

7. The movement of materials.

10. Ability to respond to stimuli, also called sensitivity.

13. Oxygen combining with another substance.

14. The process, in plants, of using light to make food.

15. Passing through the cell membrane or the walls of the intestine.

16. Exchanging gases; or getting energy by linking oxygen to food molecules.

Write in this book only if it belongs to you.
You may wish to make a copy of this page.

CHAPTER 1 INTRODUCTION
To The Pupil

PART 1 - Life Science

Life science is an attempt to understand the varied world of living things of which you and I are a part. A world inhabited by invisible creatures; some able to kill the strongest among us, some giving us an advantage over the killers! A world in which the tallest living thing is higher than you standing on top of me and 61 of your friends on top of that! (Figure 1-1)

There is so much variety and there are so many living things to look at and study that we must organize ourselves to learn and understand the wonderful world of each living ORGANISM.

BIOLOGY, the study of living things, will require an ability to measure and to organize information. As biologists we will use instruments to view one celled plants and animals; we will collect specimens to study the variety of living things; our experiments and studies will show us that the giant blue whale, the tiny ameba, the ancient bristle cone pine and you are all so different yet share the same basic life functions. Living things both great and small, plant and animal, each carry out these life functions:

1. TRANSPORT - which includes absorption and distribution of chemicals. In your body the blood in your circulatory system does the job of transport.

2. IRRITABILITY - may also be called response or regulation. Irritability is when a body reacts to a stimulus. For example: looking toward the door when you hear a knock.

3. NUTRITION - which includes the process of PHOTOSYNTHESIS in plants and INGESTION, DIGESTION and ABSORPTION in animals.

4. RESPIRATION - inside living cells respiration provides the energy for life. It also maintains the proper temperature for life through OXIDATION. Outside of cells, respiration is breathing.

5. EXCRETION - is the putting out of wastes. Excretion prevents the pollution of an organism's internal environment.

6. SYNTHESIS - a creature makes useful chemicals for secretion, regulation, and growth.

7. GROWTH - an increase in the size or number of cells. You started life as a single cell, now you are trillions and trillions of cells all working together!

8. REPRODUCTION - a life function necessary for the species but not for the individual. In the life process of reproduction a new individual of the same organism is created.

Somehow all of these life functions are blended together in each of God's creatures. The sum total of all eight life functions is called METABOLISM.

We will work at and we will study life science for these reasons: to prevent disease; to eat correctly and live a healthy life; to know and understand our fellow passengers on spacecraft earth; and to preserve life for those as yet unborn.

So that you will not waste anyone's precious time we must start our study with some rules. So that you may learn the most for our time working together in this science we must practice some skills.

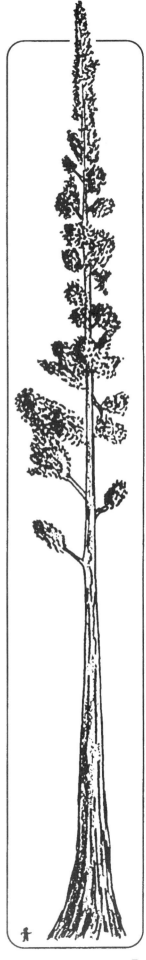

Figure 1-1 SIZES

Here is the size of Average Arnold, your everyday, all around dad, as compared to one of the California Redwoods, the tallest organisms on our planet!

PART 2 - Notebooks, Books and Labs

A well-kept notebook can be the key to success in any course of study. Ask someone for tips and instructions on how to keep a useful notebook.

The first page of your notebook is the title page. Write the course title: _Life Science_; the year; the grade; and your name. Paste pictures or news articles on this page to illustrate: metric measurement, animals, plants, food and health, and the human body. Pages two, three and four of your notebook will become the Table of Contents, to be filled in as you work.

The text is a tool for learning and study. Used correctly your book will help you do your assignments faster and more thoroughly than "Haphazard Harriet." She's a pupil too smart for her teachers. When Harriet does her assignments she just "looks for the answers" without reading the assignment first, and without using the textbook tool fully. If you wish to save time and learn more easily use each of the parts of the text correctly:

1. TITLE PAGE - the first page of a book which includes information on the title, author, publisher, place and year of publication. This information is necessary whenever you quote from a book for a report. You should always check the copyright date when using a book to look up any kind of current information. For example you will find out that Ronald Reagan is currently president in a history text published in 1988. However, even though he was extremely popular, Mr. Reagan is no longer president. You must use a book with a current copyright for current data.

2. TABLE OF CONTENTS - an outline of a book, with page numbers for each chapter, in the front of a book. Use the table of contents to find a general topic in a book. See page 5 in this book.

Figure 1-2

CONTENTS

A book's table of contents gives an outline of the work. It is a good place to look to see what general topics the book discusses that interest you.

LIFE SCIENCE
All Creatures Great And Small

TABLE OF CONTENTS

3. BODY - the main part of the book which follows the outline of the table of contents. The body is where you read in depth about a topic. The body is pages 6 to 172 in this text.

4. APPENDIX - the part of a text, found near the end of some books, containing charts, maps, or other detailed information not included in the body. For example pages 174 to 188.

5. GLOSSARY - a micro-dictionary found near the back of a book. Use the glossary to define keywords when possible, since the meaning given there will fit the usage particular to the subject of the book. If a term is not in the glossary then use a dictionary and choose the definition that fits the use of the keyword in the text.

Many words have the same "root" prefix or suffix. Learn the meaning of the root and then you will know the meanings of many words. For example, biology has two root parts: bio- which means life or living things and -ology which means the study of. Thus biology is the study of living things. You may see the same prefix in many words: biosphere, biologist, biodegradable, etc. Study Appendix I to learn the word roots important to becoming proficient in life science.

6. INDEX - an alphabetical list of all topics, including page numbers at the back of a book. The index is used to determine the pages of the body that will cover a specific topic. If a topic is not listed look up the word in the glossary. Try to determine from the definition a general topic that you may use to find the page numbers in the index. For example, if you look up guard cells in the index but do not find them listed, then look in the glossary and read: "guard cells, sausage shaped cells that open and close the stomates of leaves." Now you could look in the index for stomates, or leaves, and then find the pages that will discuss guard cells.

Sometimes it is necessary to look under a general heading instead of a specific item. In our example, perhaps under "cells" in the index you will find a sublisting for "guard" with the appropriate page numbers.

The index for _LIFE SCIENCE - All Creatures Great And Small_ begins on page 209.

In addition to this textbook we will practice using the scientific method, an organized way of solving questions and problems. The steps of the scientific method are:
1. Define the question or problem.
2. Collect data (i.e. information) through research.
3. Formulate an hypothesis (an educated guess).
4. Experiment using a control (providing a basis for

comparison) and a variable group (subjected to the variable factor being tested).

5. Express a conclusion that supports or rejects the hypothesis.

6. Share your data through written compositions and verbal reports.

Figure 1-3 SAFETY IN THE LAB

Safety is even more important than following the 8 part format for experiments. Safety rules and protective clothing must be a part of every experiment.

In our experiments we will use an eight part format. Include these eight headings in every lab that you write up:

I. **Title** - a word or phrase related to the content of the lab.

II. **Purpose** - several concise sentences that clearly explain why the experiment is being done.

III. **Materials** - a list of items that will be used up during the experiment.

IV. **Apparatus** - a list of equipment that may be used again after this procedure has been completed.

V. **Procedure** - clearly listed, step by step, instructions on how to do the experiment.

VI. **Data** - neatly organized information obtained by doing the procedure (charts, tables, graphs, calculations, observations, etc.).

VII. **Questions** - answer with full sentences any questions related to the lab.

VIII. **Conclusion** - a brief statement that sums up the results of the lab and indicates that the purpose has been fulfilled. For example, in a lab on "Testing for fats" whose purpose is "to identify common foods rich in fats," a good conclusion might be "Of the foods tested in this experiment, margarine and peanuts tested positive for fats."

See **Appendix VII** for an explanation and an example of how to plan an experiment.

BIG TREES

Each of these ten is believed to be the biggest of its kind growing in the United States today!

1. Giant Sequoia, 272 feet, Sequoia National Park, California.
2. Douglas Fir, 221 feet, Olympic National Park, Washington.
3. Ponderosa Pine, 162 feet, Lapine, Oregon
4. American Elm, 160 feet, Trigonia Tennessee.
5. Southern Cypress, 122 feet, Weakley County, Tennessee.
6. Shellbark Hickory, 122 feet, French Lick, Indiana.
7. Sugar Maple, 116 feet, Garrett County Maryland.
8. Black Cherry, 102 feet, Lawrence, Michigan.
9. White Birch, 96 feet, Lake Leelanau, Michigan.
10. Live Oak, 78 feet, Hahnville, Louisiana.

The "bigness" of each is recorded by the American Forestry Association as the sum of the height + the circumference at 4.5' + one fourth the crown spread.

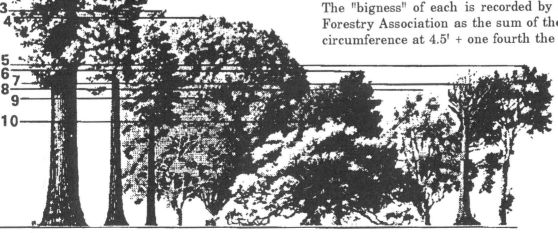

CHAPTER 1 REVIEW

OBJECTIVES:
1. **Learn the parts of a book.**
2. **Practice using LIFE SCIENCE**
   All Creatures Great And Small.
3. **Understand the Chapter 1 keywords.**

PART I. Define the following parts of a book:
    1. Title page, 2. Contents, 3. Body,
    4. Appendix, 5. Glossary, 6. Index.

PART II. Answer each question below with a neatly written, complete, sentence:

1. Which parts listed above are found in
       LIFE SCIENCE - All Creatures Great and
       Small?
2. On which page does the glossary begin?
3. How are the words in the glossary arranged?
4. Where is the index of any book located?

PART III. Write the name of one of the six parts of a book that would be the BEST section to use to find the information.

1. Which part of this book will give you the chapter that discusses cells?
2. Which part will contain the best definition of metabolism?
3. In which section might there be a chart listing the uses of plants?
4. Which part of the text will list the pages on which chloroplasts are discussed?
5. Where should a pupil look to read all about the human skeleton?
6. Which part is the best to use for the meaning of the term fetus?
7. In reading that the tallest man ever was Robert Wadlow, which section should be used to check on how old this information is?
8. Which section will give the author's name?
9. Which part gives an outline of the book?
10. Which part is a small dictionary?
11. Which section includes a chart of word parts for you to learn?
12. Which section is the main part of the book, with paragraphs, photos, and diagrams?

PART IV. Look up which chapter will discuss:
1. collections
2. fish
3. athlete's foot
4. pine trees
5. motorcycles
6. root hairs
7. how plants reproduce
8. how to use a microscope
9. vitamins and minerals
10. elements and chemicals.

PART V. Look up which page or pages discuss:
1. herbivores   6. flowering plants
2. monerans   7. euglena
3. scurvy   8. the brain
4. stomata   9. the bunsen burner
5. midgets   10. food webs

PART VI. Define each of the 16 keywords in this chapter. Keywords are emphasized in the body of the text.
Set up your definitions as shown here. You may then fold the piece of paper with the words and their meanings on opposite sides to quiz yourself as you study.

NAME	DATE
KEYWORDS CHAPTER 1	LIFE SCIENCE
1. organism	any living thing
2. biology	the study of living things
3. transport	the life function that includes the absorption and distr...

PART VII. Write the keyword from Chapter 1 that is most closely associated with each phrase.

1. After 21 days a chick hatches from an incubated egg.
2. Cows have flat molars to mash up the hay they chew.
3. Each cell of a pine tree combines oxygen with glucose to get energy.
4. A painted turtle eats an earthworm.
5. Glucose is being absorbed by the villi in the walls of your intestine.
6. You blink when a camera flash goes off.
7. A patient's heart must continue to beat if he or she is to remain alive.
8. The body breaks down the starch in French Fries to form a simple sugar.
9. Plants use chlorophyll to capture light and make their own food.
10. You exhale carbon dioxide through your mouth and nasal passages.

PART VIII. Learn the word parts in **Appendix I**. Make flash cards for each word part.

PART IX. Using a full sentence explain why salt crystals, which show growth, one of the life functions, are not alive.

CHAPTER 2 - MEASUREMENT

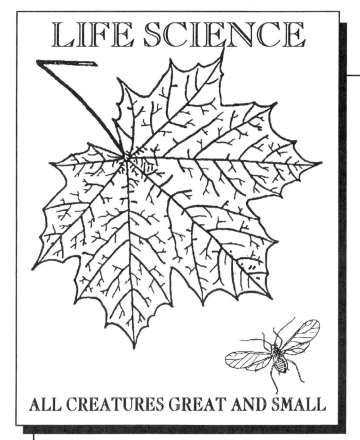

LIFE SCIENCE

ALL CREATURES GREAT AND SMALL

DOWN

1. 1000 times the basic unit.

2. Means 1/10 in the metric system.

4. A metric ruler.

5. Prefix meaning very small.

6. Basic unit of length.

7. Basic unit of liquid volume.

9. Prefix meaning very big.

13. The label part of a measurement.

Measurement Crossword Puzzle

Use the keywords from this chapter to fill in the puzzle.
See how many you know before reading the chapter!
Complete the puzzle after completing this chapter.

Write in this book only if it belongs to you.
You may wish to make a copy of this page.

ACROSS

3. Has cubic units.

6. Prefix for one thousandth.

8. Measurement based on ten.

10. Prefix meaning ten times.

11. Basic unit of mass.

12. Means 100 times the basic unit.

14. Length times width.

15. Prefix meaning one hundreth.

Chapter 2 MEASUREMENT

PART 1 - The Metric System

Metric measurement is used by industry and by scientists throughout the world, even here in our own schools! In Chemistry classes, upperclassmen must measure out 250 ml of a dilute acid, and they must be able to determine how many liters that is. A senior in Physics class often needs to change from centimeters into meters. Now you will learn the skill of using the METRIC SYSTEM, a way of measuring objects based on the number 10.

To measure the length of an object, like yourself, use a meter stick. You are probably taller than one meter stick but not as tall as two. As a matter of fact "Average Adam," your all American, everyday boy of twelve years old is exactly one and a half meter sticks tall (his cousin, Haphazard Harriet, is actually a little taller than Adam now, but won't be in a few years). The instrument for measuring length is the METER STICK. A smaller instrument is the centimeter ruler (see figure 2-1). The unit of length measurement is the METER. Note that the meter stick is divided into 10 parts called decimeters (dm), into 100 parts called centimeters (cm), and, each one meter is subdivided into 1000 parts named millimeters (mm).

What is a "unit? " If unit is not in the glossary then look up the definition in the dictionary. Make sure you know the meaning of the word UNIT, and more importantly, be sure to **include units with every measurement you write down!**

There is one problem with the meter, sometimes it takes hundreds of them to measure a distance and sometimes it takes only a tiny, tiny fraction of a meter to measure an organism. Pauline Musters, the smallest woman on record, at 18 years old, was only 0.59 meters (m) tall. But even that is big when compared to a bacillus bacterium that is only 0.000001 meters (m) long.

Having to write zero, point, zero, zero, zero, zero, zero, one meters (m) is a bit of a pain in the neck! As a result the metric system has units that are based on the meter (m) but are bigger or smaller. It is much more convienent to say one micrometer for the size of a bacillus. Also it is easier to write: 1 *u*m! *u* is the Greek letter mu, pronounced myoo (like the sound a cat makes).

Figure 2-1

A CM RULER

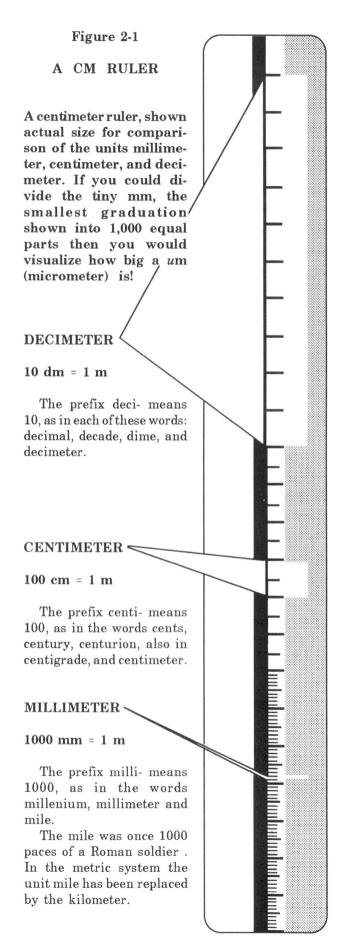

A centimeter ruler, shown actual size for comparison of the units millimeter, centimeter, and decimeter. If you could divide the tiny mm, the smallest graduation shown into 1,000 equal parts then you would visualize how big a *u*m (micrometer) is!

DECIMETER

10 dm = 1 m

The prefix deci- means 10, as in each of these words: decimal, decade, dime, and decimeter.

CENTIMETER

100 cm = 1 m

The prefix centi- means 100, as in the words cents, century, centurion, also in centigrade, and centimeter.

MILLIMETER

1000 mm = 1 m

The prefix milli- means 1000, as in the words millenium, millimeter and mile.

The mile was once 1000 paces of a Roman soldier . In the metric system the unit mile has been replaced by the kilometer.

Memorize this metric prefixes chart in order as shown:

Figure 2-2 METRIC PREFIXES CHART

Mega, ---, ---, kilo, hecto, deka,	basic unit,	deci, centi, milli, ---, ---,* micro
M_ k_ h_ da_	meter (m)	d_ c_ m_ u_
Greek prefixes mean bigger than one.	liter (l) gram (g)	**Latin prefixes mean smaller than one.**

You must know the correct abbreviations. You already know the basic unit of length is the meter (m) but what are the units for liquid volume and mass? Soda bottles come in one or two LITER (l) sizes and candy bars are often measured in GRAMS (g).

Since the metric system is based on ten, to change units is simply to move the decimal point. Use the Metric Prefixes Chart to convert from one unit to another.

For example, Average Adam is 1.5 m tall, but how many centimeters (cm) tall is Adam? Find the basic unit: meter (m) on the chart; then count the number of steps you must move to get to centimeters (cm). Note that you move two places to the right. Now move the decimal in the given, 1.5 m, two places to the right: one place 15., two places 150. and write this number with the correct units as your answer. Average Adam is 150 cm tall. Pauline Musters was 0.59 m tall, how many cm is this?

The metric system uses the **same prefixes** even though we are measuring a different quantity. The basic unit is different but the prefixes will be the same. Robert Wadlow, the tallest man on record was 7 ft 1 and 3/4 inches tall when he was 13 years old. At that time his mass was 115,666.05 grams (g). Which certainly sounds like a lot! But the gram is approximately the mass of one medium size paper clip. A better size unit for Robert's mass would be kilograms (kg). Use the **Metric Prefixes Chart**. Start at the basic unit grams (g) and count the steps to kilograms (kg). Note that you moved three places to the left. Now move the decimal point three places to the left: one place 11566.605, two places 1156.6605, three places 115.66605! This is the magnitude of your answer. Round this off to a reasonable number of places and add the units for your final answer. Thirteen year old Robert Wadlow had a mass of approximately 115.7 kg.

For comparison, the average 12 year old girl's mass is about 39.7 kg, and Average Adam would be roughly 1.45 kg less than that. As big as he was, it would take OVER one thousand two hundred (1,200) 13 year old Robert Wadlows to have a mass equal to one blue whale (139,255.2 kg). What is the mass of this blue whale in megagrams (Mg)?

You really must remember the prefixes in order with the blank spaces included. Those prefixes that mean bigger than one are Greek: MEGA (1,000,000), —, —, KILO (1,000), HECTO (100), and DEKA (10).

Latin prefixes indicate values less than one: DECI (1/10), CENTI (1/100), MILLI (1/1,000), —, —, MICRO (1/1,000,000). All of the prefixes are based on the number ten.

PART II - More Measurements

Wow - 510,070,000! Is that big! Is that big?

Measurements must always include the units. If the above is in square millimeters (mm^2) then it is only 510 square meters (m^2), just 2/3's the area of a baseball field.

But when we write 510,070,000 with the units square kilometers (km^2), now that is big! The surface area of the entire earth is approximately 510,070,000 square kilometers (km^2). To compare, Average Arnold (Average Adam's average size dad) has a skin surface area of about 1.86 m^2, that is a surface area of .00000186 km^2.

Let's try to "see" the basic idea of AREA. Use a cm ruler to measure the rectangle in figure 2-3. This rectangle is 2 cm on one side and 3 cm on the other side. If we mark off small squares that measure one centimeter on each side, we find that six of these little "square centimeters" will fit on the 2 cm by 3 cm rectangle.

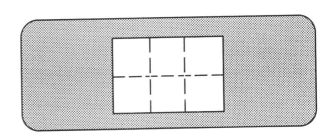

Figure 2-3 A RECTANGLE

Area is determined by multiplying the length times the width: (3 cm) (2 cm).

The units: cm times cm is called square centimeters (cm²). You must memorize the general formula for rectangular area:

AREA = LENGTH x WIDTH

When doing an area calculation, always write the formula, then substitute the numbers, with their units, finally box your answer with the correct units.

For example:

$$A = L \times W$$
$$A = (3 \text{ cm})(2 \text{ cm})$$

$$\boxed{A = 6 \text{ cm}^2}$$

Whenever additions or subtractions are done with units, the units must be the same. Also, for area or volume problems the units must be the same. For example: what is the area of the front of Figure 2-4.

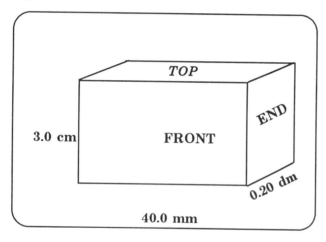

Figure 2-4 A BOX

Almost everybody knows that the formula for area is length times width:

$$A = L \times W$$
$$A = (40.0 \text{ mm}) (3.0 \text{ cm})$$

but we must change cm or mm

$$A = (4.00 \text{ cm}) (3.0 \text{ cm})$$

now we can multiply

$$\boxed{A = 12.0 \text{ cm}^2}$$

note the square centimeters.

This same idea, that units must be the same, applies to rectangular volume calculations:

VOLUME = LENGTH x WIDTH x HEIGHT

For example the volume of the box in Figure 2-4 can be calculated using the above formula.

$$V = L \times W \times H$$
$$V = (40.0 \text{ mm}) (3.0 \text{ cm}) (0.20 \text{ dm})$$

We must change all units to one kind.

$$V = (4.00 \text{ cm}) (3.0 \text{ cm}) (2.0 \text{ cm})$$

$$\boxed{V = 24 \text{ cm}^3}$$ note the units!

Metric VOLUME is measured in cubic centimeters, abbreviated cm³ or cc. You may have seen a baby bottle marked in cc's or a motorcycle that is 80 cc's. The bottle measures the volume of liquid it can hold. The motorcyle measures the volume of its cylinder, the greater the cc's, the bigger the piston, thus more power.

Figure 2-5 CUBIC CENTIMETERS

An 80 cc "bike" is small enough for learning to ride but is still powerful enough that the rider must be careful. Follow all safety rules and use protective clothing!

Liquid volume is measured in LITERS. When you memorize the volume formula you must also remember this fact:

One milliliter = one cubic centimeter

1 ml = 1 cc

So we could say that a two liter soda bottle is 2,000 ml. That is the same as 2,000 cubic centimeters.

Figure 2-6 LITERS

One and two liter soda bottles are a familiar unit of measurement in Systemae International, the metric system!

14

CHAPTER 2 REVIEW

OBJECTIVES:

1. **Know the metric prefixes.**
2. **Perform metric conversions.**
3. **Calculate area and volume.**

PART I. List the metric prefixes from the largest we've studied to the smallest. Write your list from left to right across the page.

PART II. Write each abbreviation and its meaning:

1. m	4. mm	7. ml	10. dal	13. cm^2
2. l	5. cm	8. cg	11. Mg	14. cm^3
3. g	6. dm	9. km	12. um	15. cc

PART III. Define the 16 keywords from Chapter 2.

PART IV. Write each problem. Write the answer with the correct units):

1. 1000 mm = ? m	6. 0.01 cm = ? m
2. 1000 mm = ? cm	7. 0.01 mm = ? m
3. 348 cm = ? m	8. 0.056 m = ? km
4. 5 kg = ? g	9. 0.004 Mg = ? g
5. 2.61 dl = ? cl	10. 0.025 l = ? ml

11. 2 hg = ? dag
12. 2 hl = ? dal
13. 2 hm = ? dam
14. 300 ml = ? cc
15. 4,500 cc = ? l

PART V. Answer each by writing a full sentence:
1. How many cc's are equal to one ml?
2. What is the formula for rectangular area?
3. What is the formula for rectangular volume?
4. Upon what number is the metric system based?
5. Give the root meaning of the word meter.
6. What must be included with the magnitude (i.e. number) of a measurement?
7. What is the prefix that means 1000 times?
8. Which prefix means 1/100 of?
9. Which is larger: one decimeter (1 dm) or one dekameter (1 dam)?
10. Which of these is smallest in value: hecto, micro, milli, centi?
11. Give the root meaning of the prefix centi.
12. Name two words that correctly contain the word part centi.

PART VI. Diagram and label a CM RULER. Remember to include a title; use a ruler for lines; draw in pencil; and label in ink.

PART VII. Measure the length, width, and height of another box in Fig. 2-7. Use centimeters.

Figure 2-7 ANOTHER BOX
This miniature box could hold 15 eggs of the Helena's Hummingbird, with room left over!

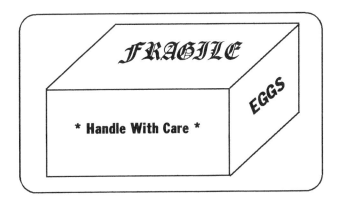

PART VIII. The correct sizes for Figure 2-7 are:
L = 5.0 cm, H = 2.2 cm, W = 2.5 cm.
Use the above values to determine the quantities requested in numbers 1-4 below.
Show all work, beginning with the formula, and ending with a box around your answer, including units.

1. What is the area of the side marked "HANDLE WITH CARE"?
2. What is the area of the side marked "EGGS"?
3. What is the area of the side marked "FRAGILE"?
4. What is the volume of the Hummingbird egg box in figure 2-7?

PART IX. Show all work.
1. What is the area, in square centimeters, of the shaded side of the block in Figure 2-8?
2. What is the area of the white top of the block?
3. What is the volume, in cubic centimeters, of the block?
4. How many milliliters of water would occupy the same volume as the block?

Figure 2-8 A BLOCK OF WOOD

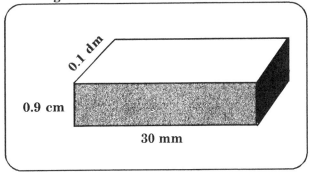

PART X. If the volume of a room is 36 cubic meters, what is its volume in cubic centimeters? Hint: draw and label a sketch of the room's possible dimensions!

CHAPTER 3 - COLLECTIONS

See Appendix X on page 186 to identify these insects.

LIFE SCIENCE

ALL CREATURES GREAT AND SMALL

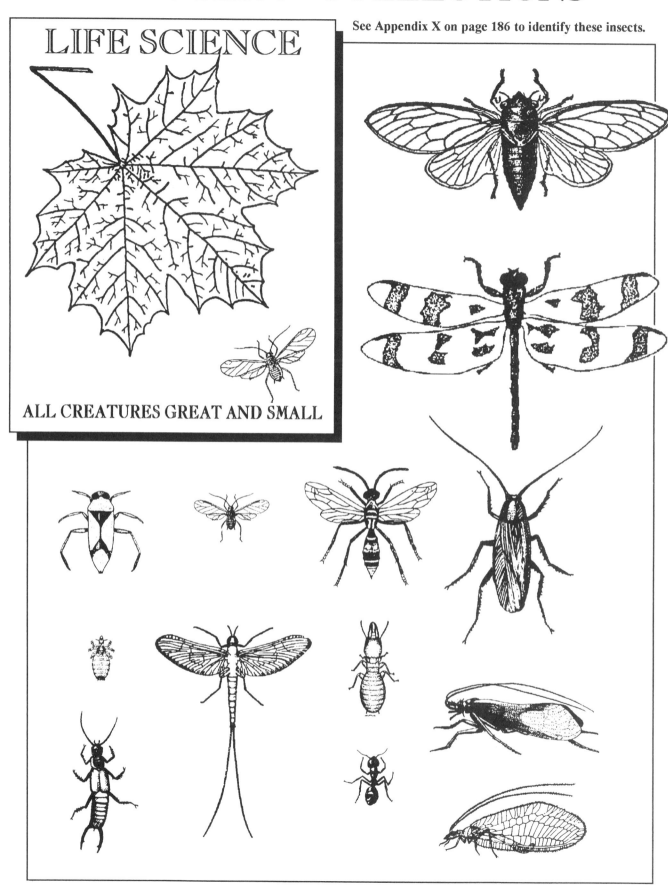

CHAPTER 3 COLLECTIONS

Bird nests were one of my first collections. I found the nest of a Phoebe (fee-bee), a soft nest of moss lined with delicate hairs and fibers. This nest however was different! Never have I found another like it. This nest still had the tiny skeletons of the baby birds in it! "What had happened to the mother bird" I wondered. Thirty years later I still have that, and many other nests. I've enjoyed the fun and exercise of finding nests in the fall of each year (why "the fall"?). I learned about the birds that made each nest. I came, like Longfellow's Little Hiawatha, to learn of "...every bird its language, learned of them and all their secrets, where they built their nests in summer, where they hid themselves in winter..." Since then hundreds of other children have enjoyed seeing my collection. They have studied the way each nest is made - each as different as the species of bird that constructed it. Collections are made to learn from, to enjoy, to preserve specimens for later, and for the beauty of the objects.

For life science class, you will collect either leaves or insects. Of course you may collect both on your own, but choose one for this class. Seeds and seashells are other interesting objects to collect on your own! For your "class collection" you must have at least 10 different specimens.

FIGURE 3-1 COLLECTIONS
Birds and their nests provide many hours of interesting discovery, collecting, and study for naturalists of any age. Understanding animal habits is one step toward a healthy appreciation of our natural environment.

LEAF COLLECTIONS

Look for one or two medium sized leaves. Never take more than one or two leaves from any one branch. Be sure to ask permission before collecting from an ornamental (a tree in someone's yard)! Remember **not** to collect poison ivy, poison oak, or poison sumac. See Appendix IX, page 185, for leaf collecting suggestions.

Figure 3-2
MAKING A LEAF COLLECTION
Steps to follow in correctly preparing leaves for a permanent collection: collect with notes, press and dry, identify and mount.

Place each leaf in a newspaper with a card showing: 1. the date collected; 2. the name of the leaf (if known); 3. special notes about where the leaf was collected; 4. the name of the person who collected the specimen. Do not allow the leaves to overlap in the newspaper. Put several pages of paper between the pages with leaves on them. Place the stack of paper and leaves in a dry warm place, with several large books on top of it.

After a week the leaves will have dried out. Remember that they are now fragile and will crumble instead of bend. Mount the leaves with a clear drying glue. Spread a thin layer of glue over every part of the back of each specimen and place it carefully on a stiff piece of paper. Be sure no excess glue is on the edges or coming through the leaf.

Write: 1. the name of the leaf; 2. the date collected; 3. the place collected; and 4. the collector's name on a piece of paper 2 cm by 4 cm. Glue the label near the leaf. Put a sheet of newspaper over the leaf and label and then put on a large book. Immediately lift the book and paper to check if any glue has come out from under the edges of the leaf or label. If it has, clean it up and use a new sheet of newspaper. Put the book back on top and allow the glue to dry. Store your collection in a DRY place.

INSECT COLLECTIONS

There are more insects on earth than there are of all other members of the animal kingdom put together. Insects reproduce rapidly. They may be found almost anywhere. Especially good places to look for insects include: on flower blossoms, in old logs and stumps, near ponds, and around outdoor lights. Spiders, because they have more than six legs, are **not** insects. Do not collect them. Use **caution** if you collect bees or wasps.

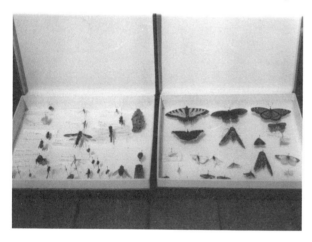

Figure 3-3 A FIRST GRADE COLLECTION A lot of time and effort went into making this young student's collection as varied and well done as you see it here. By following the instructions in this section your collection will also be interesting to view and study.

See Appendix X on pages 186-188 for insect collecting suggestions and an entomology activity

Bring the live or dead insects to class in a plastic container with your name on it. **Do not use glass** jars. This author has the scars on his right hand to clearly indicate why no glass jars may be used! You must note where, when (the date) and who collected each specimen.

Insects are killed by putting them in a killing jar. **Caution:** if a substance kills insects, it usually is not good for you to inhale! Your insects should be pinned soon after killing. Once they dry out completely the insects will be very fragile. Use a pinning board or a shoe box top. Place each pin as shown at the right.

Figure 3-4 Beetles, cockroaches, crickets.

Figure 3-5 Grasshoppers, etc. (below).

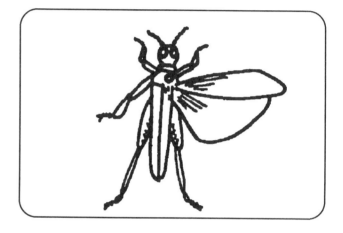

Figure 3-6 True bugs (below) Note the triangle on the back.

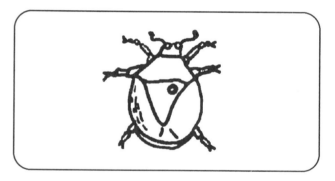

Figure 3-7 Bees, butterflies, moths, flies. (below)

LIFE SCIENCE All Creatures Great And Small

Figure 3-8 TINY INSECTS

Glue small insects, mosquitoes for example, onto a mini triangle of stiff paper.

Make your labels 1.3 cm by 2.5 cm. Write on one label: 1. where the insect was collected (the town and state); 2. the date when collected; 3. who collected it. On a second label include: 1. the name of the insect; and who identified it if different from the collector. Use the simplified key to Class Insecta to help you identify your specimens (see page 187).

Put the labels on the pin as shown in Fig. 3-9.

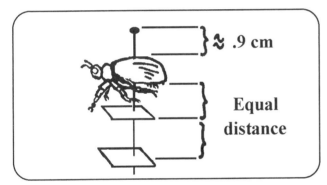

≈ .9 cm

Equal distance

Figure 3-9
LABELING AN INSECT SPECIMEN

The back of each insect should be 0.9 cm from the head of the pin and the labels spaced equally below the specimen.

Store your collection in a small box. Glue two pieces of cardboard to the bottom of your box to hold the pins in place. Keep your collection dry and cool.

Your collection should be scientifically accurate but also aesthetically pleasing. That is, you should carefully place the specimens and labels so that your collection is nice to look at!

CHAPTER 3 REVIEW

OBJECTIVES:

1. **Understand why collections are made.**

2. **Know what information is important to include in a collection.**

PART I. Put the correct heading on your paper. Use full sentences to answer each:
1. List at least three different reasons for making a collection.
2. Name three kinds of plants that you should not collect.
3. How many leaf specimens should be taken from any one branch?
4. What plants require permission before taking a leaf?
5. Name a kind of "bug" that is not an insect.
6. List two kinds of insects that require caution when collected.
7. What four pieces of data should be included with every specimen?
8. Describe a type of container that should **not** be used to collect insects.

AN INSECT PEST
Culex pungens

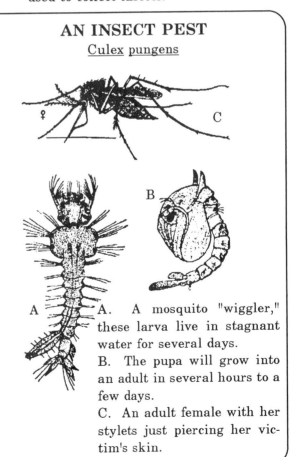

A. A mosquito "wiggler," these larva live in stagnant water for several days.
B. The pupa will grow into an adult in several hours to a few days.
C. An adult female with her stylets just piercing her victim's skin.

19

CHAPTER 4 - INSTRUMENTS

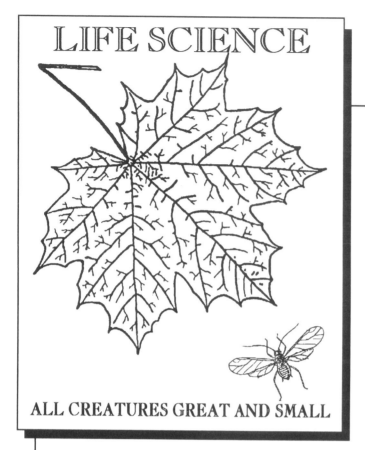

LIFE SCIENCE

ALL CREATURES GREAT AND SMALL

DOWN

2. How hot or cold compared to a standard.

5. The lense of a microscope near the eye.

7. The part of the microscope that holds the objective lenses.

8. The part of a microscope on which you place the slide.

10. One of two parts used to carry the microscope.

Instruments Crossword Puzzle

Use the keywords from this chapter to fill in the puzzle. See how many you know before reading the chapter! Complete the puzzle after completing this chapter.

Write in this book only if it belongs to you. You may wish to make a copy of this page.

ACROSS

1. A temperature scale with 0 and 100 for water's freezing and boiling points.

3. The part of a microscope that adjusts the amount of light.

4. The lense of a microscope that is close to the object.

6. The curved surface of a liquid.

9. Amount of matter in an object.

11. Markings on an instruments.

12. Also called a micrometer (.001 mm).

13. The amount of heat needed to raise 1 gram of water 1 degree C.

CHAPTER 4 INSTRUMENTS

In the next chapter, titled "Seawater," we will try to understand what it is that makes up living things. We will discover that most of your body, and that of many living things, is mainly one kind of chemical. In the following chapter on "Cells" we will investigate the building blocks of organisms. In order to successfully complete activities for each of these upcoming chapters we must be able to safely use our laboratory equipment.

PART 1 - The Pan Balance

The triple beam balance is used to measure the MASS of an object. Don't confuse mass, the amount of matter in an object; with weight, the downward force of an object due to gravity. The unit that must be included with each mass measurement is grams (g). You learned in the chapter on "Measurement" that 1000 grams may be called a kilogram (kg). The kilogram is approximately the mass of seven baseballs. It is the mass of a little less than half of a five pound bag of sugar. The gram is approximately the mass of one of Average Arnold's paper clips. We will use grams to record the mass of small objects, like a lettuce leaf. We will use kilograms for the mass of a person.

To use a triple beam balance correctly you must first know the names of its parts. Figure 4-1 illustrates the information you must know.

There are several rules that must be followed when using a balance:
1. **Always carry the balance with two hands, by the base;**
2. **Always leave the balance clean and on zero; and**
3. **Place objects on the pan gently.**

Finding the mass of solids

To find the mass of a solid object, place the unknown gently on the pan. Move the largest rider over until the pointer moves downward. Move the largest rider back one notch. Repeat with the medium sized rider, then with the smallest rider until the pointer is at the exact position on the zero scale that is was pointing to before you began. Now add the amounts indicated by each of the three riders and write your determination of the mass with the units grams (g).

Finding the mass of liquids

When measuring the mass of a liquid, a powder, or an object that will not stay on the pan, you must first determine the mass of an empty container. Then put in the liquid (or powder, or object) and find the mass of both the container and the liquid. Now subtract the mass of the empty container from the mass of the container and liquid. Write your result with the units grams (g). Study Figure 4-2 on the next page.

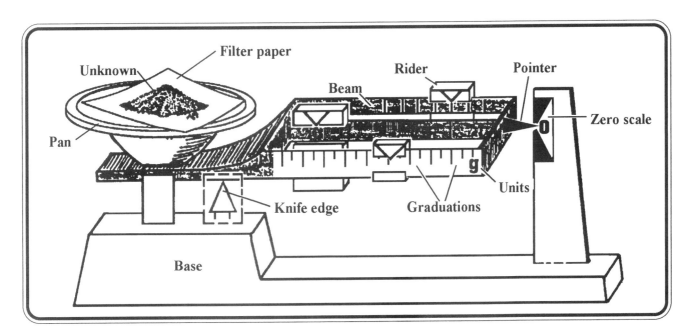

Figure 4-1 THE PAN BALANCE

Figure 4-2 MEASURING MASS

The mass of the empty container had to be recorded first. Now by subtraction the mass of the liquid may be determined.

PART 2 - The Thermometer

The two roots of the word thermometer are "thermo" meaning heat or hot and "meter" meaning to measure. The thermometer is an instrument used to determine the TEMPERATURE of an object. Try not to confuse temperature, how hot or cold compared to a standard; with heat which is an amount of energy available for transfer. Each measurement of temperature must include the correct unit. We will use CENTIGRADE degrees, °C. These degrees are sometimes called Celsius after the scientist who made up this temperature scale. You may be familiar with Fahrenheit degrees, °F which are used in our weather reports. In Chemistry and Physics courses you will be using the absolute scale measured in Kelvins (K). Fig. 4-3 shows the parts of a thermometer.

The fixed points for water are its freezing and boiling points.

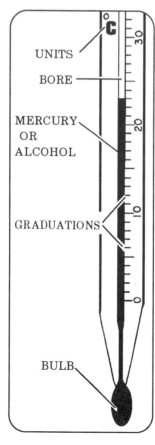

Figure 4-3
A THERMOMETER

Pure water freezes at 0 °C, 32 °F or 273 K. At one atmosphere of pressure pure water boils at 100 °C, 212 °F and 373 K.

Which is colder 0 °C or 32 °F or 273 K?

All three temperatures measure the freezing point of water, and are all the same temperature!

You must follow these four general rules when using the thermometer:

1. Always place the thermometer where it cannot roll or be knocked off the table;

2. Hold the thermometer off the bottom of the beaker when taking a reading;

3. Do not use the thermometer as a stirrer;

4. Leave the thermometer clean and dry.

PART 3 - The Graduated Cylinder

The graduated cylinder is simply a carefully marked tube of glass or plastic used to determine the volume of a liquid. The marks are called GRADUATIONS. Liquid volume, you will recall from the chapter on Measurement has the unit liter. You are familiar with the volume of one liter because soda comes in one and two liter bottles. Most graduates (graduated cylinders) are marked in 1/1000 of a liter, that is milliliters (ml). A single milliliter is about seven (7) drops of water. A fact to remember is that:

1 ml = 1 cc.

In Figure 4-4 the correct way to read the volume of the liquid is shown. Your eye must be level with the MENISCUS, and you then read the graduation by the bottom of the meniscus.

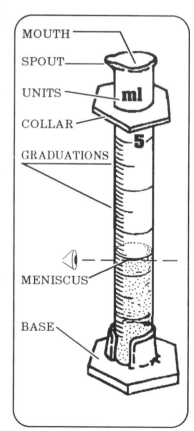

Figure 4-4 A GRADUATED CYLINDER

The correct volume is 2.4 ml. Remember to determine the value of each graduation.

The procedures below are to be followed when using the graduated cylinder:
1. **Always leave the cylinder empty and clean (drops of water may be left to air dry);**
2. **Always leave the cylinder on its side;**
3. **The collar is placed approximately 1 cm below the mouth.**

PART 4 The Bunsen Burner

The Bunsen Burner (refer to Figure 4-5) is used in many laboratories as a source of heat. Heat, measured in the units CALORIE (cal) or kilocalorie (kcal), will be needed in the chapter on "Testing for Nutrients." Not only must you know the parts of a burner and how to use it, you must be willing to follow all safety rules!

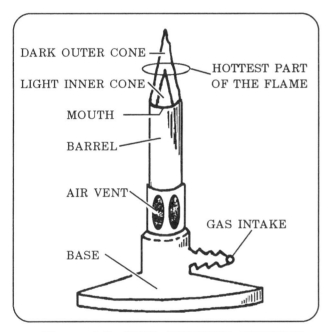

Figure 4-5 THE BUNSEN BURNER

Safety always must come first when using the Bunsen Burner:

1. **Always wear safety glasses;**
2. **Clear away all papers (and tie back loose clothing and long hair);**
3. **Never leave a lit burner unattended;**
4. **Always turn off the gas completely at the lab table valve.**

If your burner has a yellow-orange flame then you must open the air vent at the base of the barrel. The yellow flame is not as hot as the blue flame. The cooler, yellow flame also leaves soot (unburned carbon from the gas) on the glassware.

To heat a test tube use the test tube holder to keep the bottom of the test tube in the blue flame just above the lighter inner cone. Slant the tube so that the mouth does not point toward anyone. Put the hot tube in a test tube rack. Wash the test tube only after it has cooled.

When you are instructed to do so, turn off the burner immediately. Allow the barrel to cool before putting the burner away.

PART 5 The Compound Microscope

Imagine the excitement and intensity of Anton van Leeuwenhoek (lay-when-hook) when he looked into his first microscope and saw "wee beasties" so small that there are more of them on and in your body right now than there are people in the world! At first no one believed him. You will be able to see for yourself the tiny world of microbes (microscopic organisms). Life scientists often use the compound microscope to see things as small as 0.5 MICRON (called micrometer, um).

The first microscopes from the late 1600's could only make things look approximately 150 to 200 times bigger. You can determine the power of your school microscope by multiplying the strength of the EYEPIECE (or ocular) by the strength of the OBJECTIVE lens. For example, if the eyepiece is marked "10 X" and the objective in place is labeled "30 X" then the magnifying power of the scope is 10 X 30 or 300 times. We must know the parts of a microscope if we are to discuss its use and if we are to use the scopes correctly. Study figure 4-6.

The microscope is carried with one hand holding the ARM and the other holding the base. Be sure to put the scope on a flat surface. When someone else wishes to see whatever you have in view on the STAGE, move yourself out of the way. leave the microscope in one place. To prevent damage to the eyes, never use direct sunlight with the mirror. These steps will prevent damage:

1. **Start on low power and use the coarse adjustment;**

2. **When on high power (i.e. using the highest strength objective on the NOSEPIECE) use only the fine adjustment;**

3. **Clean the lenses with lense paper only (nothing else will do)!**

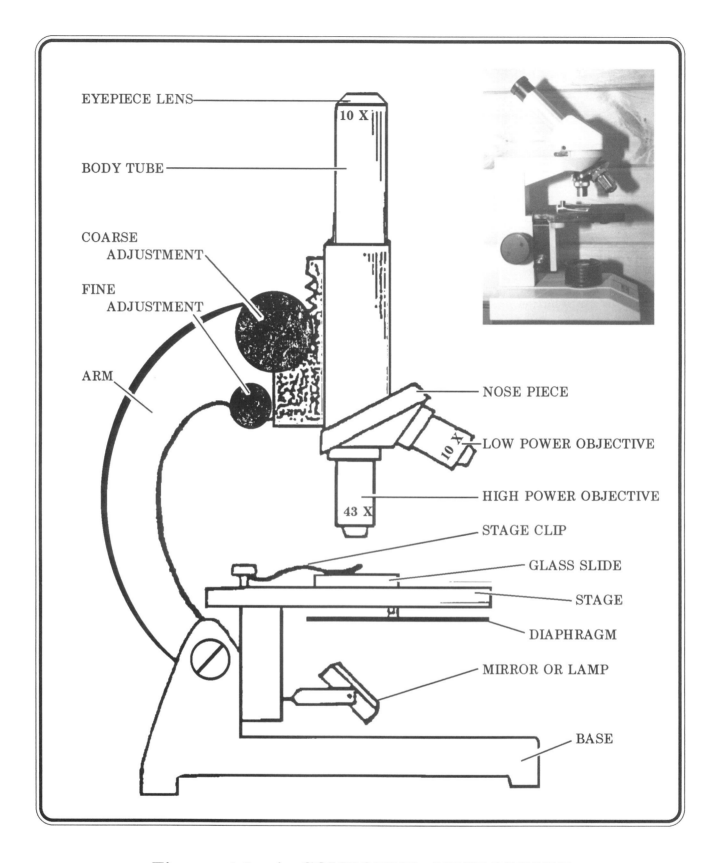

EYEPIECE LENS

10 X

BODY TUBE

COARSE ADJUSTMENT

FINE ADJUSTMENT

ARM

NOSE PIECE

10 X — LOW POWER OBJECTIVE

43 X — HIGH POWER OBJECTIVE

STAGE CLIP

GLASS SLIDE

STAGE

DIAPHRAGM

MIRROR OR LAMP

BASE

Figure 4-6   A COMPOUND MICROSCOPE

This instrument is called compound because it has more than one lens. Each microscope requires careful handling and must be kept clean and dry.

When it is time to clean up:

1. Put away all prepared slides,
2. Wash and put away your slide and cover slip;
3. Put the scope on low power;
4. Turn the coarse adjustment to put the body tube all the way down;
5. Put on the dust cover.

Figure 4-7 may help you understand what you are seeing in the microscope.

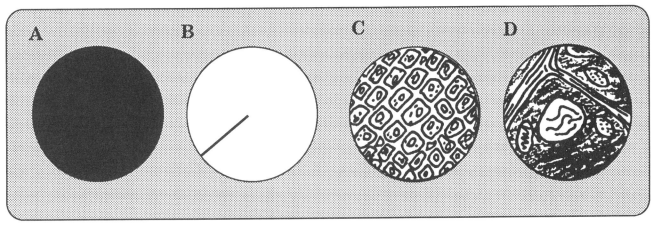

Figure 4-7 LOOKING INTO THE EYEPIECE

A - dark
If you cannot see anything as in A, then you need to adjust the mirror to reflect more light through the slide and into the objective. If the view is too bright then use the DIAPHRAGM to reduce the light.

B - pointer
The pointer, shown in B, is permanent. You must move your slide to position whatever you want someone else to see at the tip of the pointer.

C - low power
Under the low power in C there is more area but less detail. Use either focus knob when under the low power objective lens.

D - high power
In D, you will see more detail but less area. You must remember to use only the fine adjustment when on high power.

Look at Figure 4-6 and determine the magnifying power of the microscope as shown. See the answer below.
Should you use the coarse adjustment knob with the microscope set up as shown?
Bright light will "scare" many microbes away, which part allows you to reduce the light?
If you see only part of a cell under the microscope but want to see it all, should you use a higher power objective or a lower power to see more area?

ANSWERS: Lower power allows a larger field of view but less detail.
The diaphragm is used to adjust the light.
Use only the fine adjustment when on high power.
Eyepiece X Objective = Power, 10 X 43 = 430 X.

CHAPTER 4 REVIEW

OBJECTIVES:

1. **Practice metrics.**
2. **Know the parts of the lab instruments.**
3. **Know the quantity measured, and the units, for each instrument.**
4. **Correctly use and read each instrument.**

PART I. Define the 13 keywords in Chapter 4.

PART II. Answer each question with a neatly written full sentence:

1. On what number is the metric system based?

2. Name the basic metric units for length, mass, and liquid volume.

3. List the metric prefixes, largest to smallest.

PART III. Convert:
1. 5 m = ? cm
2. 1 cm = ? m
3. 100 cm = ? m
4. 1000 ml = ? l
5. 1000 l = ? ml
6. 0.05 l = ? ml
7. 3.0 g = ? cg
8. 1,450g = ? kg
9. 7.83 kg = ? g

PART IV. Sketch and label:
1. A meter stick
2. A pan balance
3. A thermometer
4. A graduated cylinder
5. A Bunsen burner
6. A compound microscope

PART V. List the unit and quantity involved with each instrument in PART IV.

PART VI. 1. Measure the length of each line in centimeters:

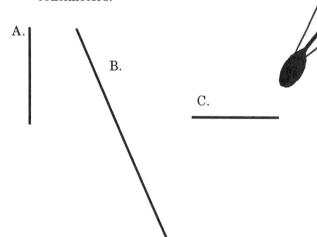

Part VII.   2. Give the mass in grams:

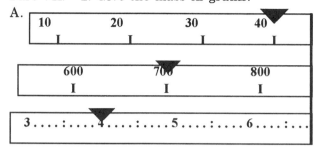

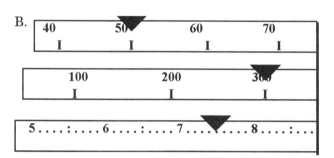

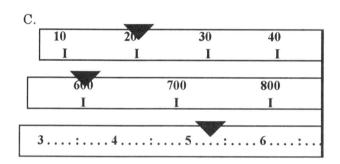

3. Read the temperature in °C:

4. Report the volume in milliliters:

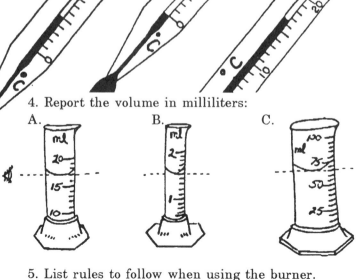

5. List rules to follow when using the burner.
6. If the eyepiece is 5X & the objective is 30X, what is the magnifying power of the scope?

CHAPTER 5 - SEAWATER

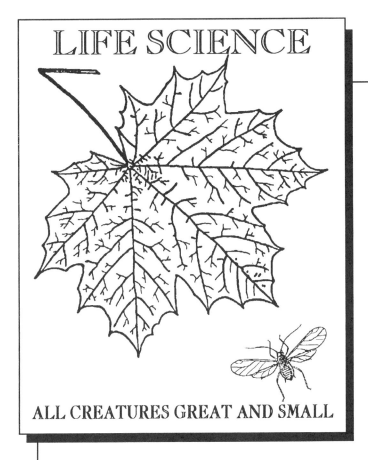

LIFE SCIENCE

ALL CREATURES GREAT AND SMALL

DOWN

2. The smallest part of a compound with all the properties of the compound.

3. A positively charged part of the nucleus of atoms.

4. Hydrogen oxide.

7. The central region of an atom.

9. A negatively charged particle in atoms that spins around in energy shells.

11. Matter with a definite volume but no definite shape.

Seawater Crossword Puzzle

Use the keywords from this chapter to fill in the puzzle. See how many you know before reading the chapter! Complete the puzzle after completing this chapter.

Write in this book only if it belongs to you. You may wish to make a copy of this page.

ACROSS

1. Two or more elements chemically combined in a definite ratio.

5. The simplest substances that make up all matter.

6. The smallest part of an element.

8. Two or more substances together in any ratio.

10. Electrons may be found here.

12. The phase of matter with the highest amount of energy.

13. A neutral particle found in the nucleus of most atoms.

14. The state of matter with a definite shape and definite volume.

ATOMS

With the best compound microscope on earth you can't even come close to seeing a molecule of water or an ATOM of sodium. With a special electron microscope, that uses a beam of electrons instead of light rays to "look" at things, you can actually magnify objects 10 million times. At that power atoms appear to be indistinct, hazy dots. How big, or shall we say, how small are atoms?

The NUCLEUS of a hydrogen atom is less than 10^{-13} m (ten to the negative thirteen meters). An iron atom is about 10^{-10} m (0.0000000001 m). The smallest "living" things called viruses are roughly 10^{-7} m. Let's try to make these sizes more understandable.

If we made the iron atom one centimeter in size, then the average virus would be 10 meters big. That would make you bigger than the distance from the earth to our moon (approximately 380,000,000 m)! How small are atoms? How many do you think could fit in one drop of water? According to chemists there are approximately 1.5×10^{22} atoms in one drop. That's 15 billion trillion! That's 15,000,000,000,000,000,000,000 atoms in one drop of water!

An atom is the smallest part of an element with all the properties of the element. As tiny as an atom is, it is made of three main pieces even smaller yet. In the dense center region of an atom, the nucleus, there are PROTONS (with a positive charge) and NEUTRONS (which are neutral, that is with no charge). Spinning crazily around the nucleus in ENERGY SHELLS are very tiny negative particles called ELECTRONS. You should be familiar with electrons because they are electricity! A beam of electrons is what forms the image on your T.V. screen. These three pieces take up very little room, and most of the atom is empty space. See figure 5-1.

Every atom that has one proton in its nucleus is the same kind of atom. If two atoms with different numbers of neutrons and electrons have the same number of protons then they are the same kind of atom. Of the more than 100 kinds of atoms, 92 may be found in nature. For life science the 15 kinds of atoms shown in figure 5-2 are the most important. You must memorize the name and symbol for each.

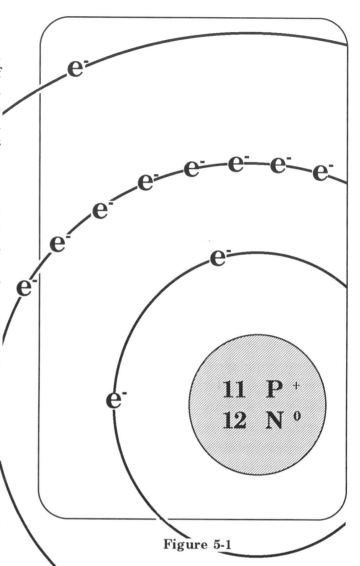

Figure 5-1

BOHR MODEL OF A SODIUM ATOM

The protons (+) and neutrons (0) are in the nucleus, the electrons (-) are spinning wildly in orbit in energy shells. Only 2 electrons may fit in the 1st shell, and only 8 in the 2nd energy shell.

Most of the atom is empty space.

Figure 5-2 SYMBOLS OF ELEMENTS

Since atoms are so tiny, we always have many of them even in a small piece of material. Many atoms of the same kind are called an element. An ELEMENT is a simple substance that cannot be broken down by ordinary chemical means. See Appendix V for all the elements.

SYMBOL	NAME In the:	PROTONS nucleus	NEUTRONS nucleus	ELECTRONS shells	NOTES
H	hydrogen	1	0	1	Exists as H_2 an explosive gas. One of two elements in water. Needed for protoplasm. About 9.5% of you is H.
C	carbon	6	6	6	A black solid. Your pencil "lead" is carbon. Approximately 18.5% of you is C. Organic compounds are C chains.
N	nitrogen	7	7	7	Exists as N_2 a stable gas. Air is 78% N_2. Needed for protein. 3% of you is N.
O	oxygen	8	8	8	Exists as O_2, a gas needed for combustion. Air is 21% O_2. About 65% of you is O.

The four elements above make up almost all of the bodies of microbes, people and the gigantic blue whale. The elements listed below are necessary in very tiny amounts.

SYMBOL	NAME	PROTONS	NEUTRONS	ELECTRONS	NOTES
Na	sodium (Latin: natrium)	11	12	11	Na is so active it is found only in compounds. Na is one element in table salt.
Mg	magnesium	12	12	12	A soft, silvery metal needed for muscle and nerve action.
P	phosphorous	15	16	15	An active nonmetal needed for bones and teeth.
S	sulfur	16	16	16	A yellow solid needed for enzymes and protoplasm.
Cl	chlorine	17	18	17	Exists as Cl_2 a poisonous gas. In salt & stomach acid.
K	potassium (L. kalium)	19	20	19	A soft, active metal needed for muscle action.
Ca	calcium	20	20	20	A metal needed for bones and teeth.
Fe	iron (L. ferrum)	26	30	26	A metal needed in the blood to carry oxygen.
Cu	copper (L. cuprum)	29	35	29	A metal needed in tiny amounts for cells to work.
Zn	zinc	30	35	30	A metal needed in small amounts for tissues to work.
I	iodine	53	74	53	Exists as I_2 a purplish solid. Needed by the thyroid gland. Turns blue-black with starch in the starch test.

MOLECULES

Just as an individual atom is a single piece of an element, a MOLECULE is one individual piece of a COMPOUND. When atoms of hydrogen (H) and oxygen (O) join they form H_2O molecules. This happens quietly in your cells and when hydrogen gas explodes. The equation is:

$$2 H_2 (g) + 1 O_2 (g) \longrightarrow 2 H_2O + energy$$

The atoms of hydrogen in the H_2 gas molecules separate (the oxygens do the same) and then two atoms of hydrogen join one atom of oxygen to make water, H_2O. Gone are the explosive GAS and the gas needed for burning. In their place is water, which when cooled is a LIQUID. Cooled below 0 °C, water becomes a SOLID.

Hydrogen and oxygen are elements. Two atoms of hydrogen joined to just one atom of oxygen make one molecule of the compound WATER. Remember, atoms are pieces of elements, molecules are pieces of compounds. There are only 92 natural elements; there are millions of compounds.

In life science, we will concentrate on just a few of the millions of compounds. About 80% of you, and other organisms, is water. If you weigh 100 pounds (45.5 kg) almost 80 of those pounds (36.4 kg) is water! You might think I'm all wet, you'd be 80% correct. Most of the rest of your physical body is made of compounds with carbon in them called organic compounds. A future chapter on nutrition will discuss the very large molecules in three groups of compounds: carbohydrates (sugars and starches); lipids (fats and oils); and proteins (hair, muscles, and enzymes).

There are several small, inorganic compounds that you should know: NaCl is table salt; HCl is hydrochloric acid; and CO_2 is carbon dioxide.

MIXTURES

The 80 percent of you that is water is not pure water. In the water of your body are dissolved salts, gases, and organic compounds. This is similar to seawater. A MIXTURE is when different kinds of compounds are together but keep their own properties. The liquid part of your body (protoplasm) is a mixture of water and many other compounds. The liquid part of your blood (plasma) is a mixture. If you had to pick just one thing on earth most like your body's mixtures, what would it be? Remember, you are mostly water. In your body are oxygen and carbon dioxide gas. Many substances are dissolved in you.

The one thing on earth most like your body's liquids is seawater! The oceans are mostly water but contain dissolved oxygen and carbon dioxide as well as organic compounds. As a matter of fact, when your life began inside of your mother, you were surrounded by a little ocean all your own, the amniotic sac. It is because of these similarities that some people think all living things must have come, way back in time, from something in the oceans. But life is much more than just seawater. Organisms, even the most simple, are very neatly organized and well planned.

Are We Afraid of Chemicals

Why has the word "chemical" become so negative to many of us? Is it because of chemical spills, chemical warfare and chemical dependency?

One reason it is hard to think positively about chemicals is because many people are unfamiliar with chemicals, at least, their names. For example, do you have tetrahydrozoline hydrochloride in your home? You may recognize this chemical if I tell you it is one brand of non-prescription eyedrops.

Some chemicals are familiar such as aspirin, rayon, gold, oxygen and caffeine. It is when we hear a name like hydrogenated glucose syrup that many of us become uneasy, only to find out that this chemical is an ingredient in many sugarless gums.

Some people try to label chemicals as good or bad. They believe that bad chemicals cause tragedies. However, no chemical is bad or good. How they are used determines whether or not chemicals will be beneficial or harmful.

Many chemicals made by man are natural also. Hydrochloric acid is used in many industrial applications, but, it is also produced in your stomach, naturally! Do not fear chemicals, learn and understand them. (Adapted from *It Matters*, Box 381, Jefferson, WI, 53549)

CHAPTER 5 REVIEW

OBJECTIVES:

1. **Appreciate the size of atoms, molecules and organisms.**

2. **Understand the relationships between**
   A. atoms and elements; and
   B. molecules, compounds; and mixtures.

3. **Know at least 15 elements necessary for all organisms.**

4. **Draw models of atoms.**

PART I. Define the 14 keywords in Chapter 5.

PART II. Draw Bohr models, and label the nucleus and energy shells of:

   1. H   2. C   3. N
   4. O   5. Cl

See Figure 5-1 for a sample **Bohr model.** Refer to Figure 5-2 for the number of subatomic particles in each kind of atom.

PART III. Answer each with a full sentence.

1. Put the following seven terms in correct order from the smallest to largest:
   molecule   atom   human   neutron
   virus   nucleus   electron.

2. Which part of an atom determines what kind of an atom it is?

3. What is most of an atom's volume?

4. What is the formula for water?

5. How many atoms are in one molecule of water?

6. How many elements are in pure water?

7. Give three examples of elements.

8. List three examples of compounds.

9. Name three mixtures.

10. What is the one mixture on earth not in living things but most like them?

PART IV. Write each statement neatly and fill in the blank with the best answer.

1. Neutrons have a 0 charge and a mass of __?__ amu (amu = atomic mass unit).

2. Protons have a __?__ charge and a mass of one amu.

3. Electrons have a __?__ charge and almost no mass.

4. The element __?__ is the most abundant in your body.

5. The air is 78% nitrogen, an element needed in your body to make __?__.

6. __?__ is an explosive gas when in its diatomic form.

7. Organic compounds contain carbon which is usually a __?__ color as a solid.

8. The element __?__ is needed for combustion.

9. When iodine turns a blue-black color then __?__ is present.

10. Letters are to words as elements are to __?__.

PART V. Write each symbol. Then correctly spell the name of the element.

1. Ca	6. I	11. P
2. C	7. Fe	12. K
3. Cl	8. Mg	13. Na
4. Cu	9. N	14. S
5. H	10. O	15. Zn

PART VI. Make a bar graph showing:
      "The Elements"

Label the horizontal axis:
      C, H, O, N, & ALL OTHERS

Label the vertical axis
      "Percent of the Human Body"

Number the vertical axis from 0 to 100.

Include a title.

Refer to Figure 5-2 for your data.

CHAPTER 6 - CELLS

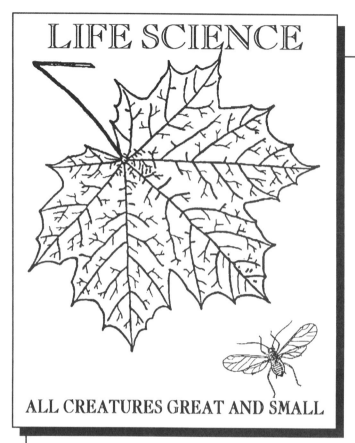

LIFE SCIENCE

ALL CREATURES GREAT AND SMALL

DOWN

1. Tube-like membranes that divide the cytoplasm.
3. The cell part where protein is made.
4. A double strand of DNA.
7. A microscopic living thing.
8. Vacuoles with digestive enzymes.
10. Movement of material from high to low concentration.
15. The part that holds all the cell parts together is the cell __?__.
17. A part of plant cells that helps support the plant.

Cells Crossword Puzzle

Use the keywords from this chapter to do the puzzle.
See how many you know before reading the chapter!
Complete the puzzle after completing this chapter.
Write in this book only if it belongs to you.
You may wish to make a copy of this page.

ACROSS

2. The part of a cell that holds the nucleus together.
5. The part of a plant cell where photosynthesis takes place.
6. The green pigment in plants.
9. Bubble-like parts of cells.
11. Term describing the cell membrane.
12. The movement of water through a cell membrane.
13. Circular movements of cytoplasm.
14. Cell parts that make secretions.
16. The dense center of a cell.
18. The basic unit of structure and function in living things.
19. A pair of spherical structures near the nucleus.
20. The liquid part of the nucleus.
21. Living matter.
22. Organelle for energy release.
23. The liquid part of the cell.

CHAPTER 6 CELLS

What would you plan to bring with you if you were going on a long submarine voyage (see Appendix I for the meanings of the parts of the word submarine)? What would you need if your vehicle were a spaceship? How about if you were just going into an underground cavern for a couple of days, what would you have to have?

To remain alive every creature, no matter how great or small, must have energy. With that energy each organism takes in food, almost all also take in oxygen gas. With that energy living things build bigger parts for themselves. With that energy every creature must get rid of waste products, including carbon dioxide gas.

What you would need on a submarine are the same things each part of your body must have: a source of energy (food), a way to use that energy, oxygen, raw materials to make new things from, and a way to get rid of carbon dioxide and other waste products. With a microscope and a drop of water from an aquarium (see Appendix I) you may observe tiny "submarines." Many of these MICROORGANISMS you may observe are made of just one CELL. Yet each cell, like a submarine or spacecraft, must get and use energy and remove wastes. For now, let's investigate the parts of a cell.

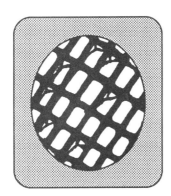

Figure 6-1 CELL WALLS OF CORK

For a science student the word cell means the unit of structure in living things. This includes all the tiny parts neatly packaged into each living cell. In the figure above only the cell walls of the dead cork cells is visible.

In 1667, Robert Hooke looked at a thin slice of cork and saw many empty boxes all packed closely together (see figure 6-1). After peering at many other plant parts through his microscope, Hooke discovered that all were made of these small boxes which he called cells. Cell means a very small room or compartment (see Appendix I). Later biologists realized that each cell in a living plant is filled with PROTOPLASM, living

material. It was discovered that animals are also made of cells but without the tiny box-like CELL WALL found only in plants. The cell wall helps support the plant's body.

Only the plant cells have tiny green parts called chloroplasts, used in photosynthesis. Inside each CHLOROPLAST is an important green chemical, CHLOROPHYLL, used by plants to capture sunlight.

Parts of Cells

Plants and animals are alike in that both are made up of cells. Your body is approximately 20 trillion individual cells each doing its own special job. Your cells are similar to all other cells in many ways. The thin CELL MEMBRANE encloses the CYTOPLASM in every living cell. The cytoplasm is where cell activities take place. A dense structure that controls the cell, the NUCLEUS, is made of NUCLEOPLASM and a NUCLEAR MEMBRANE. See Figures 6-2 & 6-3.

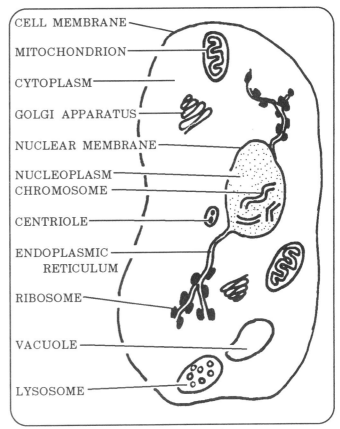

CELL MEMBRANE
MITOCHONDRION
CYTOPLASM
GOLGI APPARATUS
NUCLEAR MEMBRANE
NUCLEOPLASM
CHROMOSOME
CENTRIOLE
ENDOPLASMIC RETICULUM
RIBOSOME
VACUOLE
LYSOSOME

Figure 6-2 AN ANIMAL CELL

All of the parts shown in this animal cell are also in a plant cell except for the centrioles. The vacuoles in an animal cell are usually smaller than in plants.

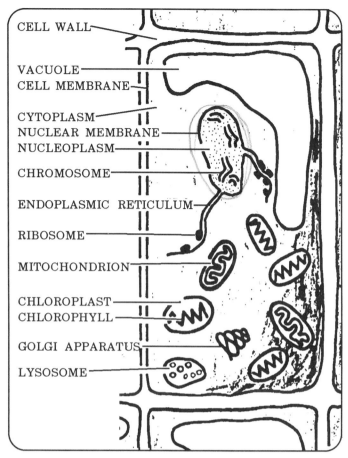

Figure 6-3 A PLANT CELL

CELL WALL
VACUOLE
CELL MEMBRANE
CYTOPLASM
NUCLEAR MEMBRANE
NUCLEOPLASM
CHROMOSOME
ENDOPLASMIC RETICULUM
RIBOSOME
MITOCHONDRION
CHLOROPLAST
CHLOROPHYLL
GOLGI APPARATUS
LYSOSOME

Plant cells have chloroplasts containing chlorophyll for making food. The vacuoles in plant cells are often larger than in animals.

Osmosis

With a good compound microscope you may be able to see some of the parts of cells illustrated in the diagrams above. The cell membrane (or plasma membrane) is SEMIPERMEABLE and will only allow certain molecules to pass into the cell. This makes each of your cell membranes very special. The cell membrane controls entry and exit from the cell. Normally, when there is a much greater concentration of a fluid in one area, the molecules move away from each other and go toward the lower concentration. DIFFUSION, this movement from higher to lower concentration (see Figure 6-4) occurs without the need for energy (passive transport). OSMOSIS is diffusion of water through a cell membrane. In osmosis the water molecules allowed through by the membrane move from higher to lower concentration.

Water, oxygen, glucose and carbon dioxide are examples of compounds whose molecules can pass through the cell membrane. By using some of its energy a cell can move materials from lower to higher concentration. Because energy is used this type of movement is called active transport.

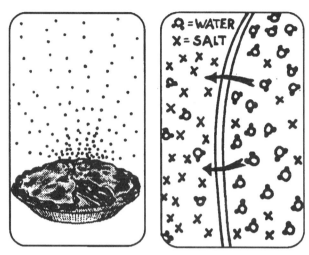

Figure 6-4 DIFFUSION AND OSMOSIS

Diffusion of the aroma from a hot apple pie illustrates how molecules move from higher to lower concentration. On the right side, osmosis causes water to move from the greater concentration of water (less salty side) to the more salty side of the membrane.

More parts of cells

The MITOCHONDRION is where the cell releases energy. Note the "mighty mitochondria" as the powerhouses of the cell. The cytoplasm is in constant circular motion called CYCLOSIS (see Appendix I). Cyclosis moves materials around the cell. VACUOLES may be empty (thus the name vacuole from "vacuum" or empty) or they may contain food or waste. The ENDOPLASMIC RETICULUM (en-doe-plas-mic ray-tic-u-lum) are tube-like parts on which reactions take place.

The two dot-like CENTRIOLES help animal cells make copies of themselves. Within the nuclear membrane, floating freely in the nucleoplasm is a spherical shape called the nucleolus. Also inside the nucleus are CHROMOSOMES, long thread-like chemicals that contain the instructions for the cell. The name chromosome comes from two Greek roots: chromas = color and soma = body. The strands of chromosomes are named colored bodies because they absorb the color very well when cells on a glass microscope slide are stained.

GOLGI BODIES, which look like stacks of pancakes, are storage centers. The LYSOSOME is a bubble-like digestion center. RIBOSOMES look like tiny dots on the endoplasmic reticulum. Ribosomes are important in making proteins.

The Cell Theory

So many parts in just one tiny cell! Some living things are just one cell. Average Adam is made of trillions of cells, and the giant redwood trees are made of many, many more cells than that! The point is **all creatures**, great and small **are made of cells**. This idea is the cell theory. The cell theory has three main statements.

1. The cell is the unit of structure and function of organisms. This means the activities we call living happen in each cell.

2. All living organisms are made up of one or more cells. This may be verified through use of the microscope.

3. Cells are made by other living cells. This statement seems obvious after studying life science in the laboratory but it causes a problem. Where did the first cell come from? The cell theory cannot explain the very beginnings of life.

Your trillions of cells are now very organized and each has a special shape to help with its function in your body. However, your body began as just one cell!

The organization of your cells and how your one, original cell came to be are discussed in the chapter on "Systems" and also in the chapter on Animal Behavior. For now, you need to be able to recognize the parts of the cell and understand the function of those parts.

CHAPTER 6 REVIEW

OBJECTIVES:
1. **Familiarity with the origin of the word cell.**
2. **Know the parts of a cell.**
3. **Identify differences in plant and animal cells.**
4. **Understand the function of cell parts.**

PART I. Diagram and label a plant cell.

PART II. Diagram and label an animal cell.

PART III. Define 23 keywords from this Chapter.

PART IV. Answer each with a full sentence.
1. What did Anton van Leeuwenhoek invent that allowed scientists to see cells?
2. Who looked at dead cork and used the term cells to describe what he saw?
3. What is the literal meaning of the word "cell?"
4. What is diffusion?
5. Is energy expended in diffusion?
6. Is diffusion passive or active transport?
7. What is osmosis?
8 & 9. List two statements of the cell theory.
10. How many cells was your body when your life began?

PART V. List and then label each term with:
　　　　N if it is part of the nucleus,
　　　　C if it is a part outside the nucleus,
　　　　P if it is a process carried out by the cell.

1. diffusion
2. chromosome
3. ribosome
4. mitochondria
5. lysosome
6. nucleoplasm
7. golgi bodies
8. cytoplasm
9. digestion
10. cyclosis
11. chloroplast
12. osmosis
13. nuclear membrane
14. vacuole
15. photosynthesis
16. cell wall
17. endoplasmic reticulum
18. protein synthesis
19. nucleolus
20. plasma membrane
21. centriole

PART VI. Answer with a full sentence using terms from PART V.
1. Which parts are only in plant cells?
2. Which part is only in animal cells?
3. Which part is usually large in plant cells but small in animal cells?
4. Which part holds genes, the instructions for how an organism looks?
5. Which part is also called the cell membrane?
6. Which part of a plant cell remains after the cell has died?
7. Which part is a green color?
8. Which part is needed in photosynthesis ?
9. Which part is the site of protein synthesis ?
10. Which part is where high energy ATP molecules are made to power the cell?
11. Which part is the area where food molecules are broken down?
12. Which part is for storing secretions?
13. Which part controls entry to the nucleus?
14. Which process is a circular movement ?
15. Which process is the movement of water through a membrane?

PART VII. Draw and fill in a chart as shown:

FUNCTIONS OF CELL ORGANELLES

Organelle	Sketch	Function

In the nucleus:

1. _____   1.   1. To hold the nucleus together

2. Nucleoplasm   2.   2. Medium for activity in the nucleus.

3. Chromosomes   3.   3. _____

Outside the nucleus:

4. _____   4.   4. Medium for activity in the cell.

5. _____   5.   5. _____

6. _____   6.   6. _____

7. _____   7.   7. Surface for chemical activity.

8. Ribosomes   8.   8. _____

9. _____   9.   9. _____

10. Lysosome   10.   10. _____

Only in animals:

11. _____   11.   11. Guides chromosomes in cell division

In plants only:

12. _____   12.   12. _____

13. _____   13.   13. _____

CHAPTER 7 - SIMPLEST CELLS

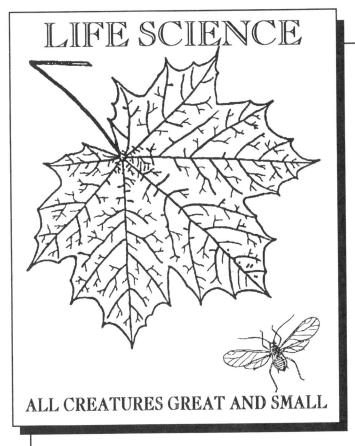

LIFE SCIENCE

ALL CREATURES GREAT AND SMALL

1. Using dead organisms as food.

2. A kingdom of organisms without nuclei.

4. A relationship in which one organism benefits at the expense of another.

5. The process of killing germs by heating milk.

6. The whip-like part of <u>Euglena</u> sp.

7. A virus that attacks bacteria.

8. A high energy molecule in cells.

9. A double strand of instructions.

13. Bumps on the roots of legumes.

15. Bacteria with thick walls.

Simplest Cells Crossword Puzzle

Use the keywords from this chapter to fill in the puzzle. See how many you know before reading the chapter! Complete the puzzle after completing this chapter.

Write in this book only if it belongs to you.
You may wish to make a copy of this page.

ACROSS

3. All the life processes at once.

7. Unicellular member of Cyanophyta.

10. DNA with a protein coat.

11. Ribonucleic acid.

12. A method of asexual reproduction in which a cell splits into two.

14. A relationship that is good for both organisms involved.

16. Organic matter in the soil.

17. A mass of bacteria.

18. A unicellular heterotroph in the Kingdom Monera, Phylum Schizomycetes.

19. Without free oxygen.

CHAPTER 7 SIMPLEST CELLS

The Necessities of Life

What are the necessary parts of an automobile? The radio? No, we could get rid of the radio. We could eliminate many of the parts of a car and it would still work. Take out the air conditioner, the windows, the spare tire, even the seats and the car can still operate. What are the necessities for the car to still work?

A car must have the gas in the tank, a source of energy. It must have the engine, a way to use the energy. It must have the transmission and wheels, a way to turn the energy into something useful. The car must have an exhaust to eliminate waste products. But all of these parts won't work without a key, to turn on the car and make it start.

The car without a key does not work. But of course, a key by itself is not going to work either.

Compare the parts of a car to the organelles and parts of a cell. The gas in the tank would be the food molecules in a food vacuole. The engine would be the mighty mitochondrion where the cell combines oxygen with glucose to make ATP molecules. The transmission and wheels would be the endoplasmic reticulum and the ribosomes where the energy in the ATPs is put to use making proteins. The exhaust system would be vacuoles and the cell membrane, which eliminate carbon dioxide and other wastes. The key is somewhat like DNA, in the chromosomes in the nucleus. This deoxyribonucleic acid turns on the cell and even instructs the cell what to do.

Is the car alive then, just like a cell? No! The cell can do more than a car. A cell can grow. A cell can repair itself, a life function we called synthesis. A cell can reproduce more cells like itself, another of the life functions. A fourth life function cells can do, and cars can't, is irritability. Cells react to changes in the environment.

VIRUSES

Viruses were mentioned back in the chapter on Seawater as the smallest "living" things. But why the double quotation marks? Living was in double quotes because viruses are really on the border between living and nonliving. A VIRUS is like the key in our comparison to a car. A virus by itself cannot do anything. A virus in the right kind of cell can turn on the cell and make the cells produce more viruses. The virus is not able to transport materials, to move, to take in food, to use the food to release energy or to excrete waste products. Viruses do not synthsize new chemicals in order to grow. The only one of the eight life functions you learned in the first chapter that a virus can perform is reproduction. But a virus can't even do that without the aid of a host cell.

A virus is a piece of DNA (or RNA, ribonucleic acid) in a protein wrapper. The DNA is a set of instructions which can control a cell's METABOLISM. See figure 7-1. Viruses that take over bacterial cells are called BACTERIOPHAGES (literally: bacteria eaters). We will study the effects of viral particles on you in the upcoming chapter on disease. We will classify viruses as a special group of almost living organisms.

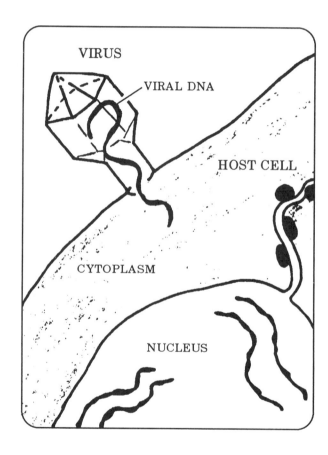

Figure 7-1 A VIRUS INVADES A CELL

The viral DNA moves into the cell and takes over the cell's metabolism. It then forces the host cell to make more viruses.

BACTERIA

The simplest living thing, a BACTERIUM, has no nuclear membrane and no organelles. Some types of bacteria have a FLAGELLUM, or even many flagella, for movement. At one time bacteria were considered part of the plant kingdom because most have a cell wall. Many bacteria get their food from dead organisms (this is called SAPROPHYTISM), or by infecting living organisms (PARASITISM). Some get their energy by "eating" minerals. A few bacteria can produce their own food by using sunlight and a purple chemical similar to chlorophyll.

The most outstanding characteristic of a bacterium is its ability to reproduce. Growing to a maximum size the single parent cell divides into two daughter cells. The process of splitting into two, called BINARY FISSION, may occur every thirty minutes under ideal conditions. There would be over 1,000,000 bacteria in just ten hours from a single parent cell! The mass of bacteria produced can be seen without a microscope. This COLONY has a characteristic color and shape which helps in identification. Colonies cannot grow forever because the necessities for life are removed as more bacteria are produced.

Remember the necessities of life: a source of energy, a way to use the energy to make new chemicals, and a way to get rid of waste products. As a bacterial colony grows larger and larger the source of energy is used up or the waste products build up to a point where the bacteria can no longer grow and undergo binary fission.

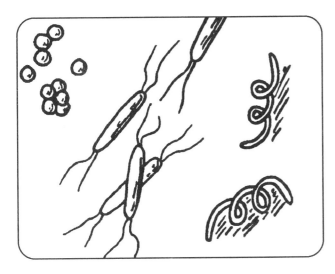

Figure 7-2 COCCI, BACILLI, SPIRILLA

Round, rod, and spiral types of bacterial cells may be seen under high magnification.

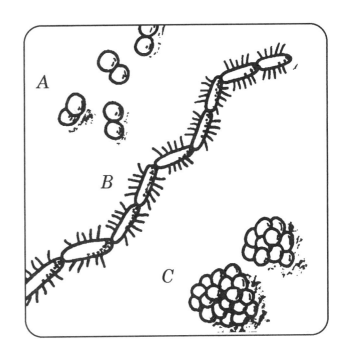

Figure 7-3 NAMING BACTERIA

Prefixes are used to describe the clusters of cells. A. diplococcus means a cluster of two cocci cells. B. Streptobacillus means a long chain of bacilli. C. Staphylococcus means a roundish clump of cocci.

Bacteria of any of the three basic shapes (see Figures 7-2 and 7-3) must have the right conditions for them to fulfill the necessities of life. Five conditions that affect bacterial growth are:

1. **Food** as a source of energy.

2. **Temperature** which allows the bacterial cell to carry out chemical reactions using the energy from the food. Very high temperatures kill bacteria (but some bacterial SPORES may survive even boiling water). The lower than room temperature of a refrigerator slows down bacterial growth but doesn't kill the microbes.

3. **Moisture** is needed for bacteria to grow. Drying out their food source slows the growth of bacteria. Too much salt or sugar in the bacteria's environment dries out the bacteria by osmosis.

4. **Light energy** is important for bacteria. Most bacteria grow better in darkness. Some are actually killed by sunlight.

5. **Oxygen** is necessary for the oxidation of food. AEROBIC bacteria get their oxygen from the air. However the tetanus bacterium (see the chapter on disease) and some others are actually killed by oxygen gas in the air. These ANAEROBIC bacteria get their oxygen from chemicals with oxygen atoms in them. Anaerobic bacteria

must survive as spores unless they end up where there is no free oxygen gas.

Now you should understand better why most foods must be kept refrigerated after opening. Foods are kept from being decayed by bacteria through a manipulation of the bacteria's environment. See figure 7-4. Before refrigerators many foods had to be "salted," some were "sugared." Many foods, such as breakfast cereals, are dried. Heating up milk at the dairy processing plant is a way to kill many of the bacteria in milk. This process, called PASTEURIZATION, is named after Louis Pasteur, a French chemist. Pasteur learned many of the things about bacteria that we use today to save food, and even lives, from the attacks of bacteria. Canned foods are cooked first at high temperatures then sealed up so that no oxygen is present. Canned foods may be good for many years. Frozen foods are kept at low temperatures but will eventually spoil.

Figure 7-4 FOOD VS. BACTERIA

Drying, salting, pasteurizing, refrigerating, freezing and canning foods are all ways of slowing bacterial decay.

You may think that bacteria equals germs. This would be incorrect. True, some bacteria are germs which cause human, animal or plant diseases; but life on earth would not continue without bacteria!

BENEFICIAL BACTERIA

You recall the necessities of life: energy, ways to use it to rearrange chemicals and excretion of wastes. There have lived on earth many millions of trillions of organisms. Their bodies contained the same oxygen, carbon, hydrogen and nitrogen atoms needed in your body. If the dinosaurs and the forests of long ago never decomposed then the chemicals needed for life today would be all used up. A fundamental idea of the chapter on ecology is that the earth's materials are in cycles. The elements needed for life go in circles from biotic (living) to abiotic (nonliving) and back again.

Life is possible only because bacteria decompose dead organisms and their products. This is the basic idea of a sewage treatment plant (figure 7-5) where bacteria are cultured to decompose the raw sewage.

Figure 7-5
BACTERIA WORK FOR PEOPLE

The large vats in a sewage treatment plant hold the sewage and bacteria while adding oxygen so that the decomposers can do their job. The bacteria break down organic compounds into simpler substances which may be added to the soil as fertilizer.

The result of this decay is the HUMUS in topsoil. Humus contains minerals and nitrates needed by plants. Nitrogen fixing bacteria are a special group that live in the NODULES of legumes like clover and peas. Nitrogen fixing bacteria take nitrogen gas from the air and "fix" it into nitrates. This helps the plants. The bacteria get their food, glucose, from the plants. Such a close relationship of two organisms, in which both live very close together and both benefit, is called MUTUALISM.

Bacteria are needed to provide many useful products including pickles, vinegar, sauerkraut, cheeses, tanned leather, linen, changing chopped corn into silage, and the production of many kinds of chemicals from molasses and sawdust.

One of the newest uses of bacteria is in genetic engineering. In this process a piece of DNA from another organism is put into a bacterial cell. The bacterial cell then produces a chemical usually made by the other organism. In the case of diabetes the object of genetic engineering is to produce human insulin in bacteria which can be injected into the diabetic whose body can't make its own hormone.

KINGDOM MONERA

Bacteria have no nuclear membrane or organelles. Similar to the bacteria, the BLUE GREEN ALGAE have no nuclear membrane and no organelles. The chlorophyll in blue green algae is not in chloroplasts but simply floating in the cytoplasm. Bacteria and blue green algae are unicellular (see Appendix I), but, the single cells sometimes stick together in clumps or filaments.

All organisms with no nuclear membrane and no organelles are grouped into the Kingdom MONERA. Monerans that carry out photosynthesis, the blue green algae, are in the Phylum Cyanophyta (see Appendix I). Monerans that cannot make their own food by photosynthesis, the bacteria, are in the Phylum Schizomycophyta. Unlike viruses, the Monerans carry out seven or eight of the life functions and may be called the simplest living things. Figure 7-6 may help you organize some of the facts that you must remember from this chapter on the Simplest Cells.

The next four chapters outline the other four kingdoms of living things.

FIGURE 7-6 KINGDOM MONERA
(At the right)

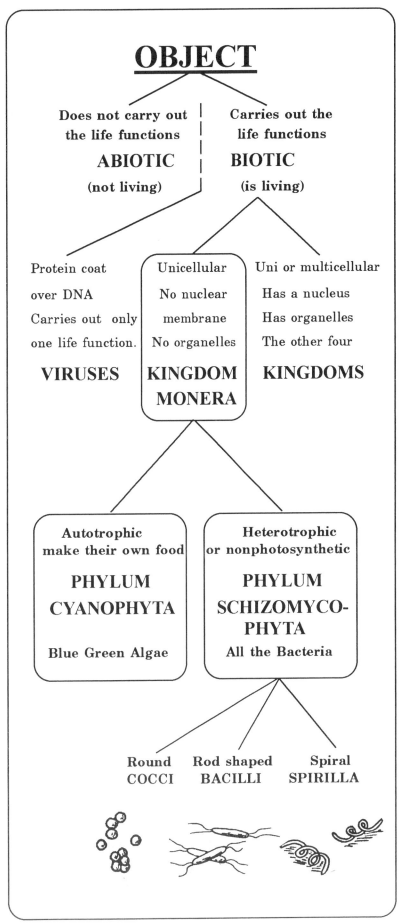

CHAPTER 7 REVIEW

OBJECTIVES:

1. Recall the life functions.

2. Learn three conditions necessary for life.

3. Know the characteristics of Monerans.

PART I. Using a full sentence, list the eight life functions (see Chapter 1 if necessary).

PART II. Use life functions from part I to answer each question with a full sentence.

1. Which is the only function done by viruses?
2. Which functions cannot be done by a car?
3. A flagellum is used for which function?
4. Which function is the most outstanding characteristic of bacteria.
5. Binary fission is one type of which function?

PART III. Using a full sentence, list the three basic necessities of life.

PART IV. Thinking of bacteria, associate one of the following environmental conditions with each statement. Answer by writing each statement followed by the condition.

FOOD   TEMPERATURE   MOISTURE
LIGHT   and   OXYGEN

1. A refrigerator helps keep food fresh.

2. Do not use a can of peas with a tiny hole in it.

3. A box of cereal is still good after a month.

4. Jars are boiled before making jelly.

5. A carpet in the sun becomes less musty.

6. Glucose is an example.

7. Pioneers ate salt pork.

8. Potato chips are in air tight bags.

9. Pasteurization.

10. Leaves, trees, frogs, birds, algae and you.

PART V. Define the 20 keywords from Chapter 7 Simplest Cells. Set up your paper as you were instructed in Chapter 1.

PART VI. Rewrite each statement using one of the 20 keywords to fill in the blank.

1. Chromosomes are made of a double stranded chemical called __?__ .

2. A __?__ carries out only one life function: reproduction.

3. Every organism must get energy. That energy in the cell is saved as __?__ molecules.

4. The tetanus bacterium is __?__, not able to use oxygen gas from the air.

5. Kingdom __?__ contains organisms without a nuclear membrane.

6. Phylum Cyanophyta contains the __?__ which have chlorophyll but no chloroplasts.

7. A bacterium may form a __?__ to survive drying out.

8. Milk from the farm is sent to the dairy for __?__ before going to the market.

9. __?__ is the relationship between nitrogen fixing bacteria and clover in which both benefit.

10. The DNA of viral particles invades host cells and takes over its __?__.

11. A bacterial cell can undergo __?__ approximately every 30 minutes.

12. Some bacilli use a __?__ to move around.

13. Without __?__ soil is not as fertile.

14. In __?__ the microbe harms its host.

15. __?__ is short for ribonucleic acid.

PART VII. Neatly write a paragraph explaining four ways bacteria are useful and beneficial for mankind.

CHAPTER 8 - PROTISTS

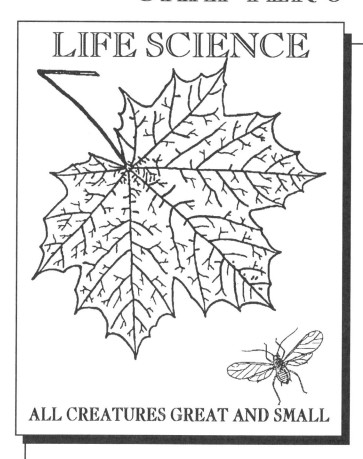

LIFE SCIENCE

ALL CREATURES GREAT AND SMALL

Protists Crossword Puzzle

Use the keywords from this chapter to fill in the puzzle. See how many you know before reading the chapter! Complete the puzzle after completing this chapter.

ACROSS

1. A type of reproduction in which nuclear material is exchanged.

3. Subdivisions of a class.

6. Greek word meaning group.

7. Whip-like structure in Euglena.

9. A small nucleus in Paramecium.

10. _?_ nomenclature: two names.

12. Hair like structures used for locomotion by some protists.

14. The science of naming things.

16. Part of protists for excretion.

20. The five largest taxons.

21. Light sensitive part of Euglena.

CHAPTER 8 PROTISTS
A Microscopic Menagerie

The Kingdom Monera contains organisms without a well defined nucleus and no organelles. We call Monerans the simplest living things. Now we will investigate a group of microbes that are truly the first complete cells in the current system of classification. This large number of similar organisms is Kingdom Protista.

You may see from **Appendix I** that the root of Protista is the Greek "proto" which means first. Thus the first complete unicellular organisms in our system of naming are called protists.

TAXONOMY

Before we look into the microscopic world of the Kingdom Protista we must understand the worldwide system used to group living things. Aristotle, a Greek from 350 years before Christ, gathered organisms from many parts of the world. He and his students tried to arrange the plants and animals into some kind of reasonable order. Greek for order is "taxis" and Aristotle is considered the starting point of TAXONOMY (see Appendix I). Theophrastus, one of Aristotle's interested students, based his writings about plants on detailed study and careful classifications. Almost 2000 years later an English botanist, John Ray, classified nearly all of the plants around Cambridge. Because of Ray the word species came to mean one kind of organism.

Building on John Ray's start, Carolus Linnaeus developed the basis for the modern system of taxonomy. Just when Linnaeus was studying living things people began using a surname as well as a first name. Linnaeus decided to use two names for each different kind of organism. This two name system of naming is called BINOMIAL NOMENCLATURE. In 1735 Linnaeus published a book, *Systemae Naturae*, in which he named thousands of plants and animals. We still use most of those names today. The most important thing Linnaeus did was to use a seven TAXON system with Latin names, the last two of which are called the scientific name.

The naming of organisms is important so that there is no confusion in trying to control diseases and pests. Taxonomy is necessary if we are to successfully preserve wildlife in our environment. Just think, with over 200 000 kinds of beetles, just one of the thousands of kinds of insects, there certainly could be confusion! Remember that any system of classification must separate well over a million known organisms.

All these creatures, from the great dinosaurs to the tiny monerans, are put into just 5 giant groups called KINGDOMS. In the last chapter we noted that a kingdom may be divided into smaller taxons, called PHYLA. Even in this chapter on protists, and the next on fungi, we will not use the other five taxons. For our work on plants and animals however, we must know that each phylum may be divided into CLASSES, each class into ORDERS, each order into FAMILIES, each family is divided into GENERA, and each genus into SPECIES.

You will see in Figure 8-1 that the genus and species, the **scientific name**, are always **underlined**. The **first letter** of the **genus** name is **capitalized**. The **species** name is always **lowercase**. Sometimes you may see "Ameba sp." which indicates that there are several species referred to but all of them are amebas.

EXAMPLE	RED OAK	HOUSE FLY	HUMAN
Name	(Quercus rubra)	(Musca domestica)	(Homo sapiens)
TAXONS			
Kingdom	Plantae	Animalia	Animalia
Phylum	Tracheophyta	Arthropoda	Chordata
Subphylum	Spermopsida	—————	Vertebrata
Class	Angiospermae	Insecta	Mammalia
Subclass	Dicotyledonae	—————	—————
Order	Fagales	Diptera	Primates
Family	Fagaceae	Muscidae	Hominidae
Genus	Quercus	Musca	Homo
species	rubra	domestica	sapiens

Figure 8-1 SAMPLE CLASSIFICATIONS

Kingdoms are the largest divisions and contain varied organisms that only have a few characteristics in common. Species is the smallest taxon, containing 1 kind of organism.

Figure 8-2 TAXON NAMES
Use the saying to remember the groups in order.

5 of	King	Phillip's	Classes	Ordered	Frozen	Grape	sodas
	Kingdom	Phylum	Class	Order	Family	Genus	species

Perhaps a comparison will help you understand how the taxons go together. Let our country be one of the kingdoms, then the states could be phyla, this county the class, this town an order, your street the family. Your home could be the genus and your room would be the species taxon. Study figure 8-2 to memorize the taxon names in order.

How would you separate all living things? Some creatures live on land, many can fly, a great number of organisms are herbivores (plant eaters). Shall we put everything found in the sky into the same group? That will put a bat, a housefly and a blue jay all in the same small taxon! The wings of each organism are actually very different from the others. A fly's wings are a thin membrane; the bat's, a fold of furry skin; and the last is covered with feathers. These three organisms are very different. We cannot correctly group organisms by where they are found, nor by what they can do, nor even by what they eat!

Think back to how we divided the bacteria and the blue green algae from all the other living things. They have no nuclear membrane and no real organelles. Then we divided these monerans because some have chlorophyll (Cyanophyta) but the bacteria (Schizomycophyta) do not. Scientists use the structure of organisms for classification. Using structure as the basis of taxonomy indicates that killer whales are more like us than they are like fish! We will see in the chapter on the Kingdom Animalia why this is true.

KINGDOM PROTISTA

To belong to the varied Kingdom PROTISTA an organism must have a nuclear membrane and organelles. But wait, you have those! You're not a protist. There is one more characteristic of protists: most of them are UNICELLULAR or very, very simple MULTICELLULAR organisms. Each cell of a protist does everything for itself. In the more complex organisms, you or a fly or an oak, there are special cells for special jobs.

Look at Figure 8-3, the main phyla of protists.

You will not be required to memorize all those long names, but you should be able to describe what all those phyla of the Kingdom Protista have in common. The euglena, ameba, and paramecium all have organelles, a nuclear membrane and a unicellular body.

PHYLUM - COMMON NAME - NOTES

EXAMPLE

Euglenophyta - Euglenoids - Plant and animal like **Euglena** (Fig. 8-7)

Chrysophyta - Golden algae - Have chloroplasts **Chromulina**

Pyrrophyta - Dinoflagellates - Two flagella **Ceratium**

Sarcodina - Ameboid protozoa - Have pseudopods **Ameba** (Fig. 8-4)

Ciliata - Ciliates - Move by cilia **Paramecium** (Fig. 8-6)

Mastigophora - Zooflagellates - Most are parasites **Trypanosoma**

Sporozoa - Sporozoans - All are parasites **Plasmodium**

Myxomycota - Slime molds - Decay organisms **Physarum**

Figure 8-3 KINGDOM PROTISTA

All the members of Kingdom Protista are unicellular or simple multicellular organisms with organelles and each cell has a nuclear membrane (See figures 8-4, 8-6 and 8-7).

AMEBA

A simple microorganism that has inspired many science fiction creatures is the ameba. Actually there are many species in the genus Ameba. The name ameba means "no shape" or "changing shape." This protozoan uses a PSEUDOPOD for locomotion. See Figure 8-4. An ameba ingests its food by engulfing it (Figure 8-5). It's contractile vacuole is a bubble like organelle that squeezes excess water out of the ameba. To reproduce, the ameba splits into two after making copies of the DNA in its nucleus.

PARAMECIUM

The paramecium is one of the most complex protists. If you take some sediment from the bottom of a pond with some pond water you may see both the ameba and the paramecium. Add some grass to the culture as well. The paramecia will be on the bottom debris feeding on bacteria. The amebas concentrate on the decaying grass. Figure 8-6 shows the slipper like shape of the paramecium. Its unicellular body is covered with tiny, short "hair-like" structures, CILIA, used for locomotion. Unlike the ever changing shapeless ameba, the paramecium has a rather stiff cell membrane called a PELLICLE with an oral groove in it. This complex little creature has two nuclei in each cell: one is a MACRONUCLEUS and the other a MICRONUCLEUS. The paramecium contains star like CONTRACTILE VACUOLES used to excrete life's waste products. The paramecium often undergoes binary fission, splitting into two, or it may reproduce by CONJUGATION. The micronucleus is needed during conjugation, which is a type of sexual reproduction.

See Figure 8-6 on the next page.

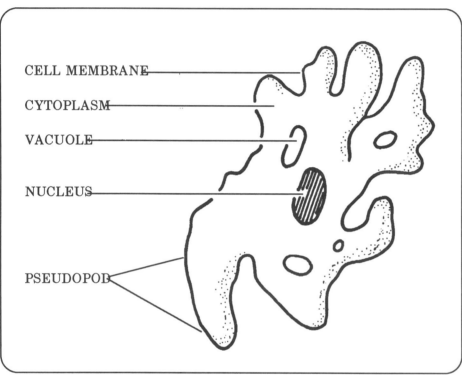

CELL MEMBRANE
CYTOPLASM
VACUOLE
NUCLEUS
PSEUDOPOD

Figure 8-4 AN AMEBA
The ameba moves by flowing its cytoplasm
into one of its "false feet."

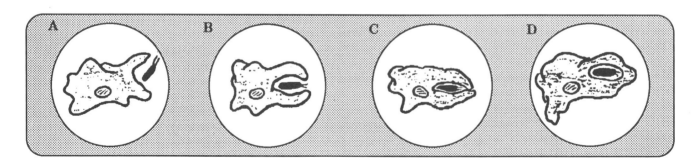

Figure 8-5 THE ENGULFING PROCESS

Like the "blob" of science fiction fame, the ameba flows over and around an unlucky flagellate!

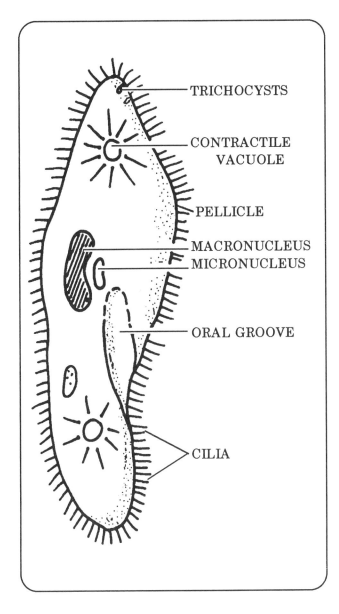

Figure 8-6 THE PARAMECIUM

The paramecium is a microscopic protozoan that feeds on monerans. It is one of the more complex members of **Kingdom Protista.**

EUGLENA

The euglena is an in between plant and animal protist. It contains both chloroplasts for making food and a gullet for ingesting food. The euglena also has an EYESPOT. It has a soft pellicle with spiral shaped thicker parts. The most noticable part of the euglena is its one long FLAGELLUM. See figure 8-7. The euglena reproduces by binary fission.

Figure 8-7 THE EUGLENA
(BELOW)

The euglena has the ability to make food through photosynthesis. Like you and I however, it must ingest some of the amino acids it needs. Like the paramecium, euglena has a pellicle. As a result it has a definite shape.

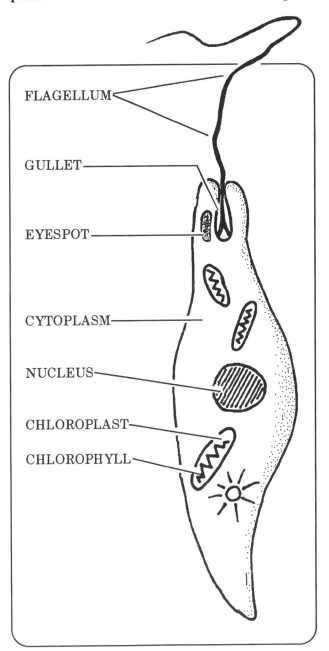

CHAPTER 8 REVIEW

OBJECTIVES:
1. **Understand the concept of classification.**
2. **Identify characteristics of the Kingdom Protista.**
3. **Diagram and label three different protists.**

PART I. Define the "taxonomy terminology."
1. binomial nomenclature
2. taxon
3. taxonomy
4. kingdoms
5. phyla
6. classes
7. orders
8. families
9. genera
10. species

PART II. Use a full sentence and terms from part I to answer each question.
1. What is the science of naming creatures?
2. Which taxon contains just 1 kind of organism?
3. What is the term for using two names to identify an organism?
4. What are the two taxons used in a scientific name?
5. Which division is largest?
6. There are only 5 of which group?
7. Families are subdivisions of which group?
8. Animals which are almost, but not exactly the same, would be in which groups together?
9. Which taxon could contain animals that are most different?
10. Different protists in the same phylum must also belong to the same ___?___. (Which one of the other taxons?)

PART III. Answer each with a full sentence.
1. Which ancient Greek started the first orderly classification of living things?
2. What was the most important thing Carolus Linnaeus did for taxonomy?
3. Which 2 taxons make up the scientific name?
4. Are the house fly and the human in the same kingdom?
5. Can the red oak and an unborn baby be in the same species?
6. List three rules for writing scientific names correctly.
7. What is your scientific name?
8. What do scientists use as the basis for classifying organisms?
9. Explain the basis for why the Monerans were placed into a separate Kingdom.
10. Are two organisms in the same genus very similar or very different?

PART IV. Diagram and label an ameba.

PART V. Diagram and label a paramecium.

PART VI. Diagram and label the euglena.

PART VII. Define the following "protist parts and processes."
1. cilia
2. conjugation
3. contractile vacuole
4. eyespot
5. flagellum
6. macronucleus
7. micronucleus
8. multicellular
9. pellicle
10. Protista
11. pseudopod
12. trichocysts
13. unicellular

PART VIII. If false, change the *italicized* word to make the statement true. Neatly write each full statement once it is true.

1. Kingdom *Monera* has unicellular organisms with organelles.

2. Diatoms and golden algae belong to the same *Phylum*.

3. Euglena, ameba, and paramecium belong to the same *Phylum*.

4. The ameba moves by means of a *flagellum*.

5. The *paramecium* has cilia for locomotion.

6. The euglena has a *flagellum* to help it perform the life function of irritability.

7. The *ameba* is both plant and animal like.

8. The ameba can reproduce by *binary fission*.

9. All *protists* have a nucleus, with a membrane, that controls the cell.

10. The oak tree and the paramecium share *two* of the same taxons.

CHAPTER 9 - THE FUNGI

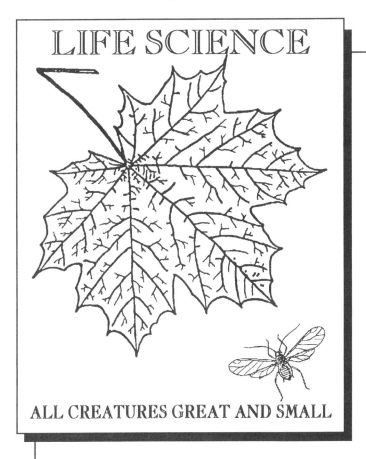

LIFE SCIENCE

ALL CREATURES GREAT AND SMALL

DOWN

1. Root-like structures of fungi.

2. Asexual reproduction in which the cytoplasm is divided unequally.

3. The ring on the stipe of a fungus.

4. The chemical in the cell walls of fungi.

6. Organism that must feed on other organisms to survive.

10. The "stem" of a mushroom.

11. Tiny single cells that can produce a whole new fungus.

13. A fan shaped mass of hyphae.

15. The rounded top part of a fungus.

The Fungi Crossword Puzzle

Use the keywords from this chapter to fill in the puzzle. See how many you know before reading the chapter! Complete the puzzle after completing this chapter.

ACROSS

2. Club shaped structures on which some fungi produce spores.

5. A mass of hyphae.

7. Kingdom of heterotrophs with chitinous cell walls.

8. A person who studies fungi.

9. A sac-like structure where spores are produced in some fungi.

12. Thin part of a mushroom that produces spores.

14. Thread-like body of a fungus.

16. A cup-like structure at the base of the stipe of some fungi.

Write in this book only if it belongs to you.
You may wish to make a copy of this page.

CHAPTER 9 THE FUNGI
Almost Plants

Dead Man's Fingers, Witches' Snot, Destroying Angel, Death Cap,... These almost sound like the names of rock groups Average Adam tells his friends not to listen to! (See Figure 9-1) Actually they are the names of members of the kingdom FUNGI. Unlike the Monera, fungi have a nuclear membrane and organelles. Unlike the Protista, most fungi have a cell wall made of CHITIN. Each member of the varied Kingdom Fungi is HETEROTROPHIC. Each assimilates nutrients digested outside of the cells. Many members of the fungi have specialized cells in a multicellular stage of their life cycle.

Figure 9-1 DEAD MAN'S FINGERS
Xylaria polymorpha, a woodland Ascomycete sometimes appears just like its name sounds.

You, like Average Adam, may not wish to become a MYCOLOGIST but fungi are a part of your life! You should recognize mushrooms, puffballs, toadstools, mold and yeast as fungi.

You should know that fungi help in making bread and wine. You may have suffered from athlete's foot or ringworm, these fungal parasites are discussed in the Chapter on diseases. Helpful and harmful drugs are made from fungi. Like the bacteria, the fungi are decay organisms that decompose organic chemicals into the simple substances needed to keep life going on earth.

The four main phyla of Kingdom Fungi are named according to how their members reproduce. See Figure 9-3 on the next page. Zygomycota is made of two words: zygo = zygote, mycota = fungus. Black bread mold (Rhizopus sp.) is one

of these conjugation fungi. All the members of Phylum Zygomycota use conjugation to combine nuclear material and form a zygote.

Saprolegnia, a water mold, has a non-motile egg cell that is fertilized for reproduction. The egg cell causes this phylum of fungi to be called Oomycota or "egg fungi."

Most species of fungi are members of Phylum Ascomycota. Now you already know that "mycota" means fungus. "Asco" is from a root word ASCUS meaning sack. The spores produced for reproduction are inside a microscopic sack and thus the Phylum Ascomycota are the "sac fungi."

Yeast is an Ascomycete that can also reproduce by BUDDING. See Figure 9-2. Every time you eat a roll or bread you are ingesting yeast that was added live to the dough to make it rise.

Saccharomyces cerevisiae, a species of yeast, can carry out anaerobic respiration in which the sugar in grape juice is converted into wine. The alcohol and carbon dioxide are actually the waste products left when the yeast uses energy from the glucose in the grape juice.

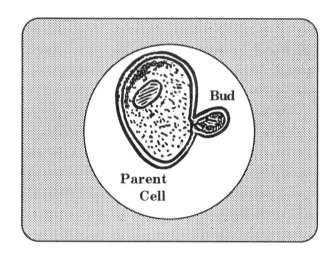

Figure 9-2 BUDDING IN YEAST
Budding as a form of asexual reproduction, is similar to binary fission except the cytoplasm is not evenly divided between the parent cell and the bud.

Budding, a form of asexual reproduction, is similar to binary fission, except the cytoplasm is unevenly divided between the parent cell bud.

In 1928 Dr. Alexander Fleming had an experiment that failed because his bacterial cultures were being killed by a mold, Penicillium notatum. That failure turned into one of the

continued on page 52

Figure 9-3 THE PHYLA OF KINGDOM FUNGI

This is a very simplified key leaving out most technical details and some groups of fungi.

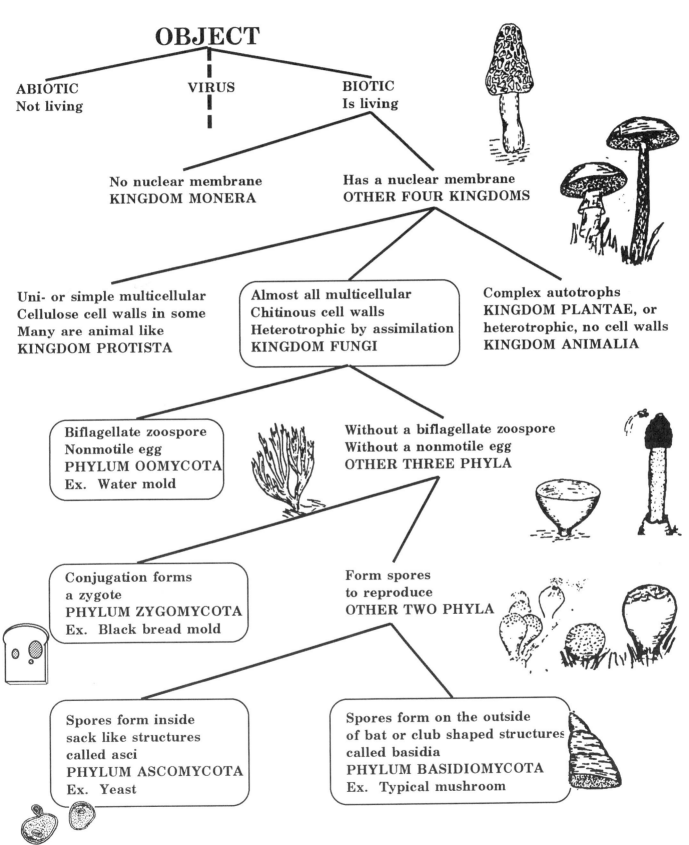

OBJECT

ABIOTIC
Not living

VIRUS

BIOTIC
Is living

No nuclear membrane
KINGDOM MONERA

Has a nuclear membrane
OTHER FOUR KINGDOMS

Uni- or simple multicellular
Cellulose cell walls in some
Many are animal like
KINGDOM PROTISTA

Almost all multicellular
Chitinous cell walls
Heterotrophic by assimilation
KINGDOM FUNGI

Complex autotrophs
KINGDOM PLANTAE, or
heterotrophic, no cell walls
KINGDOM ANIMALIA

Biflagellate zoospore
Nonmotile egg
PHYLUM OOMYCOTA
Ex. Water mold

Without a biflagellate zoospore
Without a nonmotile egg
OTHER THREE PHYLA

Conjugation forms
a zygote
PHYLUM ZYGOMYCOTA
Ex. Black bread mold

Form spores
to reproduce
OTHER TWO PHYLA

Spores form inside
sack like structures
called asci
PHYLUM ASCOMYCOTA
Ex. Yeast

Spores form on the outside
of bat or club shaped structures
called basidia
PHYLUM BASIDIOMYCOTA
Ex. Typical mushroom

greatest life saving discoveries of all time. Dr. Fleming named the bacterial killing agent penicillin. Today penicillin is produced using a different species but the very same genus.

The most familiar fungi produce tiny spores on microscopic "baseball bats" called basidia. The Phylum Basidiomycota, or club fungi, are named that because of the shape of the basidia.

Mushrooms are the most obvious basidiomycete fungi of all. Next time someone gets a pizza with mushrooms, see if you can identify some of these parts. The CAP is the unbrella shaped top. Underneath the cap are the GILLS. The stem is correctly termed a STIPE and it often has a ring around it below the cap called the ANNULUS. Sometimes there is a cup like structure at the bottom called a VOLVA. See Figure 9-4. These structures are all made of thin filaments of cells called HYPHAE. A mass of hyphae is called MYCELIUM. Root like hyphae, RHIZOIDS break off when you pick a mushroom from the ground.

Figure 9-5 A STINK HORN
Insects attracted to this sticky, and stinky, fungus help spread the spores. All fungi are heterotrophs and need a food source.

Under the bark of a dead tree you may see a beautiful fan shaped STOLON formed of hyphae. The single cells used to make a new mushroom, SPORES are formed on the BASIDIA on the gills. Not all fungi have gills (Figure 9-5).

The gilled mushroom is Average Arnold's idea of a fungus. However, fungi come in many shapes and colors. Some people would call Amantia phalloides a toadstool because it is poisonous. Its nickname, death cap, clearly indicates the need to be an expert before deciding to eat any wild fungi. Figure 9-6 shows a bracket fungus used by artists. You may have stomped on some puffballs (Lycoperdon sp.) and sent millions of spores into the air. Some basidiomycetes that cause plant diseases are called rusts and smuts. Wheat rust (Puccina graminis) and corn smut (Ustilago maydis) are two of the most important fungal parasites of agricultural crops in America.

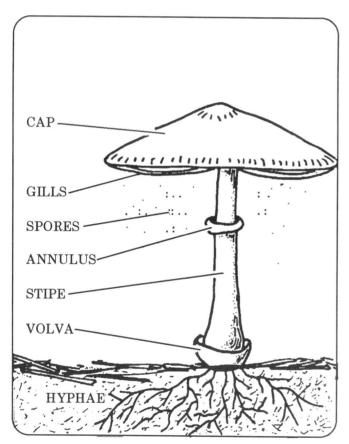

Figure 9-4 A TYPICAL MUSHROOM

Mushrooms are the best known members of the Phylum Basidiomycota. They serve an important ecological role as decomposers.

Figure 9-6 ARTIST'S CONK

Ganoderma applanatum is a common type of club fungus which grows like a shelf on dead trees.

CHAPTER 9 REVIEW

OBJECTIVES:

1. Know the characteristics of Kingdom Fungi

2. List beneficial fungi.

3. Carefully diagram and label a generalized mushroom.

PART I. Using full sentences, explain how fungi are different from monerans.

PART II. Using full sentences, explain how fungi are different from protistans.

PART III. Using a full sentence, list four characteristics of Kingdom Fungi.

PART IV. Diagram and label a generalized mushroom.

PART V. Define the 17 keywords from Chapter 9 Fungi.

Part VI. Write each statement neatly using one of the keywords to fill in the blank.
1. The _?_ are plant like organisms without true roots, stems, or leaves and no chlorophyll.
2. A __?__ is fascinated by the variety and wierdness of fungi, and so she studies them in detail.
3. Fungi must assimilate already digested foods because they are __?__.
4. The ring on some mushrooms is called an __?__ from the same root word that is in annual, meaning 1 ring around the sun.
5. The __?__ holds the cap up off the ground.
6. Almost all fungi are made of thin strands called __?__.
7. If you place a mushroom's cap on a piece of paper you may see a __?__ print after a day.
8. Blue Green Algae have a cellulose cell wall but fungi have __?__ in their cell walls.
9. The sac shaped structure containing spores in the Ascomycetes is called an __?__.
10. In the Basidiomycetes the spores form on club shaped structures called __?__.

PART VII. Writing a paragraph with complete sentences, describe five (5) ways that fungi are involved in your life.

NOTICE: CONTINUE READING ONLY IF YOU HAVE A TOADSTOOL TEMPERMENT, A MUSHROOM MENTALITY, OR A MUSTY, MOLDY, MYCOLOGICAL MADNESS!

The Kingdom Fungi is well known for including important decomposers. There is a fungus among'us, Ann Ulus, who wishes to ascus a few rotten riddles.

1. Why did Average Adam, with his toy gun, need some mushrooms?
2. Why were the police investigating the fan shaped hyphae?
3. What did the yeast cell say to the baker?
4. Why did Haphazard Harriet think fungi were fish?
5. What do you call a boy who is always joking?
6. What did Average Arnold say when he had to pay a lot to the doctor?
7. Why couldn't the cell in the ascus pay to go to the movies?
8. What did Mrs. Franklin tell Benjamin when it began to thunder?
9. What is the name of the special class where Eskimos teach their dogs to pull their dog sleds?

Answers

1. He needed CAPS.
2. It was STOLON (stolen).
3. This BUD's for you.
4. They have GILLS.
5. FUNGI (fun guy).
6. That was a HYPHAE (high fee).
7. Because she'SPORE (she's poor).
8. Bring your CHITIN (kite in).
9. MUSHROOM ("mush'i" room)

CHAPTER 10 - PLANTS
(part A)

The Crossword for part B is on page 69.

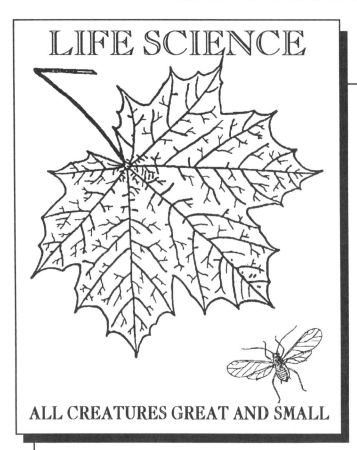

LIFE SCIENCE

ALL CREATURES GREAT AND SMALL

DOWN

2. A single cell that can produce a new moss or fern.
3. Literally means "naked seed."
4. The system of tube-like cells in plants.
6. Another name for most evergreens.
8. A class of Tracheophytes that do not produce seeds. (ex. ferns).
10. A phylum of plants with no vascular system (ex. mosses and ferns).
11. The kingdom of autotrophs with cellulose cell walls.
12. A seed leaf.
13. Spores are made inside of these.
18. Plants with two cotyledons.

Introduction Crossword Puzzle

Use the keywords from this chapter to fill in the puzzle.
See how many you know before reading the chapter!
Complete the puzzle after completing this chapter.

ACROSS

1. An underground, horizontal stem that can produce a new plant.
5. Plants with one cotyledon and flower parts in threes.
7. The phylum of plants with a vascular system.
9. Clusters of sporangia on the undersides of fern fronds.
14. Root-like structure on mosses.
15. Organisms that make food.
16. A class of Phylum Tracheophyta with seeds hidden in a fruit.
17. A starch storage area in algae.
19. The leafy part of a fern.
20. A symbiotic relationship which benefits both organisms.

Write in this book only if it belongs to you.
You may wish to make a copy of this page.

Chapter 10 PLANTS
The Autotrophs

PART A - TAXONOMY

PLANTS

For a moment try to think of all the things you use that are made from, or result from, plants. Looking at Figure 10-1 may remind you of some plant uses.

Figure 10-1 PLANT USES
Plants and their products are a big part of any picture where people live and play.

With a little help I thought of more than 150 uses we make of plants. To see if you came up with uses that I didn't think of, check **Appendix VI**. The fact is that our lives are intertwined with the plant kingdom so closely that we could not live without plants. The action of plants in preventing erosion and maintaining water sheds is often overlooked. Every time you munch on a snack these 2 uses of plants allowed it to happen.

Food uses are approximately one half of my list of plant uses. Of course beef, pork, fish, lobsters, clams, shrimp and other animal products all depend on plants. All members of the Kingdom PLANTAE are AUTOTROPHS. That means they are "self feeders." Plants make their own food through photosynthesis. They make all of our food too, even though some plant food is changed into animal food before we eat it! There's more on how plants take sunlight and make food in a future chapter on nutrition. Right now our goal is to clearly answer: What is a plant? Then we will briefly outline the different kinds of plants.

Unlike the monerans, plants have nuclear membranes and organelles. Unlike protistans, the plants have multicellular bodies with special cells for special jobs. Unlike fungi, plants have cellulose cell walls and chlorophyll. Because plants contain chlorophyll, they can make their own food. See Figure 10-2 for an outline of the classification of the Kingdom Plantae.

Figure 10-2 KINGDOM PLANTAE

All members of the huge plant kingdom have several important structural characteristics in common.

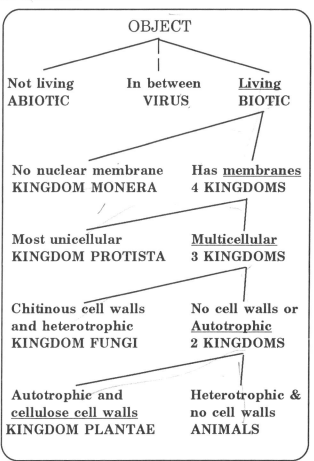

ALGAE

The plant kingdom contains a tremendous variety of creatures, some great, some small; but all are autotrophs with cellulose cell walls. There are five main phyla in the Kingdom Plantae. One, Phylum Chlorophyta gets its name because of chlorophyll, the green chemical needed for photosynthesis. The Green Algae is a commonly used name for Phylum Chlorophyta. Some of these green algae are important starting points for the food chains in ponds and lakes near you.

One green algae, Spirogyra sp., also called pond silk, is interesting to study under the microscope. Looking at Figure 10-3 you should be able to identify the cell wall (1) and the chloroplast (2). The ribbon like chloroplast is in the shape of a spiral, thus the name - Spirogyra! With a compound microscope you could see for yourself the dense nucleus (3), and sometimes a vacuole (4), as well as the cell wall and the spiral chloroplast.

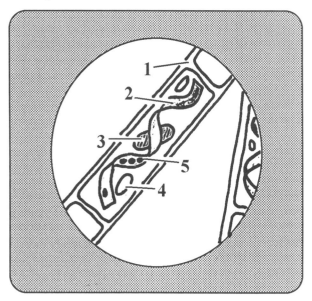

Figure 10-3 SPIROGYRA
A member of the Phylum Chlorophyta, the Spirogyra is one of the more complex green algae that exists as filaments in freshwater ponds and lakes.

A PYRENOID in spirogyra is a storage area for starch. Pyrenoids (see #5 in Figure 10-3) are only visible if the algae has been in light for several hours before being viewed. In addition, to see the starch bodies, they must be stained with iodine first. The brown iodine solution turns blue-black when it reacts with starch molecules.

Chlorella is another of the members of Phylum Chlorophyta. These tiny spherical green algae have been studied intensely as scientists have tried to understand photosynthesis. Chlorella gets its name from its one big chloroplast containing lots of chlorophyll. See Figure 10-5

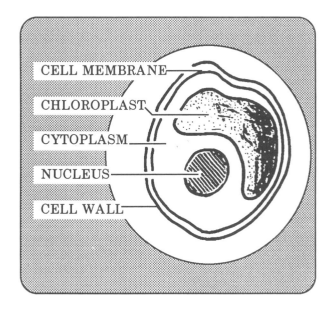

Figure 10-5 CHLORELLA

Spirogyra reproduces asexually by binary fission. It can at times reproduce sexually as shown in the life cycle diagram. The zygospore, a thick walled part, contains a zygote, or new individual. The zygote has a unique, new combination of DNA.

Figure 10-4 SPIROGYRA'S LIFE CYCLE

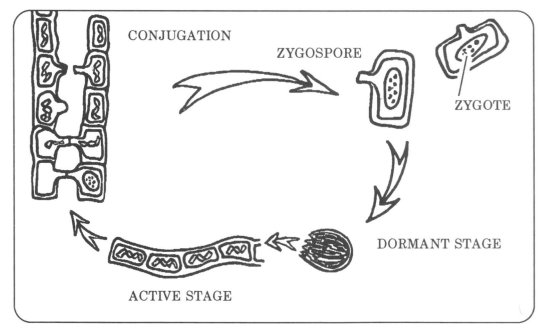

CONJUGATION

ZYGOSPORE

ZYGOTE

DORMANT STAGE

ACTIVE STAGE

<u>Protococcus</u> is a simple green algae that you may find almost anywhere. The green coloring on the North side of many tree trunks and on damp boards or even some rocks is due to millions of individual cells of <u>Protococcus</u>. This algae is so small that even with a good microsope you will only see its cell wall and chloroplast. But that's enough to know it belongs to Kingdom Plantae!

<u>Fucus</u> sp., brown algae in Phylum Phaeophyta, may be seen in the cool ocean waters off New York and New England.

Agar, used to make agar medium for culturing bacteria, is made from a red algae in the Phylum Rhodophyta. Members of Rhodophyta, for example Irish Moss (<u>Chondrus</u> sp.), have chlorophyll just like other plants. But in the red algae, red pigments cover up the green color.

LICHENS

Some green algae live in very close association with fungi. The fungal hyphae provide a shady, humid environment for the algae. The algae make food for themselves, and are also used by the fungi as a food source. Two organisms living so close for the benefit of both is MUTUALISM. You will recall an example of mutualism when we discussed nitrifying bacteria in the nodules on the roots of legumes.

Lichens are a case of mutualism where the two organisms are living so close together that many people think they are one creature. Lichens have even been classified and given scientific names as if they are one organism. For example, <u>Cetraria</u> sp. is a common grayish lichen (Figure 10-6) that grows on boulders. The northern parts of North America, Europe and Asia are covered by <u>Cladonia</u> <u>rangiferina</u>, known as Reindeer lichen. See Figure 10-7.

Figure 10-6

SHIELD LICHEN

<u>Cetraria</u> <u>glauca</u>, on maple may also be found on bare rocks because of the mutualism in which the algae makes the food while the fungus provides the moist and shaded area required by the algae to keep on living.

Figure 10-7 REINDEER LICHEN
Reindeer lichen, <u>Cladonia</u> <u>rangiferina</u>, may be found as far south as New York State.

Figure 10-8 SOIL MAKERS British soldier lichen, <u>Cladonia</u> <u>cristatella</u>, with its poisonous red caps helps begin the formation of new soil on bare rocks.

MOSSES

In the Phylum BRYOPHYTA are three classes which include liverworts, hornworts and mosses. A common hornwort (<u>Phaeoceros</u> <u>laevis</u>) and the common liverwort (<u>Marchantia</u> <u>polymorpha</u>) are probably no more common to you than they are to Average Adam. These members of Phylum Bryophyta are small, green and grow very close to the ground. Because of their small size most people don't notice hornworts and liverworts.

Members of Phylum Bryophyta tend to be small since they have no VASCULAR SYSTEM. That is, bryophytes have no special tubes for moving liquids through their bodies. Bryophytes do not have true stems, roots, or leaves. They reproduce by alternation of generations. The sperm cells must swim through a film of water to reach the egg cell. The new organism is the single celled zygote. The zygote grows and produces spores which grow into the part of a bryophyte that you can see easily.

The most familiar bryophytes are mosses. Like the liverworts and hornworts, mosses have no vascular system and need a film of water for reproduction. That explains why mosses are almost always found in the woods or under porches and in shady areas where it stays moist. That also explains why mosses get only a few centimeters tall. Without a vascular system water cannot be raised very high above the ground. RHIZOIDS are tiny root like structures that hold the mosses to the ground. See figure 10-9.

Figure 10-10 BRACKEN

Crushed up bracken fern is a natural insect repellant when rubbed on the arms, neck and ankles.

Figure 10-11 shows the FROND of a sensitive fern. Each frond is divided into sections sometimes mistakenly called leaves. Each small part of the frond is a leaflet, correctly termed pinnae.

Figure 10-9 A MOSS

Haircap moss, Polytricum commune, is one familiar member of Phylum Bryophyta, Class Musci: the mosses.

FERNS

Ferns are often found where mosses and the other bryophytes grow. However, ferns are a very different kind of organism in one major way! Ferns have a vascular system.

Fossil evidence indicates that at one time there were forests of tree sized ferns! These fern forests seem to have been abundant when the dinosaurs ruled the earth. The special tube like cells in the vascular system allow ferns to grow taller than mosses. Today, one of the tallest ferns you will find is Pteridium aquilinum, called common bracken. The bracken fern (see Figure 10-10) grows up to two meters high, taller than Average Arnold, your average sized dad!

Figure 10-11 A FERN FROND

The entire fan like piece of the sensitive fern, Onoclea sensibilis, is the frond.

The undersides of some fronds are dotted with small brown bumps, SORI, made of clusters of SPORANGIA containing the SPORES. Some ferns have their sori on a separate stalk. You may try to pull up a frond and find that it is attached to several neighbors by a horizontal, underground stem called a RHIZOME. The small, root like rhizoids anchor the fern to the ground (Figure 10-12).

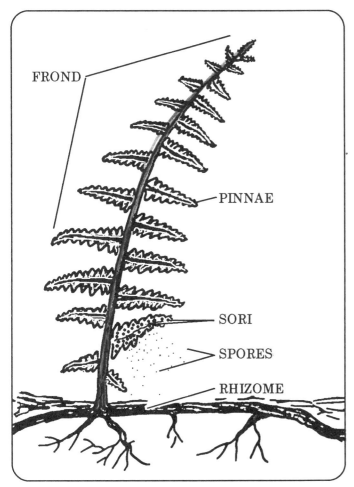

Figure 10-12 A TYPICAL FERN
All the parts of a fern may be seen in this diagram of the New York fern. It's scientific name is <u>Thelypteris</u> <u>noveboracensis</u>

The ferns grow taller than the mosses because of their vascular systems, but they still need a film of water to reproduce. That is why ferns are found with mosses in wet, humid places.

PHYLUM TRACHEOPHYTA

Similar to the ferns and like the flowering plants that we will study, the conifers have a vascular system. All plants with vascular systems belong to the plant kingdom's Phylum TRACHEOPHYTA. Wisk ferns, club mosses (Figure 10-13) and horsetails (Figure 10-14) are three subphyla of the phylum Tracheophyta. A fourth subphylum, named Pteropsida, contains almost all of the plants you are familiar with. The ferns, because they don't make seeds, are in Class FILICINEAE.

Figure 10-13
WOLF'S CLAW

Like the ferns this club moss, <u>Lycopodium</u> <u>clavatum</u> cannot make seeds and must reproduce by spores. Unlike the mosses however, the club moss has a vascular system.

Figure 10-14
FIELD
HORSETAIL

The field horsetail, <u>Equisetum</u> <u>arvense</u>, is a common horsetail that is poisonous to farm animals. It grows along roadways in the moist ditches and in wet land areas.

Plants with seeds **not** inside a fruit are all in the Class GYMNOSPERMAE. Gymno is a Greek word part meaning naked, and spermae means seed. Look at a pine cone (see the back cover) and you can see the seeds that are between the scales of the cone. That is, the seeds are "naked," not hidden. Most gymnosperms are commonly called conifers because they have cones.

Plants **with** seeds inside a fruit are grouped in the Class ANGIOSPERMAE. Angio means hidden, so angiospermae means "hidden seed." Plants that have hidden seeds, that is the angiosperms, are the flowering plants.

CONIFERS

Unlike the ferns, conifers do not need a film of water to reproduce. The name CONIFER comes from two root words: coni meaning cone, and fer from a Latin word meaning "to carry" or to have. You should be familiar with the word ferry from the same Latin root. A ferry carries things. A conifer carries, or has, cones.

The conifers are gymnosperms. You already know the root words in gymnosperm, but why is a gymnasium called a gym? It has the same root, gymno, meaning naked because the ancient Greeks would strip before wrestling or running against their opponents.

Most conifers are evergreens, meaning some of their needles or scaly leaves stay on over each winter. See Figure 10-15. The conifers are the most important plants to both the lumber and the paper industries. The largest live creature on earth is a conifer (see Figure 1-1 in Chapter 1). The oldest tree is a conifer: a bristle cone pine (<u>Pinus</u> <u>longaeva</u>) in California that began growing over 2,600 years before Christ was born.

Figure 10-15 A TYPICAL CONIFER

<u>Picea</u> <u>pungens</u> or blue spruce is very often planted as an ornamental tree on lawns. A vascular plant that bears its seeds on the scales of a cone, the blue spruce gets its species name from its sharp needles. Pungent means "sharp" or "to prick."

FLOWERING PLANTS

Every single plant food listed in **Appendix VI** is a member of the colorful Phylum Angiospermae. The flowering plants are not only the most obvious, but at this time, are the dominant plants on earth. The flowers, see Figure 10-16, may be almost unnoticable. If they are a gift for your mother be sure to get some of the pretty, bright, blossoms as shown in Figure 10-17. Flowers are special plant organs designed for reproduction that we will study in detail in one of the chapters on reproduction.

**Figure 10-16
GRASSES ARE
FLOWERING
PLANTS**

Grasses, like many trees, have very tiny, often green, flowers that are easily overlooked. Yet every flower, no matter how small, is a complex plant organ needed for the continuation of that species of plant.

There was a movie once, *Please Don't Eat the Daisies*, but actually daisies are one of the few composite flowers that are entirely edible!

Figure 10-17 AMERICAN FIELD DAISY

It is a lot easier to identify <u>Chrysanthemum leuconthemum</u> than it is to say its scientific name!

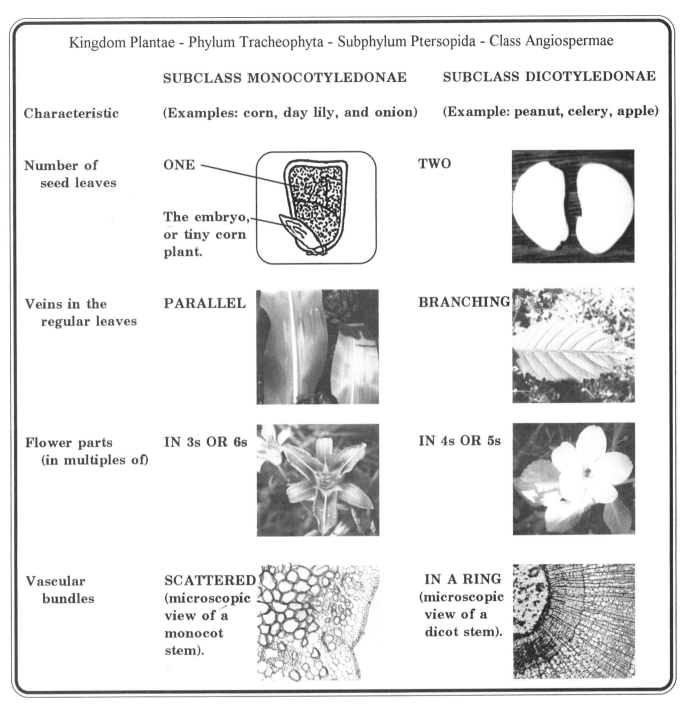

Kingdom Plantae - Phylum Tracheophyta - Subphylum Ptersopida - Class Angiospermae

Characteristic	SUBCLASS MONOCOTYLEDONAE (Examples: corn, day lily, and onion)		SUBCLASS DICOTYLEDONAE (Example: peanut, celery, apple)	
Number of seed leaves	ONE — The embryo, or tiny corn plant.		TWO	
Veins in the regular leaves	PARALLEL		BRANCHING	
Flower parts (in multiples of)	IN 3s OR 6s		IN 4s OR 5s	
Vascular bundles	SCATTERED (microscopic view of a monocot stem).		IN A RING (microscopic view of a dicot stem).	

Figure 10-18 MONOCOTS VS. DICOTS

The Class Angiospermae is easily divided into two Subclasses based on the structure of the seeds. Figure 10-18 outlines what you must memorize about each MONOCOT and DICOT.

You should already know from playing monopoly that the prefix mono means one. Di-, as in dissect, means two. COTYLEDON is the correct term for the special seed leaf used for storage in a seed. Now you can deduce the meaning of the word Monocotyledonae to be "one seed leaf" and subclass Dicotyledonae means "two seed leaves."

The next time you have peas, beans, or even a few peanuts, be sure to remove the seed coat and you will see the two cotyledons that you are eating for their stored up food! It is actually quite interesting that every plant with one cotyledon has parallel veins. If a plant has branching veins it always has two seed leaves and its vascular tissue is in a ring. These regular and consistent patterns of structure used to classify monocots and dicots are evidence that these organisms were designed according to an intelligent plan.

Chapter 10 PLANTS

PART B - PLANT ORGANIZATION

CELLS TO SYSTEMS

The organization of the beautiful and complex bodies of the gymnosperms and angiosperms begins with atoms. A small number of different kinds of atoms, you will recall, make up many kinds of molecules. Those molecules make up the organelles which together form the cell (Figure 10-19).

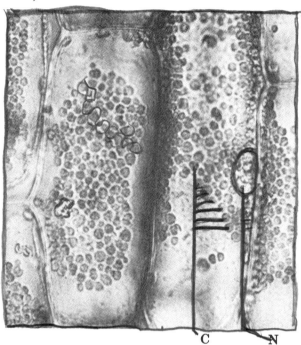

Figure 10-19
ORGANELLES ARE PARTS OF CELLS

All living things are made of cells. These cells of <u>Elodea</u> sp., an aquarium plant, contain a nucleus (N), chloroplasts (C), vacuoles and other parts too small to be seen at a magnification of 680 times.

Most cells of the monerans, protistans, and fungi are generalized. That is, each cell does all the jobs that have to be done for itself. The shape of one cell and the next is very similar.

The cells of the members of the plant kingdom, especially the Tracheophytes, are specialized. These cells have different shapes for different jobs as illustrated in Figure 10-20.

A lot of cells with the same shape, all doing the same job form TISSUE. Tissues working together to perform a life function are called an

Figure 10-20
SHAPE IS RELATED TO FUNCTION

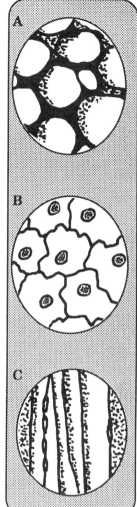

Cells for storage (A) are fat and more or less round in shape. These are cortex cells.

Cells for protection (B) join together closely like the pieces of a living puzzle. These are epidermal cells.

Cells for the transporting of liquids (C) are shaped like a soda straw. These are xylem (zi' lem) cells.

ORGAN. A group of organs form a SYSTEM. All the systems of a creature, working together, form the organism.

No matter what their shape or function, living cells must take in materials, carry out respiration and excrete wastes. The specialized parts of the more advanced plants help them carry out the life functions better so that every cell may stay alive.

ROOTS

In Figure 10-21 there are two types of root systems. One is specialized for storage of food materials, the other type is especially good for absorption.

The familiar carrot TAP ROOT, very similar to the one shown, is a plant organ made of several tissues. The tap root's main function is the storage of food. Tap roots do have small side roots, called secondary roots, that help with absorption.

The thin FIBROUS ROOT system of grasses is better designed for absorption of water and minerals from the soil. Each tiny root can only store a little bit of food.

Either type of root system anchors the plant in the ground, and this helps prevent erosion.

Figure 10-21 ROOT SYSTEMS

On the left is a tap root designed for storage. On the right is a fibrous root system, especially good for absorption.

Unlike the rhizoids of ferns, the root systems of tracheophytes are true roots, a complex group of organs made of tissues. The XYLEM tissue transports water and dissolved minerals. Firewood is mostly dead xylem cells. The PHLOEM (pronounced: flō em) cells bring dissolved food down from the leaves to living cells in the roots.

Read this carefully: the phollowing may help you remember this phact - "phood phlows in phloem." Once you remember that food is in the phloem then you know the water is in the xylem.

Looking at Figure 10-22 you will observe a ROOT CAP which protects the tip of the root. Behind the root cap is the meristematic region, which is simply an area of cell division. All the cells in the meristematic region look nearly the same. Behind the meristematic region is the zone of elongation where the new cells grow longer and push the root cap through the soil. Behind the zone of elongation is the zone of differentiation. In the zone of differentiation cells take on different shapes depending on the function they will do. ROOT HAIRS will also be seen from this point and beyond on healthy, fresh roots. Root hairs are extremely important in absorption of water and minerals from the soil. See Fig. 10-22.

If you are going to transplant a tree or flower, it is critical that you keep the roots moist so that the delicate root hairs stay alive. If they dry out the root hairs die. New root hairs grow as the root grows, but the old ones cannot be revived.

The PITH cells are large loose cells designed for storing food. Pith cells are similar in shape to the cortex cells in Figure 10-20. The epidermal cells are tough and fit close together for protection of the tissues underneath.

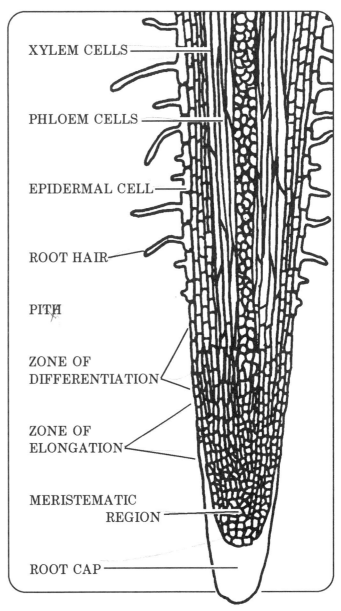

Figure 10-22 A ROOT LONGISECTION

The complex structure of a true root shows different kinds of tissues organized to form the root. Cells in one kind of tissue tend to have the same shape.

STEMS

In plants that live for one or two years, called annuals and biennials, the stems are soft. In the perennials, which live for many years the stems are hard. Annuals and biennials have HERBACEOUS STEMS (Figure 10-23) while perennials have WOODY STEMS (Figure 10-24).

Figure 10-23 HERBACEOUS STEMS

Timothy hay, Phleum pratense, has sweet, green herbaceous stems that farm animals eat, and Huckleberry Finn types chew on.

Figure 10-24 A WOODY STEM

This elm, Ulmus americana, lives for many years as do most trees. This perennial's woody stem contains cells that formed before the American Indians won the battle of the Little Big Horn!

Stems are used for support, transport, storage and, if green, photosynthesis. Stems, like roots, have pith, xylem and phloem tissues.

In Figure 10-25 the inside of a woody stem is magnified with the pith to the right. The thin circle of CAMBIUM is a special area of cell division between the lighter xylem and the dark bark on the left. It is similar to the meristematic zone in the root. The rugged BARK is made of dead cells that protect for the tissue underneath.

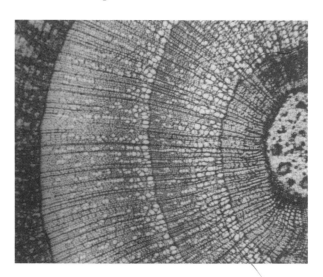

Figure 10-25 CROSS SECTION OF A WOODY STEM (50X)

The stem of Tilia americana, known as American basswood, shows the rings typical of a woody stem. The annual ring is due to a difference in the size of the spring xylem and the xylem which grows in the dry summer.

Some stems have become specialized to do one function more than others. The rhizome, BULB, TUBER, and corm are all specialized stems.

Figure 10-26 SPECIAL STEMS
An onion bulb, Allium cepa, and a potato tuber, Solanum tuberosum, are underground stems used for storage by the plant, and for food by mankind.

LEAVES

Leaves come in so many sizes and shapes that it is hard to believe they have the same tissues and carry out the same functions. Green leaves are used to produce food and to exchange gases. Leaves are green because of chlorophyll. The autumn colors of leaves show up when the chlorophyll is no longer made in the leaf. In the chloroplast, but hidden in the spring and summer by chlorophyll's green color, are two other colors. Xanthophyll is yellow and carotene is orange. The name carrot is related to the root word for carotene. The red PIGMENT in some leaves is anthocyanin, located in the vacuoles. The brown color of dead leaves is caused by tannic acid.

The veins and shapes of leaves are used in taxonomy to name plants. A simple leaf has one blade on each petiole (Figure 10-27). A compound leaf has three or more leaflets on a petiole.

The veins may be palmate, like the spread out fingers of your palm; or pinnate, like a pinion feather; or parallel, where the large veins all go the same direction, parallel to each other. The veins in a leaf are the ends of the vascular system that began in the zone of differentiation in the root.

Figure 10-27 LEAF SHAPES AND VEINS

A true leaf has a bud in the axil, or angle, of the petiole. The bigtoothed aspen, Populus grandidentata, to the left; and quaking aspen, P. tremuloides, to the right; are both simple leaves with pinnate venation. Bigtoothed has a toothed edge while the quaking aspen has a serrated edge.

Just like the root and stem, leaves are a complex organ made of many different tissues. Study Figure 10-29 of a leaf cross section on the next page. The PALISADE LAYER got its name because under a microscope it appears like a wall or cliff; which is what palisade means! The most important function of leaves is to carry out photosynthesis. The palisade layer is where most of this food making takes place.

The SPONGY LAYER has lots of loose cells where oxygen and carbon dioxide are exchanged and water is released. The upper and the lower epidermis are protective layers on the top and bottom. Some leaves have a waxy coating on their upper epidermis called a CUTICLE that helps protect the leaf. The cuticle also helps prevent the loss of too much water.

The lower epidermis has openings, stomates, to let water and oxygen out and carbon dioxide and oxygen in! A stomate is pictured in figure 10-30 on the next page.

Some plant stems have LENTICELS (Figure 10-28) which are openings in the bark similar to stomates in the leaves.

Figure 10-28 LENTICELS

The young stem of yellow birch, Betula lutea, clearly shows the lenticels. The twigs of yellow birch were the original source for the flavoring in birch beer soda.

Excellent examples of how shape is related to function are the guard cells of a STOMATE. The job of guard cells is to regulate TRANSPIRATION, the evaporation of water from the leaves of plants. Guard cells are sausage shaped. The side of the cell membrane toward the stomate is thicker than the other side. See figure 10-30.

When the guard cells become turgid with excess water they open the stomate. To see how this works put a piece of tape on a partially blown up balloon. The balloon must be a sausage shaped one. With the tape on, as you now blow up the balloon it will bend because one side stretches more than the side with the tape. The thicker

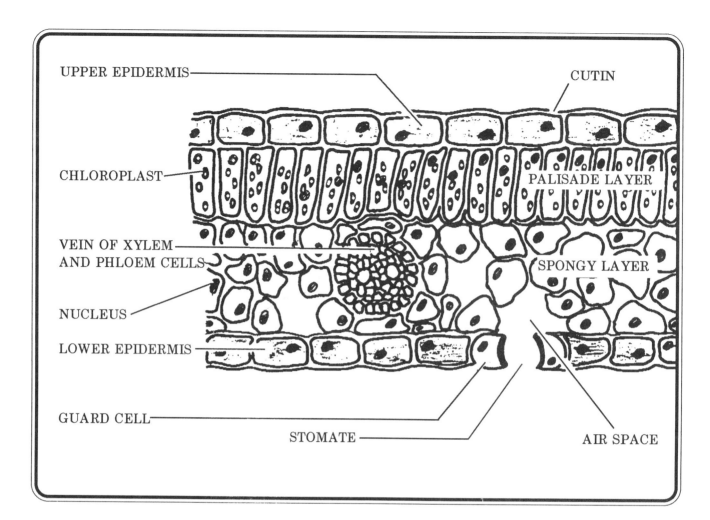

UPPER EPIDERMIS

CUTIN

CHLOROPLAST

PALISADE LAYER

VEIN OF XYLEM
AND PHLOEM CELLS

SPONGY LAYER

NUCLEUS

LOWER EPIDERMIS

GUARD CELL

STOMATE

AIR SPACE

Figure 10-29 A LEAF CROSS SECTION

side of the guard cell stretches least and the cell bends, opening the stomate. As a plant dries out the guard cells become flaccid and the stomate closes. This slows transpiration and keeps water in the plant. The reason most evergreens have needle like leaves is because they must survive the winter when the ground water is frozen. The narrow needles of conifers do not transpire as much as broad leaves.

The systems and organs of plants, made of various tissues, all work together to allow plants to make food. Food the plant itself needs; food all creatures, great and small, must have to live. The next chapter discusses the more complex organisms on earth that depend on plants to make their food.

Figure 10-30 GUARD CELLS

Stomates (S), openings in the lower epidermis of leaves, are opened and closed by guard cells (G). Chloroplasts are labelled (C).

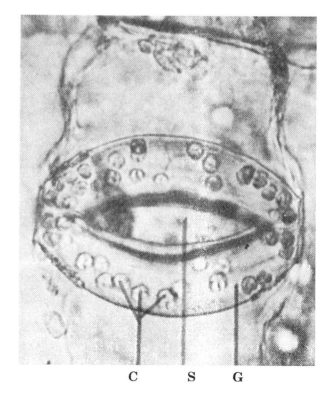

C   S   G

CHAPTER 10 REVIEW

Objectives for Part A:
1. **Know the major subdivisions of Kingdom Plantae.**
2. **Understand how taxonomy is based on the structures of organisms.**
3. **Distinguish between monocots and dicots.**

PART I A. List at least five different plants used as food.

PART II A. Define the 20 keywords from part A of Chapter 10 - Plants.

PART III A. Using a full sentence for each part below, explain how plants are different from: 1. Monerans;
                   2. Protistans;
                   3. Fungi;
                   4. Animals.

PART IV A. Diagram and label:
                   1. <u>Spirogyra</u> sp.
                   2. a fern.

PART V A. If false, change the *italicized* word to make the statement true. Neatly write each full statement once it is true.
1. *Heterotroph* means "self feeder."
2. In photosynthesis, plants use light energy to make *food.*
3. Plants have nuclear membranes, *fungi* do not.
4. Plants have *chitinous* cell walls, fungi do not.
5. Plants have *chlorophyll* but fungi do not.
6. Phylum Chlorophyta is the *green* algae.
7. *Chlorella* has a spiral chloroplast.
8. *Sugar*, in the pyrenoids, turns iodine blue-black.
9. Lichens, containing both algae and fungi, are a good example of *transpiration.*
10. *Lichens* are organisms that can live on bare rocks.

PART VI A. Neatly write out each sentence, filling in the blanks with the best answer.
1. Liverworts, hornworts and mosses are in the Phylum __?__.
2. Mosses tend to be short because they have no __?__.
3. All bryophytes need a film of water for __?__.
4. What appear to be tiny roots on a moss are actually __?__.

5. Haircap moss is in the Kingdom __?__.
6. Haircap moss is in the Phylum __?__.
7. Haircap moss is in the Class __?__.
8. The Genus for the haircap moss is __?__.
9. The species name for the haircap moss is _?_.
10. __?__ is the scientific name for the haircap moss.

PART VII A. Write each sentence neatly, using a keyword to fill in the blanks.
1. Ferns belong to the Kingdom __?__.
2. New York fern is a member of the Phylum __?__.
3. Unlike mosses, ferns have a __?__ for transport of liquids.
4. The fan like leaf of a fern is called a __?__.
5. A horizontal underground stem that connects some ferns is a __?__.
6. __?__ are small dots on the undersides of certain pinnae.
7. The __?__ are a number of spores clustered in the sori.
8. The common bracken fern is in the class _?_.
9. Instead of seeds, ferns reproduce by __?__.
10 Because ferns make their own food we can call them __?__.

PART VIII A. Write a short paragraph explaining why ferns usually grow only where it is shady and moist. Include an explanation of why ferns can grow taller than mosses.

PART IX A. Answer each question by writing a full sentence.
1. What is the one characteristic all Tracheophytes have in common?
2. Which of these three main classes of Phylum Tracheophyta do **not** produce seeds:
                   Filicineae,
                   Gymnospermae and/or
                   Angiospermae?
3. What is the meaning of the root word "gymno?"
4. What is the literal meaning of the word angiosperm?
5. What Class contains the conifers?
6. What Class is also called the flowering plants?
7. What are the seeds hidden inside of, in the flowering plants?
8. Give two important uses of conifers.
9. What is the meaning of the subphylum name Monocotyledonae?
10. Are dicots angiosperms?

Objectives for Part B:
1. **Understand the organization of the bodies of living creatures.**
2. **List and know the parts of a plant: root, stem and leaf.**
3. **Outline the plant kingdom's subdivisions and their main characteristics.**

PART I B. Neatly rewrite the following list in order from smallest to largest:
atoms, cells, molecules, organelles, organism, organs, systems, tissues.

PART II B. Define the 23 keywords in Part B of Chapter 10 - Plants.

PART III B. Write each sentence neatly, filling in the blank with one of the keywords. A keyword may be used more than once.
1. Many similar shaped cells form a __?__, which in turn forms an organ.
2. A __?__ system is very good for absorption.
3. A carrot is an example of a __?__ in which food is stored.
4. Food flows in the __?__.
5. A 2 X 4 piece of lumber is made of __?__ cells.
6. Healthy roots have lots of tiny __?__ to aid in absorption.
7. Plants that live only 1 or 2 years have __?__.
8. Perennials have __?__ on their stems, a thick layer of dead cells for protection of the tissues underneath.
9. The onion is a special underground stem called a __?__.
10. Chlorophyll is a green __?__ needed for photosynthesis.
11. Most photosynthesis occurs in the __?__, made of tall cells under the upper epidermis.
12. At night oxygen gets into a leaf through the __?__.
13. _?_ is the evaporation of water from plants.
14. The flower is a special reproductive __?__ of the angiosperms.
15. The xylem and __?__ tissues together make up the vascular system of tracheophytes.

PART IV B. Diagram and label a leaf.

PART V B. Diagram and label a woody stem.

PART VI B. Diagram and label a root.

PART VII B. Write a short paragraph of full sentences that explains where guard cells may be found, what their function is, and how their shape helps them do their function. Include a title and correctly use five (5) of these terms in your essay:
flaccid, guard cell, lower epidermis, spongy layer, stomate, transpiration, turgid.

PART I C. Overall review:
Rewrite this chart and fill in the 15 missing labels:

```
                          Object
      __1__          Virus           BIOTIC
   (not living)        |            (living)

No nuclear membrane          Have membranes
Kingdom __2__                Other 4 kingdoms

Mostly unicellular           mostly multicellular
Kingdom __3__                Other 3 kingdoms

Chitinous cell walls         No cell walls or
and heterotrophic            autotrophic
Kingdom __4__

Cellulose cell walls         No cell walls
and autotrophic              and heterotrophic
Kingdom __5__                Kingdom Animalia

Simple structure             Complex structure
mostly aquatic               many terrestrial

Green     Brown     Red
Phylum    Phylum    Phylum
__6__     Phaeophyta Rhodophyta

No vascular system           Have a vascular system
Phylum __7__                 Phylum __8__
(The Mosses)

Reproduce by spores          Reproduce by seeds
Class Filicineae
(The __9__)

Seeds exposed in cone   Seeds hidden inside fruit
Class __10__            Class __11__
(The Conifers)         (Flowering Plants)

One seed leaf          Two seed leaves
Subclass __12__        Subclass __14__
Example: __13__        Example: __15__
```

CHAPTER 10 - THE PLANTS, part B, CROSSWORD

ACROSS

2. Tube-like cells that carry food down from the leaves of plants.
5. A large root used for storage.
6. Tiny parts of root cells used for absorption.
10. Evaporation from plants.
13. A group of organs doing one job.
15. A thick layer of dead cells that protects woody stems.
16. Small openings in the bark of young stems.
18. Special underground stem used for storage, for example, the potato.
20. An opening on the lower side of a leaf through which gases move.
22. Many small roots all about the same size.
23. A coloring matter.

DOWN

1. A waxy layer on a leaf.
3. A group of tissues working together.
4. A protective layer of cells on the end of a root.
7. The soft stem of annuals.
8. Tissue that carries water up from the roots.
9. The part of a leaf where most photosynthesis takes place.
11. The soft center of a stem.
12. Part of the leaf where gases are exchanged.
14. A group of cells all doing one job.
17. The hard stem of perennials.
19. A layer of cells between the xylem and phloem that makes new cells.
21. For example, an onion.

SCIENCE OF SORTS

The ancient Egyptians are credited with making the first leavened bread. Legend has it that spores from yeast, floating in the air settled on dough and caused the flat, hard loaves into soft, light bread.

Aspirin was invented by Felix Hoffmann to relieve his father's pain. A basic constituent of the analgesic comes from the spirea plant which led to the trade name "aspirin."

Nuts are excellent sources of unsaturated fats, minerals, vitamins and protein

Your body has 206 bones, the largest is the femur in your leg.

It takes 17 muscles to smile;, 43 muscles are required to frown; so relax some of the more than 600 muscles in your body and SMILE!

CHAPTER 11 - ANIMALS

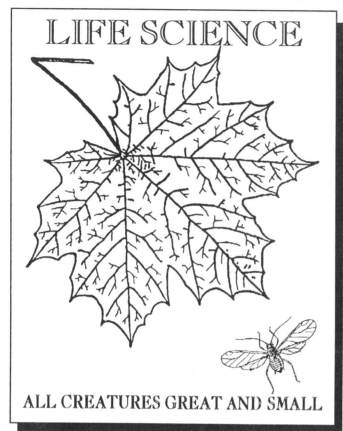

LIFE SCIENCE

ALL CREATURES GREAT AND SMALL

DOWN

1. A "feathery" organ used to exchange gases under water.
2. Small openings.
3. Organisms that maintain a body temperature at a constant level.
5. Front end.
6. The process of changing shape.
7. A meat eater.
9. An organism that eats all kinds of foods.
10. Back end.
12. Attached by the base.
14. An organism whose body is the same as the temperature of the environment.
17. To be dormant in hot weather.
19. An organ used to exchange gases in air.
21. The immature form of an insect that undergoes incomplete metamorphosis.

Animals Crossword Puzzle

Use the keywords from this chapter to fill in the puzzle. See how many you know before reading the chapter! Complete the puzzle after completing this chapter.

ACROSS

2. An immature resting stage in insect metamorphosis.
4. Also called a caterpillar.
8. The process of growing a missing part of the body.
11. Symmetry in which the object may be cut into two similar parts.
13. Eater of insects.
15. Eater of plants.
16. To become dormant in cold weather.
18. Symmetry with sameness along the radii of a circle.
20. A long part of some invertebrates, sometimes with a stinger.
22. Top or back.
23. Bottom or lower.
24. An organ formed by an unborn mammal to get food and oxygen.

Write in this book only if it belongs to you.

CHAPTER 11 ANIMALS
The Heterotrophs

ANIMAL KINGDOM

The longest of all animals is over 54 m long! That is longer than a line that starts on the front cover of this book and is drawn across the bottom of every page, both sides, to the back. This long sea creature almost looks like a wide pencil line. Its scientific name, Lineus longissimus, means the long line.

The ribbon worm, Lineus, is not very impressive in terms of overall size. Neither are the most numerous type of animal, marine nematodes, which are nearly microscopic in size. The most massive animal to ever live is the Sulphur-bottom whale, also called the blue whale. It would take approximately 1900 Average Arnolds to add up to just one of these giant creatures! How many elephants do you think are as big as just one blue whale? Don't just guess. Use this data to calculate your answer: it would take over 86 Average Arnolds to equal one elephant.

Animals great and small, long and short, common and rare, all share several characteristics. The classification of animals begins with these characteristics of the Kingdom ANIMALIA:

1. Animals are **multicellular**, their many cells have nuclear membranes and **organelles**;
2. Animals are **heterotrophic**, lacking chloroplasts, animals must ingest food;
3. Animals are made of numerous tiny cells with **no cell walls**.

TAXONOMY REFRESHER

Carolus Linnaeus used Latin names and seven taxons to group plants and animals according to their structure. Because the gigantic blue whale is multicellular and eats small shrimp-like krill by the tons, this whale is in the Kingdom Animalia. Having a spinal cord in a backbone like fish, frogs and flamingoes, the blue whale is part of the Phylum Chordata, Subphylum Vertebrata. But the big "blue" doesn't have scales as fish do! Its giant heart has four chambers, one more than a frog's heart. Mrs. Sulphur-bottom gives birth to her little baby (longer than your classroom!) unlike the egg laying flamingo!

The facts that blue whales live in the ocean like fish, and are good swimmers like frogs, are not what are important in classifying them. Even if it were the Pink whale, instead of Blue, it would not be in the same class as the flamingo!

Animals are classified according to their structure. A whale, warm blooded and with hair, is more like you than the fish, frog or flamingo. As a result it is in the same taxonomic class as people: Class Mammalia.

The whale shares Order Cetacea with the very similar porpoises and dolphins, all with flippers. The giant Blue whale, like the other baleen whales, has no teeth and is in the Family Balaenidae. Figure 11-1 at the top of the next page compares the taxons for several animals.

The object of the chart in Figure 11-1 is **not** that you memorize a lot of big names. There are four main ideas that the **EXAMPLES OF TAXONS** chart should help you to understand:

1. As two creatures have more and more structures that are similar, the **more alike** they are, the **more taxons** they have **in common**;
2. Organisms in the same class must be in the same phylum and kingdom, etc.;
3. Any two different living things will **not** have the same seven taxons;
4. The **genus and species names**, together, are the scientific name for each kind of organism.

SPONGES

Remember that conifer meant "cone bearer." The Phylum PORIFERA means "pore bearer." A PORE is a small opening. The porifera are the sponges, which, as adults, are full of holes. The young sponge is a larvae that swims around finding a place to settle. The adult sponge, full of pores, is SESSILE (Figure 11-2).

There are no organs or systems in a sponge. A sponge can regrow if it is cut into pieces because

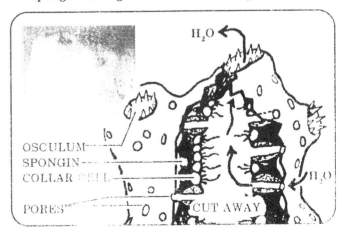

Figure 11-2 A SPONGE

Each collar cell uses its flagellum to move water, containing food, into the pores and out of the osculum.

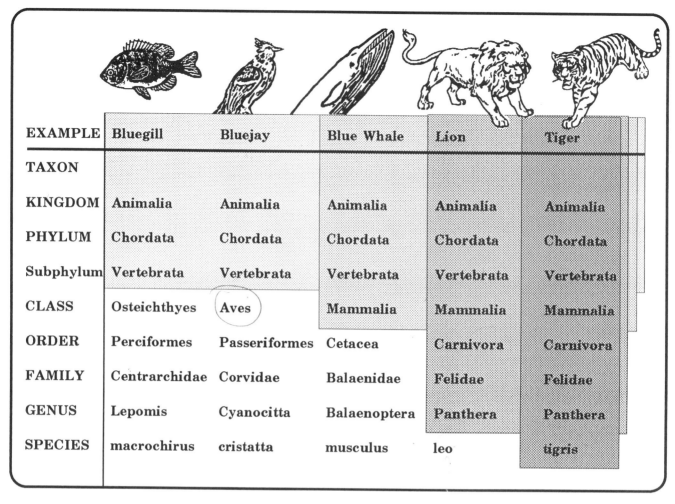

EXAMPLE	Bluegill	Bluejay	Blue Whale	Lion	Tiger
TAXON					
KINGDOM	Animalia	Animalia	Animalia	Animalia	Animalia
PHYLUM	Chordata	Chordata	Chordata	Chordata	Chordata
Subphylum	Vertebrata	Vertebrata	Vertebrata	Vertebrata	Vertebrata
CLASS	Osteichthyes	Aves	Mammalia	Mammalia	Mammalia
ORDER	Perciformes	Passeriformes	Cetacea	Carnivora	Carnivora
FAMILY	Centrarchidae	Corvidae	Balaenidae	Felidae	Felidae
GENUS	Lepomis	Cyanocitta	Balaenoptera	Panthera	Panthera
SPECIES	macrochirus	cristatta	musculus	leo	tigris

Figure 11-1 EXAMPLES OF TAXONS

The shading indicates the similarity between the different organisms. The greater the similarty the more taxons both creatures share. Taxonomy, based on structures, helps indicate which animals are most closely related. The whale is related more closely to a tiger than to the blue gill! One kind of organism, the tiger for example, has a set of seven taxons that no other animal may share. The lion shares six of the same taxons, indicating that the lion and tiger are similar.

its body plan is so simple. REGENERATION is only possible in the lower animals. Your body is much too complex to regenerate anything except skin and small pieces of muscle. Figure 11-2 shows the parts of a sponge and a photo of a sponge's skeleton. Their soft skeletons, made of a chemical called spongin, are useful in washing the family car! Sponges have no nervous system, thus no eyes, no ears, no nose and no tongue. Spongilla sp. is an example of a freshwater sponge.

JELLYFISH

Hopefully you have never been stung by a jellyfish's nematocyst, a stinging cell on the end of one of the tentacles of a jellyfish. Washed up on a beach a jellyfish looks like a lump of clearish jelly. But in the water the graceful bag like body, with each TENTACLE waving in the currents, displays its RADIAL SYMMETRY. Like the sponges, jellyfish have only two layers of cells. The jelly like substance in between the two cell layers gives them their common name. Inside the bag like body is the gastrovascular cavity where digestion occurs. Jellyfish belong to the Phylum COELENTERATA (bag like body).

Hydra is a freshwater coelenterate which is often sessile but can move by a somersault action. Hydra may reproduce by budding to produce offspring genetically the same as the parent. Sexual reproduction occurs when testes, and at a different time in the same Hydra, ovaries, form in the ectoderm. Most jellyfish are marine. They float freely with their mouth and tentacles downward. Hydra has no eyes, ears, nose or tongue but does have sensitive skin with a nerve net (See Figure 11-3 below).

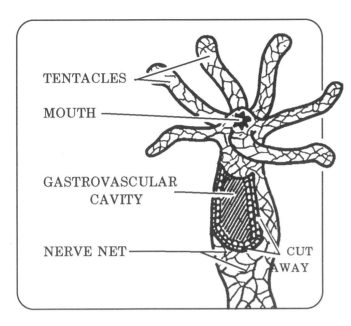

Figure 11-3 HYDRA

Due to its many tentacles, Hydra littoralis is named after a mythological creature with many heads.

FLATWORMS

The Phylum PLATYHELMINTHES contains creatures that are more complex than the Porifera and Coelenterata. The flatworms have three basic cell layers, just as your body has. Their common name refers to the platyhelmintes' ribbon like body, with no segments. To remember the name, think "platy for flaty!"

The beef tapeworm (Taenia saginata) is actually quite complex when compared to Hydra or Spongilla. For one thing, flat worms are made of three main cell layers.

Since the USDA (United States Department of Agriculture) inspects meat that goes to market Taenia is no longer as common in humans as it used to be. The beef tapeworm, like other parasitic flatworms has a sucker like head called a scolex. In reproduction part of the tapeworm changes into a proglottid, a special section containing the newly fertilized egg cells. The proglottids break off inside the human intestine.

When excreted, they may be ingested by a cow to start the life cycle over again.

Planaria is a small flatworm that looks cross eyed (Figure 11-4). Actually, Planaria's two DORSAL eyespots are sensitive to light but are not like the eyes of more complex animals. The nervous system which includes the eyespots is much more developed than in the Porifera and Coelenteratata.

Between the outer and inner layer of cells is a third layer, the mesoderm, which means "middle skin." The digestive tract has only one opening, which is labelled the mouth, and is on the VENTRAL side. The first part of the dead end digestive tube is the PHARYNX (fair inks).

Planaria is hermaphroditic! Although not as bad as it sounds, it is interesting to understand where such a word came from. Hermes was a handsome Greek god and Aphrodite was the Greek goddess of love and beauty. Hermaphroditic means having both male and female characteristics. We could call the sponges and jellyfish hermaphroditic also because, like Planaria, the same organism can make sperm and egg cells.

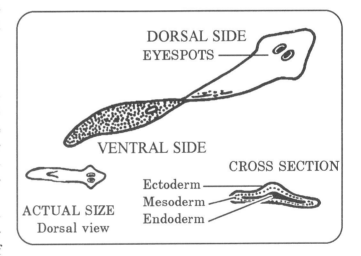

Figure 11-4 PLANARIA
Planaria and other members of the Phylum Platyhelminthes have three basic cell layers.

Figure 11-5 A DOG TAPEWORM
(BELOW)
The typical flat shape and ribbon like body of a flatworm is evident in this pet parasite.

Members of Phylum Platyhelminthes may be cut into two similar halves. This is a type of symmetry termed BILATERAL SYMMETRY. "Bi-" as used in bicycle means two. Lateral means side. Bilateral symmetry is found in most of the more complex animals. Flatworms like Planaria are still not too complicated to regenerate missing parts. In *Animals Without Backbones* by Ralph Buchsbaum you can see a photograph of a five headed planaria grown in the lab by partially cutting the head and allowing regeneration!

ROUNDWORMS

Nematodes are the most abundant animals on earth. There are more than 1,000,000 in each shovel full of garden soil. I'll bet you have never even heard of nematodes, let alone seen one! Hopefully you have never suffered from any parasitic nematodes.

NEMATODA means "form of a thread;" and is a good name for these tiny round worms in the Phylum Nematoda. No respiratory or circulatory systems are present but these round worms have a complete digestive system with two openings.

Figure 11-6
HOOKWORM

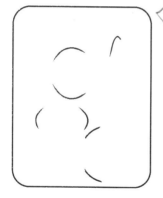

Necator americanus, or "killer of Americans" has a tiny thread like body, yet is more complex than flatworms, jellyfish or sponges.

Hookworm was once a common parasite in the southern United States. The nematode sticks to bare feet and bores through the sole of the foot. Inside its host, sexual reproduction produces zygotes which are eliminated with the solid waste. Shoes and sewage treatment plants have greatly reduced infestations of hookworm.

When Moses told the Jewish tribes not to eat pork perhaps he was protecting them from a nematode that infests pork, Trichina spiralis. Thorough cooking of pork products has made pork worm less of a threat in the United States today. Trichina is still in most pork products but is killed by the heat in well cooked meat.

SEGMENTED WORMS

The segmented worms have bodies made of many rings. For example, the earthworm, Lumbricus terrestris, has the typical segmented body that is the outstanding structure of the Phylum ANNELIDA. Annelida is from the root word annus. Annus is Latin for "circuit" or ring around the sun. Our word annual, meaning one circuit around the sun, has the same origin. We used the term annulus to name the ring around the stipe of some mushrooms. Annelida refers to the ringed bodies of the segmented worms.

Earthworms are a lot more important than just fishing bait! This lowly annelid adds organic matter to dirt particles. It opens the soil up for air and water to enter, and mixes the soil. Our list of plant uses and our understanding that plants are the autotrophs pointed out that we depend on plants for food. Plants, of course, depend on the soil to grow! Good soil is formed by the action of the common annelid, or earthworm.

Annelids are much more complex than the phyla we investigated earlier. Refer to Figure 11-7 to see the parts of an annelid. Inside the third segment of Lumbricus is a simple brain connected to a ventral nerve cord and many nerve cells throughout the body. There are five "hearts" connected to an artery on bottom and to a dorsal blood vessel with valves. This blood system is a

Figure 11-7
ANNELID ANATOMY

Lumbricus terrestris, the earthworm, has circulatory, digestive, nervous and excretory systems but no skeletal system. (below)

ANTERIOR END   DORSAL SIDE

MOUTH   CLITELLUM   POSTERIOR END

      ANUS

SETAE   SEGMENT

VENTRAL SIDE

closed system, as is yours.

The worm's digestive system is the most complex yet (of the phyla studied so far). Like the nematodes there is an ANTERIOR opening, the mouth; and a POSTERIOR opening, the anus. With no jaws or teeth, the pharynx is used to draw in the food, which moves through the esophagus, crop, gizzard, and, at the 19th segment, into the intestine. Nephridia are tubes used to excrete nitrogen compounds. The mucus covered skin is used for breathing. Stiff little bristles called setae are used for locomotion. The clitellum (see Figure 11-7) is a specialized region used for reproduction. Like poriferans, coelenterates, and platyhelminthes, annelids are hermaphroditic. They will not fertilize their own egg cells.

The familiar earthworm is really a complex and important part of the living world that connects us to the abiotic soil.

MOLLUSKS

Phylum MOLLUSCA contains the soft bodied animals with a muscular foot. The mollusk body is muscular but not segmented. The soft body often has a hard shell.

Snails, with just one shell, are univalves. Clams and oysters are bivalves because they have two shells. The octopus and squid are both called cephalopods (sef al o pods) which means literally "head-foot."

Figure 11-8 shows the univalve and bivalve shells of some mollusks. An important, and, for many people, favorite, use of mollusks is as food!

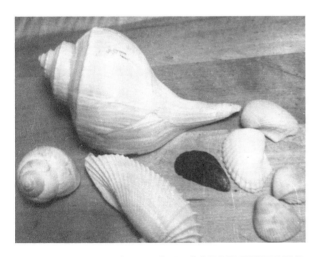

Figure 11-8 MOLLUSK COLLECTIBLES

Sea shells are interesting and beautiful for the amateur as well as the expert naturalist.

ARTHROPODS

Podos means foot. We used that root word in pseudopod, the "false foot" of the ameba; and in cephalopod, the "head-foot" bodies of octopi and squid. The crabs, spiders, thousand leggers and insects all belong to the Phylum ARTHROPODA. Poda means foot, but what does "arthro-" mean? Arthro- comes from a Greek word that means jointed. Arthropoda means jointed foot, like a suit of armor. The outstanding structure of Phylum Arthropoda is a chitinous EXOSKELETON. This skeleton on the outside, like a suit of armor, can only bend at the joints.

There are more kinds of these joint footed animals than of all other kinds together. But wait. Didn't we say that an unheard of marine nematode is the most numerous animal of all? We did, and that's correct! There are many more of that one kind of nematode than of any other species of animal. But there are more species of arthropods than of any other phylum of animals.

The five main classes of the Phylum Arthropoda are compared in Figure 11-9 on the next page. Just about everybody can find their most "unfavorite" creatures on this list. Also on this list are important natural controls that kill and eat pests who destroy our foods; plant pollinators that give us bountiful fruit and vegetable harvests; and pests that cause us to support a multibillion dollar chemical industry.

The arthropods are as beautiful as a butterfly, as deadly as a scorpion, as nasty as a cockroach, and as interesting as a whirllygig on a cool pond.

The arthropods boast species that can communicate with great precision. The figure eight dance of the honey bee is still being studied to discover how the bee directs others from the hive straight to a food source. The arthropods include insects with complex societies. Ants, for example, show division of labor and a type of caste system.

Arthropods, insects in particular, are disease vectors of major importance. Diseases carried by flies, ticks and mosquitoes have only been understood since the late 1800s. Some of these diseases carried by insect vectors are being investigated today. More about disease in another chapter.

Arthropods are often a person's favorite dish when they go out to eat at a restaurant. You have probably had lobster or crabs for dinner, leaving behind the chitinous exoskeleton that is the trademark of all the arthropods. Such great variety in this one Phylum requires a closer look.

PHYLUM ARTHROPODA - ALL HAVE CHITINOUS EXOSKELETONS

CLASS	STRUCTURE	EXAMPLES	NOTES
ARACHNIDA Spiders & ticks	Two body parts Eight legs 8 simple eyes	House spider- _Theridon lepidariorum_ Dog tick-_Dermacentor variabilis_	Spiders control pests Ticks and mites are parasites & vectors.
CRUSTACEA Crabs, lobsters & crayfish	Two body parts Four antennae 10 legs (2 special)	Coast lobster-_Homarus americanus_ Eastern crayfish-_Cambaris bartoni_	Important food sources for humans.
CHILOPODA Hundred leggers	Flattened body 1 pair of legs on each segment	Common centipede - _Lithobius_ sp.	Hundred leggers are carnivorous.
DIPLOPODA Thousand leggers	Rounded body 2 pair of legs on each segment	Large millipede - _Spirobolus marginatus_	Thousand leggers are herbivorous; "di" refers to 2 pair/seg.
INSECTA Insects	Three body parts Six legs Two antennae	House fly - _Musca domestica_ Carpenter ant - _Camponotus herculeanus_	Insecta means cut inward, referring to the three body parts.

Figure 11-9 CLASSES OF ARTHROPODS

All of the examples given above have the general characteristics of the Phylum Arthropoda and Kingdom Animalia. They all have exoskeletons, they all ingest food.

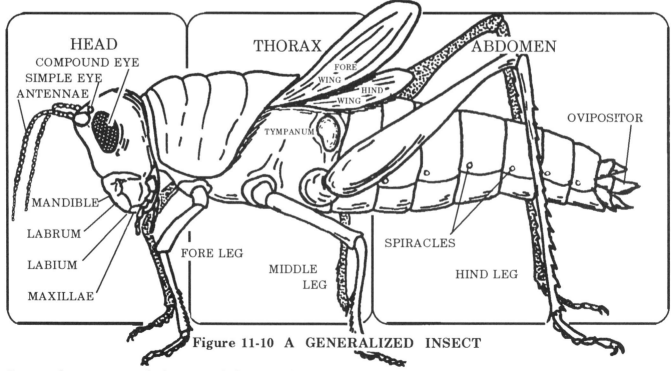

Figure 11-10 A GENERALIZED INSECT

Insects have an exoskeleton and three body parts with six legs on the thorax, or middle section.

The Class Insecta is huge in terms of number of species. Insects can be found almost anywhere on earth where there is life. The great variety of insect body shapes are illustrated in Figure 11-11.

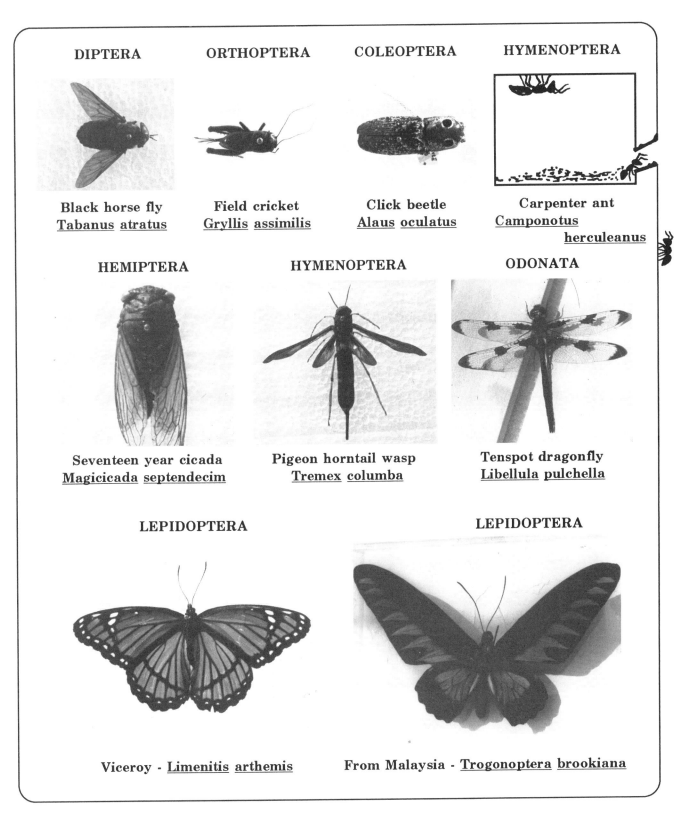

DIPTERA

Black horse fly
Tabanus atratus

ORTHOPTERA

Field cricket
Gryllis assimilis

COLEOPTERA

Click beetle
Alaus oculatus

HYMENOPTERA

Carpenter ant
Camponotus
herculeanus

HEMIPTERA

Seventeen year cicada
Magicicada septendecim

HYMENOPTERA

Pigeon horntail wasp
Tremex columba

ODONATA

Tenspot dragonfly
Libellula pulchella

LEPIDOPTERA

Viceroy - Limenitis arthemis

LEPIDOPTERA

From Malaysia - Trogonoptera brookiana

Figure 11-11 SOME ORDERS OF INSECTS

Each order contains many families each of which contains many genera and species of insects.

Insects change their shapes during different stages of their lives. METAMORPHOSIS means the process of changing shape. Figure 11-12 shows a model of complete metamorphosis which involves four stages: egg --> larva --> pupa --> adult. Sometimes an insect LARVA is referred to as a caterpiller. The PUPA of a butterfly is called a chrysalis and that of a moth is a cocoon.

Figure 11-12
COMPLETE METAMORPHOSIS

This model of the four stages of complete metamorphosis represents the life cycle of the Monarch butterfly, Danaus plexippus.

The familiar red legged grasshopper, Melanopus femurrubrum, undergoes what is called incomplete metamorphosis in which the young, called a NYMPH, looks almost like the adult. After hatching from the egg a nymph grows and molts until it reaches adult size.

STARFISH

Starfish and their marine relatives the pretty sand dollars and prickly sea urchins (Figure 11-13) are animals with spiny skin and radial symmetry. The phylum name ECHINODERMATA means "spiny skin." We've seen the root word "**derma**" for skin in several terms: the lower and upper epi**dermis** of leaves, the ecto**derm** or outer layer of cells in animals, the endo**derm** or inner layer of cells, and the meso**derm** or "middle skin" in all animals from the flatworms to you! Say the phylum name so that it sounds like this:

$$\bar{e}\bar{e} - k\bar{i} - n\bar{o} - der - ma - ta$$

Figure 11-13
PHYLUM ECHINODERMATA

The sand dollar is just a skeleton and its spiny skin is gone. The bumps on the starfish are its spines. The sea urchin could be called the porcupine of the sea!

Each ray of a starfish has tube feet on the ventral side, with the mouth located at the center. On the top is a round dot near the center. This dot is the sieve plate used to filter water. Echinoderms display radial symmetry, meaning they can be cut like a pizza into similar pieces.

Clams and other mollusks are favorite foods of the starfish. Fishermen used to try to kill the starfish by chopping them up and throwing the pieces back into the sea. By regeneration each piece of the starfish would grow back its missing parts! By not understanding the life science of a starfish, the fishermen were actually helping these pesky echinoderms reproduce asexually.

MARINE WORMS

Phylum Hemichordata, or "almost chordates," are a small group of animals similar in some ways to echinoderms and in other ways like the most complex animals - the chordates. The phylum is characterized by bilateral symmetry and a stomochord. All are marine; acorn worm is an example. For now, we will omit the hemichordates, just as we have skipped some of the less well known phyla of the animal kingdom.

CHORDATES

All animals with a dorsal nerve cord, internal skeleton and, at some point in their development, gill slits, belong to the Phylum CHORDATA. Chordata refers to the nerve cord down the back of these animals. Chordates have complex bodies with bilateral symmetry. There are several chordates without a backbone in special subphyla. You, and most familiar animals, belong to the Subphylum VERTEBRATA. Each piece of the backbone is a vertebra, thus the subphylum name is Vertebrata (See Figure 11-14 below).

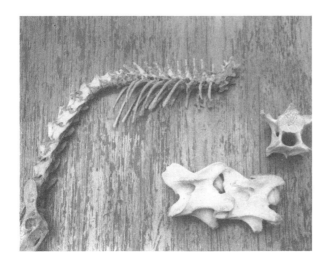

Figure 11-14 VERTEBRAE

The backbone of a cat, and several vertebrae from the backbone of a cow, protected the dorsal nerve cord of these vertebrates when they were alive.

The Phylum Chordata, Subphylum Vertebrata is divided into seven main classes.

LAMPREYS

Class AGNATHA - COLD BLOODED, jawless animals with gills. Lampreys and hagfish are jawless fish.

SHARKS

Class CHONDRICHTHYES - cold blooded fish with jaws and GILLS. Sharks and sting rays are called cartilagenous fish because their skeletons are made of cartilage instead of bone. These fish have gill slits with no cover over them. See Figure 11-18 at the end of this section.

FISH

Class OSTEICHTHYES - cold blooded animals with gills and scales and with a skeleton of bone. The word part "ichthyes" means fish. So an ichthyologist is a person who studies fish, and osteichthyes ("osteo" means bone) are the bony fish.

An operculum covers the gills of the bony fish, unlike the exposed gill slits of the model used to film the horror movie *Jaws*. The great white shark is **not** a member of Class Osteichthyes because its skeleton is **not** bone.

AMPHIBIANS

Class AMPHIBIA - cold blooded animals with a moist soft skin. The young have gills, the adults breathe with LUNGS.

Can you determine the meaning of amphibia? It is made of two word roots: amphi- and -bio. You may know what an amphibious airplane is, or perhaps you are ambidextrous. An amphibious plane can land on water or solid ground. If you are ambidextrous, you can write with both your left and your right hands. Amphi (or ambi) means double or both. Bio means life. Class Amphibia is so named because its members live both in water and on land.

A female frog, with lungs, lays her eggs in water. The tadpoles that form have gills. As they grow the tadpoles develop lungs. See the newt, another amphibian, pictured in Figure 11-18 at the end of this chapter.

In winter frogs HIBERNATE in the mud of ponds and streams. In the summer, if the weather gets too hot and dry, the frogs may ESTIVATE. Estivation, like hibernation, is when an organism's metabolism slows way down and the animal survives without eating. Estivation occurs in the summertime, hibernation in the winter.

At one time people believed that frogs could form automatically out of mud. This mistaken theory of spontaneous generation may have been caused in part by the habit of frogs to estivate. In 1668 Francesco Redi of Italy proved that living things do not spontaneously arise from nonliving things. His experiment with pieces of meat and flies showed that animals are generated only by other living animals.

REPTILES

The name for the Class REPTILIA means "creeping animals." All reptiles, great and small, are cold blooded. Most have a three chambered heart, and dry scaly skin. Reptiles only have lungs and they do not return to the water to reproduce. Lizards, turtles and many snakes (Figure 11-18) lay leathery eggs on land after internal fertilization.

Crocodiles and alligators are CARNIVORES, as are many snakes. Many of the lizards are INSECTIVORES. Turtles (see Figure 11-18) tend to be OMNIVORES, that is they will eat many different kinds of foods. An animal that eats just plants is an HERBIVORE.

BIRDS

Birds are good aviators. Aviation refers to flying. An aviary is a large bird cage. The Latin word avis means bird, and the Class AVES is for the birds! Now that we have aves figured out, what do you suppose is the name of a person who studies birds? Would you believe ornithologist? An ornithologist is a person who studies birds (Figure 11-15). The root word in this case is from the Greek word for bird, ornithos.

Members of Class Aves all have feathers, but they also have scales! Bird feet are scaly. Birds are WARM BLOODED and most can fly.

Figure 11-15 AN ORNITHOLOGIST

Dr. Heinz Meng is a well known ornithologist who is especially interested in birds of prey.

The varied beaks and feet of birds are excellent examples of how shape is related to function. A sparrow hawk's talons are designed for grabbing (Figure 11-18), a pheasant's feet are good for walking (Figure 11-18), and a duck's webbed foot is a perfect paddle (Figure 11-18). In the same order we see a sharp hooked beak for tearing meat, a stout pointed beak for seeds, and a spoon shaped beak for scooping up mud.

The familiar robin's nest is evidence of bird reproduction by laying eggs on land. Unlike reptiles, bird eggs have fragile shells, and the young of most birds require parental care.

Figure 11-16 A ROBIN'S NEST

The mud & grass nest of <u>Turdus</u> <u>migratorius</u> contains the light blue eggs that will, if left undisturbed, hatch into robin chicks.

Eagles and other birds of prey, now protected species, are favorite topics for artists. See photos of four different eagles inside the back cover of this book.

MAMMALS

Class MAMMALIA, like the birds, are warm blooded animals with a four chambered heart. Unlike birds, or any other animals, mammals have hair and mammary glands. These mammary glands produce milk to feed the young that are born alive (Figure 11-17). Because of selective breeding, a modern cow's mammary glands produce enough milk to provide us with ice cream, cheeses, whipped cream, butter, whole and skim milk, in addition to feeding her calf.

Figure 11-17 MAMMALS

The mammary glands of a cow, Bos taurus, are inside the udder. Mammary glands are the structural characteristic used to place animals into the taxonomic Class Mammalia.

Actually the platypus and the spiny anteater are a couple of egg laying mammals, subclass Protheria. The opossum (Didelphis virginiana) kangaroo and koala have a subclass of their own, Metatheria, because they have a pouch for their young. Most mammals live inside their mother before birth, attached to a placenta, and belong to subclass Eutheria (for examples see the right side of Figure 11-18 on page 83).

The PLACENTA is visible in Figures 11-19 and 11-20. Your belly button is the point where you were attached to your placenta by the umbilical cord as your life began inside your mother. Although you, and the other placental mammals, received food and oxygen while inside, the placenta ensured that your blood never mixed with your mother's. An embryo can actually have a different blood type than the mother!

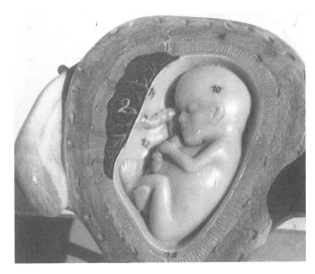

Figure 11-19 A PLACENTA

The placenta (2) is visible in this accurate model of a 10 to 11 week old unborn human, Homo sapiens, a placental mammal.

Figure 11-20 FETAL PIG

The unborn pig is still attached to its umbilical cord but has been taken out of the uterus.

The opossum has no placenta and the tiny baby opossum must crawl into the mother's pouch to grow. This difference is why there are subclasses in the Class Mammalia.

Class Mammalia is divided into orders on the basis of teeth types and the shape of the legs, feet and hands. People belong to the Order Primates along with the monkeys and apes.

The mammals are a large, interesting class of animals. Come to think of it, your science class is a class of interesting mammals!

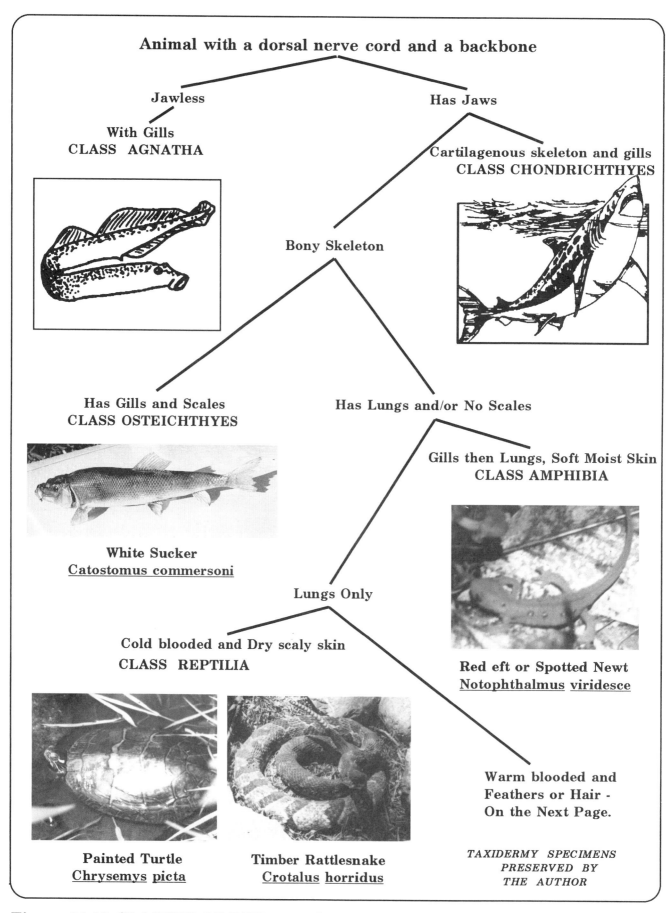

Animal with a dorsal nerve cord and a backbone

Jawless

Has Jaws

With Gills
CLASS AGNATHA

Cartilagenous skeleton and gills
CLASS CHONDRICHTHYES

Bony Skeleton

Has Gills and Scales
CLASS OSTEICHTHYES

Has Lungs and/or No Scales

Gills then Lungs, Soft Moist Skin
CLASS AMPHIBIA

White Sucker
Catostomus commersoni

Lungs Only

Cold blooded and Dry scaly skin
CLASS REPTILIA

Red eft or Spotted Newt
Notophthalmus viridesce

Warm blooded and
Feathers or Hair -
On the Next Page.

Painted Turtle
Chrysemys picta

Timber Rattlesnake
Crotalus horridus

*TAXIDERMY SPECIMENS
PRESERVED BY
THE AUTHOR*

Figure 11-18 CLASSES OF PHYLUM CHORDATA, SUBPHYLUM VETEBRATA

CLASSES OF PHYLUM CHORDATA, SUBPHYLUM VERTEBRATA
CONTINUED

Has Feathers and Lays Eggs
Warm blooded
CLASS AVES

Has Hair and Bears Live Young
Feeds Its Young on Milk
CLASS MAMMALIA

Little Brown Bat - <u>Myotis</u> <u>lucifugus</u>

Female Kestrel or
Sparrow Hawk
<u>Falco</u> <u>sparverius</u>

Unborn
Human

<u>Homo</u>
<u>sapiens</u>

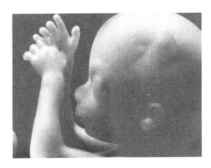

Short Eared Owl
<u>Asio</u> <u>flammeus</u>

Eastern
Cottontail
Rabbit

<u>Sylvilagus</u>
<u>floridanus</u>

Male Cardinal
<u>Cardinalis</u> <u>cardinalis</u>

Black Duck
<u>Anas</u> <u>rubripes</u>

Male Pheasant
<u>Phasianus</u> <u>colchicus</u>

Porcupine
<u>Erethizon</u> <u>dorsatum</u>

CHAPTER 11 REVIEW

OBJECTIVES:

1. **Distinguish between an animal and other creatures.**

2. **Know the major phyla of Kingdom Animalia.**

3. **Understand how structure is the basis for taxonomy.**

4. **Familiarity with the diversity of animals.**

5. **List examples of the classes of vertebrates.**

6. **Study keywords through their origins and word parts.**

PART I. Distinguish between Kingdom Animalia and the other four kingdoms by listing 3 of the main characteristics of animals.

PART II. Using Figure 11-1 answer each question with a sentence.
1. Are the bluegill and blue jay in the same order?
2. An animal called the pumpkinseed is in the Genus Lepomis. Which animal from Figure 11-1 is the pumpkinseed most like?
3. A chicken is in the same class as the blue jay. Must it also be in the same phylum?
4. How many kinds of organisms will be in the Genus Balaenoptera **and** species musculus?
5. What is the scientific name of a tiger?

PART III. Make a chart as shown below and complete by filling in the nine major phyla of the Kingdom Animalia. Omit Hemichordata.

Part III - PHYLA OF THE ANIMAL KINGDOM

PHYLUM	NAME	CHARACTERISTICS	EXAMPLE
1. Porifera sp.	sponges	body full of pores	Spongilla
2. ...			
3. ...			
4. ...			
5. ...			
6. ...			
7. ...			
8. ...			
9. ...			

PART IV Neatly rewrite each statement below. Correctly spell the phylum name below that best matches the statement in the margin in front of each question number.

Annelida	Echinodermata	Porifera
Arthropoda	Molluska	or use
Chordata	Nematoda	All of these
Coelenterata	Platyhelminthes	None of these

Remember to use the terms above.
1. Pore bearers
2. Has a skeleton of spongin
3. Heterotrophic
4. Has cell walls made of chitin
5. A sac like body
6. The tapeworm's head is a scolex
7. Angiospermae
8. Carry out respiration
9. Most abundant animals on earth
10. Also called round worms
11. Have chloroplasts
12. Segmented worms
13. Important in forming good soil
14. Lack nuclear membranes
15. Soft bodied with a muscular foot
16. Made of cells
17. Have a chitinous exoskeleton
18. Joint legged animals
19. Spiny skinned animals
20. Creatures with a dorsal nerve
21. Insects
22. Birds
23. Snakes
24. Frogs
25. Sponges
26. Fish
27. Crustacea
28. Reproduces
29. Spiders
30. Ameba
31. Monocots
32. Mammals
33. Jellyfish
34. Planaria
35. Hookworm
36. Lumbricus
37. Butterfly
38. Sharks
39. Placentals
40. Homo sapiens

PART V. Diagram and label:
   1. A sponge; and 2. Hydra.

PART VI. Diagram and label the external anatomy of an earthworm.

PART VII. Diagram and label a generalized insect.

PART VIII. Write a short paragraph using complete sentences to explain **complete metamorphosis**. Include: diagram, title & labels.

PART IX. Write a short paragraph in which you name and describe the special organ you used when living inside your mother before birth. Name three other examples of animals whose young use the same kind of organ. Name at least one mammal that does not use this organ to live inside its mother.

PART X. Define these keywords. Layout the page as you were instructed in Chapter 1:

Agnatha	Chondrichthyes	Nematoda
Amphibia	Chordata	Osteichthyes
Animalia	Coelenterata	Platyhelminthes
Annelida	Echinodermata	Porifera
Arthropoda	Mammalia	Reptilia
Aves	Molluska	Vertebrata

PART XI. Answer each question by using one of the keywords from Part X in a full sentence.

   1. Which terms are names of kingdoms?
   2. Which are the names of phyla?
   3. Which are names of subphyla?
   4. Which are classes?
   5. Which term includes all the rest?

PART XII. Define the following keywords:

	metamorphosis
anterior	nymph
bilateral symmetry	omnivore
carnivore	placenta
cold blooded	pore
dorsal	posterior
estivate	pupa
gill	radial symmetry
herbivore	regeneration
hibernate	sessile
insectivore	tentacle
larva	ventral
lung	warm blooded

PART XIII. Write each sentence neatly filling in the blank with a keyword from Part XII.

1. A person who eats a Whopper hamburger, with lettuce, tomato, pickles and all the toppings is an __?__.
2. When John the Baptist lived in the desert on locusts (Class Insecta) he was an __?__.
3. When you are "glued to your seat" at an exciting part of *The Lion King* movie, you are _?_.
4. A __?__ nerve cord is in a chordate's back.
5. Sponges are full of __?__.
6. A __?__ is the stage of a butterfly before it becomes an adult.
7. Young amphibians breathe underwater by means of __?__.
8. On a cool night, snakes and other reptiles slow down because they are __?__.
9. Your belly button is where your umbilical cord once attached you to your __?__.
10. Starfish and pizza both have __?__.

PART XIV. CLASSIFICATION REPORT

Write a report on an animal. The topic must be agreed to by your instructor. The report is to include:

   1. Title page with heading and artwork;

   2. Table of contents with page numbers;

   3. Full classification of your animal;

   4. Description of the animal that shows why it is classified into each of its taxons;

   5. Special notes about your animal that are interesting, unusual or important;

   6. At least three quotations following the form given in class;

   7. A diagram, map, graph, or chart related to your topic and referred to in your report;

   8. A glossary containing at least 5 of the vocabulary words from this chapter.

CHAPTER 12 - NUTRITION

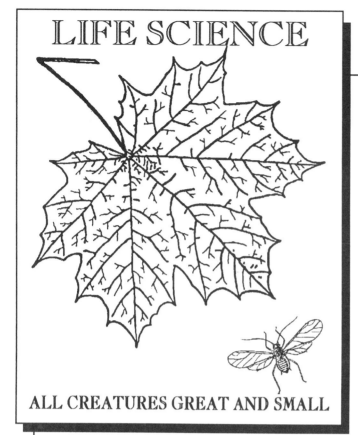

LIFE SCIENCE

ALL CREATURES GREAT AND SMALL

DOWN

DOWN

1. Organic compound needed by an organism in small amounts.

2. Carbon-hydrogen-oxygen compounds with two hydrogens for each oxygen.

4. A simple sugar, made of one ring.

6. Hydrogen oxide.

8. A type of acid, containing nitrogen, which is found in proteins.

9. A unit of heat measurement.

11. A complex sugar made of two rings.

13. Also called "blood" sugar.

16. Any substance needed by an organism.

Nutrition Crossword Puzzle

ACROSS

3. The taking in of predigested food.

5. Many sugar molecules fastened into one long molecule.

7. Lipids.

10. Breaking down complex foods.

12. A starch made of glucose molecules.

14. Combining oxygen and glucose in a cell to release energy.

15. The taking in of food.

17. Passing through the walls of the intestine.

18. Long chains of amino acids.

19. Process of getting and using food.

Use the keywords from this chapter to fill in the puzzle. See how many you know before reading the chapter! Complete the puzzle after completing this chapter. Write in this book only if it belongs to you.

CHAPTER 12 NUTRITION
Living Chemistry

NUTRIENT GROUPS

Nutrition! What do you think when you hear nutrition? Carrots? Spinach? Liver? Or do you think candy, cake, ice cream? There is a lot more to the topic of NUTRITION than just things you don't or do like to eat.

There are five basic NUTRIENT groups. Most foods are a combination of these five groups.

WATER

Approximately 80 percent of Average Adam is WATER. Of course, that means if you weigh 88 pounds, that is a mass of 40 kg, then over 70 lbs or 32 kg of you is water! This water is not pure but is filled with dissolved chemicals of all sorts.

Pure water is made of molecules with 2 hydrogen atoms fastened to one oxygen atom (See below, Figure 12-1). There are many billions of molecules of water in one tiny drop!

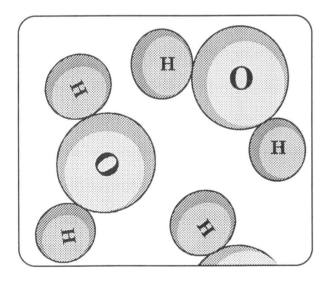

Figure 12-1 WATER

The low energy molecules of water, hydrogen oxide, are necessary for every form of life known to mankind.

Similar to a swimming pool, the watery part of your blood, the plasma must maintain a proper pH. The cytoplasm and nucleoplasm must maintain an electrolyte balance. That means there must be the correct amount of atoms with positive charges as compared to those atoms with negative charges. You will recall from our discussion of osmosis that the concentration of ions controls the flow of water into or out of cells. In a future chapter we will investigate how your kidneys work like the filter on a swimming pool, only better!

Humans can often survive up to a month without food but only a few can last more than 4 days without water. Depending on your size you should, for your body to work its best, drink four to eight glasses of pure water a day.

FATS

Fats and oils are special compounds used for the long term storage of energy in a living system. When your body takes in too much chemical energy much of the excess will be saved in FAT molecules. These molecules are made of carbon (C), hydrogen (H) and oxygen (O) atoms, with many more hydrogens than oxygens.

Fats are also good insulators. That blue whale from the last chapter lives most of its life in the cold waters near the Antarctic. As a warm blooded animal the whale must maintain its body temperature higher than that of the water it is in. The blubber, whale fat, like a good coat or the insulation in a house, keeps the heat inside from moving outward to the water. The blue whale and its relatives have all become endangered species because of the modern technology used to track and catch them. Whales are hunted for several reasons. One is for the tons of blubber on each whale. Whale oil is used in lamps and stoves. These uses point out the fact that fats and oils are high energy compounds.

Ducks, like those pictured in Figure 11-18 of the last chapter also have thick layers of fat allowing them to swim in ice cold water.

Oils and fats are very similar chemicals. Oils are simply liquids at room temperature. Oils help lubricate and soften the skin. As a teenager your body may get carried away with its oil production for a couple of years. But washing carefully and regularly will keep this excess oil from being a real problem. Without the oils your skin would quickly dry out and crack — like the bottom of a dried up mud puddle! Fats are part of your cell membranes.

Fats and oils are in your diet every day. French fries, potato chips and foods cooked in oil supply this nutrient in ample amounts. Bacon is mostly fat. Oil and vinegar salad dressing is another source of oils in modern diets (Fig. 12-2).

Figure 12-2 FATS AND OILS

Bacon, nuts, butter, ice cream and cooking oil all provide ample fats and oils in Average Arnold's diet.

PROTEINS

Have you ever seen a PROTEIN? Have you ever looked into a mirror? See that handsome face, that beautiful hair? Protein! Your muscles, skin and hair are proteins. But, what, exactly, are proteins?

Proteins are large molecules made of smaller pieces called AMINO ACIDS (Figure 12-3). There are 22 amino acids necessary for your body to work and grow.

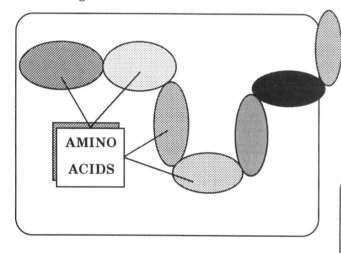

Figure 12-3 A PROTEIN MOLECULE

Proteins are made of many smaller pieces called amino acids. The order of the amino acids makes human protein different from that of each other species of living thing.

A single protein molecule is made of hundreds, even thousands, of amino acids. Many different proteins may be made from the same 22 amino acids, similar to making millions of words from just 26 different letters.

Your body can make some of the amino acids it needs but the so called essential amino acids may be obtained only through your diet. Meat, eggs and milk are necessary in a balanced diet if you are to get the essential amino acids your body requires.

Proteins, built up from amino acids, are made of carbon, hydrogen, oxygen and nitrogen (N). Some proteins have sulfur (S) or phosphorus (P) in them but nitrogen is always in every protein.

Hemoglobin is a protein in the blood that has iron (Fe) in it. Hemoglobin is the protein in your red blood cells that carries the oxygen to every cell in your body. The formula for hemoglobin gives an idea of how complex protein molecules are: $C_{3032}H_{4816}O_{872}N_{780}S_8Fe_4$. You don't have to know the formula, but you should know that nitrogen must be present if the molecule is a protein. If hemoglobin is to carry oxygen your diet must provide the iron necessary for the "hemo" protein.

Use Figure 12-4 to help you remember some of the ideas discussed here. The enzymes referred to in Figure 12-4 are chemicals in your cells that help certain reactions occur. Your life would be over if your enzymes stopped working. A temperature of 106 °F (41.5 °C), or more, can change the shape of enzymes so they can no longer perform their job. If a person's temp. rises that high it is critical that she or he receive immediate treatment to lower their body temperature.

Figure 12-4 (Below)
PROTEIN FOOD FOR THOUGHT
This figure can help you recall protein facts but studying is the best method for learning. Remember the "N" in protein is for nitrogen.

	H	H	P			A
	a	e	r		S	m
	i	m	o		k	i
P	R	O	T	E	I	N
	l	g	o	n	n	o
	a	l	p	z		A
	s	o	l	y		c
	m	b	a	m		i
	a	i	s	e		d
Membranes		n	m	s		

CARBOHYDRATES

A CARBOHYDRATE is any of the chemicals in the body made of carbon, oxygen and hydrogen, with two hydrogens for each oxygen. Thus the name carb - o - hydr - ate means **carb**-on, **o**-xygen and **hydr**-ogen. Unlike water, carbohydrates always have carbon. Carbohydrates have no nitrogen as in proteins. Carbohydrates have only two hydrogens for each oxygen, not like fats with many more hydrogens. Smaller carbohydrates are sugars while bigger ones are starches.

Sugars

For us, the most important carbohydrate is the simple sugar glucose. Sometimes called blood sugar, GLUCOSE is the "gasoline" for the body's engine. Your body can change other carbohydrates, fats and even proteins into glucose!

The white sugar used for tea or to make cookies is sucrose. Sucrose is a complex sugar that your body breaks into glucose so it can use its chemical energy to stay alive. Glucose is VERY important (Fig. 12-5).

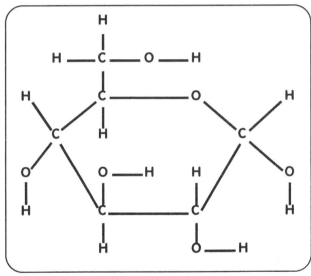

Figure 12-5 GLUCOSE
The structure of just one glucose molecule is represented above. $C_6H_{12}O_6$ is the molecular formula. Billions of glucose molecules were turned into carbon dioxide and water just during the time it took to read this caption. Your cells oxidize glucose to get energy.

In Figure 12-5 you see only one sugar ring. This indicates that glucose, like fructose (fruit sugar), is a simple sugar, or MONOSACCHARIDE. Sucrose, and lactose (milk sugar) are DISACCHARIDES. The name disaccharide indicates that there are two sugar rings in one molecule of sucrose or lactose.

Starches

Much of what you eat is starch. Potatoes, crackers, bread, cereal, spagetti, rice and noodles are mainly starch (Figure 12-6). Wood and paper also contain starch. The chemicals in starches are many, many sugar rings fastened together in long chains.

Your body cannot use, right at noon time, all the glucose it makes from the starches in your lunch. It must use some glucose each instant from lunch until you eat again. As a result your body takes many of the glucose molecules and joins them into a giant POLYSACCHARIDE called glycogen. GLYCOGEN is a starch made from many glucose molecules. Glycogen is how your body saves glucose energy for a short time. If your body takes in too much energy regularly, then it makes fats to save the energy.

Cellulose is the starch in wood. Paper is made from the cellulose fibers in the wood. Your body cannot breakdown the cellulose in wood or paper like it can break down the starches in wheat, rice or potato products. As a result, wood and paper are not nutrients for humans (this includes Junior High School students!). There are animals, fungi and some bacteria that can use wood or paper as a nutrient source.

Figure 12-6 STARCHES

The starchy foods pictured must all be broken down by your body before being used as glucose to run the engines of life in each cell.

VITAMINS AND MINERALS

A VITAMIN is a complex organic molecule needed by your body in small amounts. The next chapter discusses what happens when you are missing a vitamin or don't get enough of a vitamin. Some vitamins are co-enzymes, they help your enzymes.

The table below outlines the more common vitamins, their source and their effects in your body.

Figure 12-7 VITAMINS

VITAMIN	MAIN FOOD SOURCES	AFFECTS
A - carotene	carrots, milk	the eyes
B$_1$ - thiamine	cereals, milk	the nerves
B$_2$ - riboflavin	cereals, eggs	the skin
C - ascorbic acid	oranges, lemons, limes	the gums and capillaries
D - calciferol	liver oil, milk	the bones
E - tocopherol	wheat germ	reproduction
K - vitamin K	Spinach, lettuce	the blood
P-P - niacin	fish, meat, milk	digestion

In terms of life science, a mineral is an inorganic compound or element necessary for an organism in small amounts. Diseases will result from a lack of these minerals just as they will if an organism lacks a vitamin. Some necessary minerals are listed in Figure 12-8.

Figure 12-8 MINERALS

MINERAL & SYMBOL		MAIN FOOD SOURCES	AFFECTS
Calcium	Ca	milk and milk products	bones and teeth
Chlorine	Cl	table salt	digestion
Iodine	I	fish, iodized salt	thyroid gland
Iron	Fe	raisins, spinach, other greens	hemoglobin in red blood cell
Magnesium	Mg	green vegetables	muscles and nerves
Phosphorus	P	milk, green vegetables	bones & teeth
Potassium	K	milk	muscle action
Sodium	Na	table salt	heart beat
Sulfur	S	green vegetables	enzymes

ENERGY FOR LIFE

Nutrition requires more than just the chemicals needed to build a living body. Every living creature, great or small, must have energy. Living things use adenosine triphosphate, ATP, as a way to store energy once it has been released from the chemical bonds of food. Every living cell; moneran, protistan, fungal, plant or animal; must get energy to stay alive. Almost all cells use the process of cellular respiration to break down food molecules into simple low energy products. In this process, energy is released and held in ATP's until used for one of the life functions.

The amount of energy in food is measured by how much heat it could produce when burned. The unit for heat is the CALORIE. Average Adam needs approximately 3,500 calories per day. While the average high school girl needs about 900 calories less than Average Adam.

Cellular Respiration

You now know that $C_6H_{12}O_6$, glucose, is the chemical food used for energy. Oxygen is needed by each cell to combine with the glucose and release the energy in the sugar's bonds. For animals, the carbon dioxide and water formed are waste products. Cellular respiration is written chemically as:

$$6O_2 + C_6H_{12}O_6 \longrightarrow 6CO_2 + 6H_2O + ENERGY.$$

This reaction takes place in the "mighty" mitochondria of each living cell. The energy is "tied up" in the phosphate bonds of the ATP molecule.

INGESTION of fats, proteins and carbohydrates by animals is followed by DIGESTION in which glucose is a product. Then ABSORPTION of the glucose into the cells occurs. Finally the process of CELLULAR RESPIRATION as shown in the chemical equation above releases the energy in the glucose for use by the cell. The Fungi and many of the Monera and Protista simply take in foods that are already digested, this is called ASSIMILATION. Any organism that must take in food by ingestion or assimilation is a heterotroph, and may be said to be heterotrophic.

Those creatures that make their own food we called autotrophs. The plants, and some monerans and protists are autotrophic. Even though they can make their own food, autotrophic organisms must carry out cellular respiration to keep cells alive.

Photosynthesis

The opposite of respiration is photosynthesis. In respiration a more complex chemical is broken down to release the energy in its bonds. In photosynthesis, light energy is used to take simpler chemicals and make a more complex compound with higher energy bonds. The chemical equation for photosynthesis is:

$$6CO_2 + 12H_2O \xrightarrow[\text{LIGHT}]{\text{Chlorophyll}} C_6H_{12}O_6 + 6O_2 + 6H_2O.$$

Chlorophyll, the green pigment in autotrophic cells helps "capture" the light energy which is used to split the water into hydrogen atoms and oxygen atoms. Since light is required, this part is called the light phase. The hydrogen atoms then combine with six carbon dioxide molecules to make glucose. Since light is not needed, this part of photosynthesis is the dark phase. Oxygen is given off as a waste product of photosynthesis. The glucose has more energy than the carbon dioxide and water. Photosynthesis can occur only in autotrophic cells. Fungi, animals and some monerans and protists cannot make their own food. The Kingdom Plantae is the beginning of almost all food chains through which each heterotroph eventually gets energy from sunlight to keep its cells working. (Figure 12-9). Plants begin food chains because plants are photosynthetic. In other words, you are actually a solar powered machine!

Figure 12-9
AUTOTROPHS AND HETEROTROPHS
Sunlight is used by autotrophs, like the green club moss shown here (upper left), to make the food all the heterotrophs need. The Indian pipe (center), without chlorophyll, must grow on the remains of green plants.

CHAPTER 12 REVIEW

OBJECTIVES:

1. **Identify the five major nutrient groups.**

2. **Know examples of each type of nutrient.**

3. **Compare and contrast respiration and photosynthesis.**

4. **Understand the similarities and differences between autotrophs and heterotrophs.**

PART I. List the five nutrient groups and the name of an example for that group.

PART II. Define the 19 keywords in Chapter 12 - Nutrition.

PART III. Use a keyword to fill in each blank.

1. Approximately 80% of most living things is __?__.
2. Lubrication, insulation and long term storage of energy are all functions of __?__.
3. The nitrogen containing pieces of proteins are called __?__.
4. $C_6H_{12}O_6$ is the formula for __?__.
5. The general name for any simple sugar made of just one sugar ring is __?__.
6. Wood is not a __?__ for you because humans cannot digest wood.
7. __?__ are long chains of amino acids.
8. __?__ is the process of dissolved food moving through a cell membrane.
9. The term __?__ describes the act of taking a bite of a hamburger.
10. Photosynthesis is the opposite of __?__.

PART IV. If necessary change the *italicized* word to make the statement true. Write each full statement neatly, once it is true.

1. Hydrogen oxide is another name for *starch*.
2. Only a small number of *amino acids* make up thousands of proteins.
3. *Iodine* is the mineral in hemoglobin that carries oxygen.
4. *Proteins* are made of carbon, oxygen and hydrogen only with the hydrogen to oxygen in a two to one ratio.
5. Sucrose is a *monosaccharide*.
6. Glycogen is a *starch* made from glucose molecules.
7. Sodium and chlorine are *minerals* in table salt.
8. *Ascorbic acid* is another name for Vitamin C.
9. *Thiamine* is another name for the Vitamin A in carrots.
10. Milk and milk products are a good source of *iron* needed for strong bones.
11. ATP is a molecule used to hold *energy*.
12. *Glucose* is combined with oxygen in cellular respiration.
13. Chlorophyll is needed for *respiration*.
14. In photosynthesis, *carbon dioxide* is given off as a waste.
15. Human beings are *autotrophs*.

PART V. Write the chemical equation for cellular respiration.

PART VI. Write the equation for photosynthesis.

PART VII. Write a short essay describing the similarities and differences between how a green corn plant and a cow get their energy. Correctly use at least five of these terms:

ATP	HETEROTROPH
AUTOTROPH	MONOSACCHARIDE
CHLOROPHYLL	PHOTOSYNTHESIS
GLUCOSE	RESPIRATION

PART VIII. Match each phrase in column A with
the best vitamin or mineral in column B.
Write out both the phrase and the
vitamin or mineral as your answer.
Terms may be used more than once.

A   B

1. Ascorbic acid.   A. Vitamin A
2. Builds strong bones and teeth. B. Vitamin B1
3. Helps control heartbeat. C. Vitamin C
4. Found in citrus fruits (limes). D. Vitamin D
5. Is in hemoglobin.   E. Calcium (Ca)
6. Needed for the thyroid gland. F. Iodine (I)
7. Helps nerves work properly. G. Iron (Fe)
8. Is in table salt.   H. Sodium (Na)
9. Is a disaccharide.   I. None of these
10. Is a fat.

PART IX. Write each statement below. In the
margin identify which nutrient group is
most closely associated with the state
ment. Use the letters below.

C = carbohydrates   F = fats and oils
P = protein   V = vitamins and minerals
W = water   X = none of these

1. Glucose and fructose are simple sugars.
2. Makes up 80% of your body.
3. Hair and fingernails contain nitrogen.
4. In cellulose the hydrogen to oxygen is in a two
to one ratio.
5. Meats are made of amino acids.
6. A high fever can destroy human enzymes.
7. Carotene helps the eyes.
8. Glycogen is a starch.
9. Meats, eggs and milk are necessary to provide
amino acids your body cannot make.
10. Enzymes help chemical reactions take place
at low temperatures.

PART X. Identify each of the nutritional groups
pictured at the right. Write a complete
sentence to answer.
For example:
In the example, the vegetables are a good
source of <u>vitamins</u>.

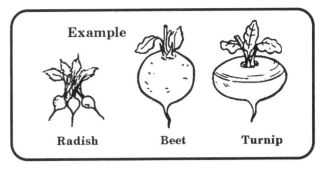

Example

Radish   Beet   Turnip

A.

B.

C.

D.

CHAPTER 13 - DISEASE

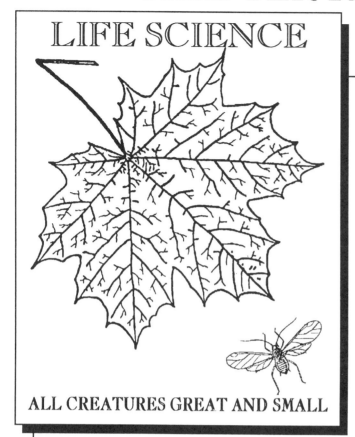

LIFE SCIENCE

ALL CREATURES GREAT AND SMALL

DOWN

1. Proteins for fighting pathogens.

2. Disease transmission by touching.

3. Any condition in which one of the life functions may not be carried out correctly.

5. Catching a disease by using the clothes of a sick person.

6. The outer layer of skin.

8. Any disease causing organisms.

10. Able to be transmitted from one person to another.

13. An organism that carries a germ from one host to another.

Disease Crossword Puzzle

Use the keywords from this chapter to fill in the puzzle.
See how many you know before reading the chapter!
Complete the puzzle after completing this chapter.
Write in this book only if it belongs to you.
You may wish to make a copy of this page.

ACROSS

4. Not able to be transmitted from one person to another.

7. Chemicals that can kill microbes.

8. White blood cells.

9. A substance that stops infection.

11. An organism attacked by pathogens.

12. Tiny drops of liquid.

14. Substance used to give immunity.

15. Ability to resist disease.

16. A small but very deep wound.

CHAPTER 13 DISEASE
The Fight For Life

NONINFECTIOUS DISEASES

Deficiency Disease

When a plant or animal lacks a part of one of the nutrient groups then their body cannot carry out all the life functions successfully. Figure 13-1 shows the effects of lacking protein in a diet.

**Figure 13-1
DEFICIENCY
DISEASE**

This child's diet lacks protein. As a result the stomach bloats and the muscles are underdeveloped. (UNICEF)

Deficiency diseases are not contagious and often can be cured by improving the diet. A glass of milk once a day can prevent the malnutrition shown in Figure 13-1. Any DISEASE that is not able to be "caught" by contact with the person who has it, or by things they touched, is called NONINFECTIOUS. Deficiency diseases are noninfectious. Figure 13-2 lists some human deficiency diseases and the nutrient that is missing.

Figure 13-2 DEFICIENCY DISEASES

Any of the deficiency diseases may be prevented by a good diet. Scurvy was one of the very first deficiency diseases to be figured out. It became a major problem during the age of exploration when sailors spent months at sea with no fresh fruits or good vegetables. James Lind, a Scottish doctor, knew that the Dutch used citrus fruits as a regular part of the diet on their ships. Lind tried hard to convince the British navy to do the same. In 1795, the year after Lind died, England's warships all carried lime juice for each sailor. Seventy years later all British ships gave their sailors lime juice and scurvy began to disappear. British sailors then became known as "limeys" and their teeth stopped falling out on long voyages!

Many years later in 1932 Charles Glen King isolated vitamin C from lemons. Oranges and lemons are even a better source of vitamin C than limes. Today babies fed by bottles instead of on their mother's milk sometimes get scurvy. Orange juice in the diet can prevent scurvy.

Many people supplement their daily intake of food with a multiple vitamin pill. This is acceptable for any vitamins that are water soluble. Ingesting an excess of soluble vitamins will not harm you because your excretory system will eliminate the excess.

Environmental Diseases

Some disease is caused by the environment. In Pennsylvania there are a number of cases of black lung disease resulting from working in coal mines. Both smoking (Figure 13-3) and drinking alcohol have been related to LUNG CANCER as well as other diseases.

DISEASE	SYMPTOMS	CAUSE	CURE
ANEMIA	tired, pale	lack of iron (Fe) causes a shortage of hemoglobin for red blood cells.	eat leafy greens.
BERIBERI	nerve problems	lack of vitamin B1 causes a malfunction of the nerves.	eat grains, and milk.
GOITER	large swelling on the throat	deficiency of Iodine (I) causes the thyroid gland to grow extra large.	use iodized salt, eat fish.
NIGHT BLINDNESS	inability to see at nighttime	deficiency of vitamin A, carotene, impairs the eyes.	eat carrots.
RICKETS	soft teeth and bones	lack of vitamin D, calciferol, causes the bones and teeth to loose calcium.	drink milk.
SCURVY	deficiency of vitamin C	allows breakdown of capillaries.	eat oranges, use lemons and limes.

**Figure 13-3
CIGARETTE
EFFECTS**

**Toxic chemicals
and the tar in
cigarette smoke
are a threat to
each person's
health, not just
the user's lungs.**

"SMOKING OR
NONSMOKING?"

Skin cancer may be caused by over exposure to strong sunlight. Environmental diseases may be avioded by not smoking or drinking alcohol, by careful care of our environment, and by use of safety clothing and equipment when painting or using other chemicals.

Functional Disorders

Other diseases that you cannot "catch" from someone who has them are functional disorders. For example, an ALLERGY, may be inherited but you will not "catch" an allergy from someone. The chart in Figure 13-4 lists diseases that cannot always be cured, but are no threat to others!

Figure 13-4 FUNCTIONAL DISORDERS

Acromegaly	overactive pituitary in adults.
Allergies	overactive immune system.
Blindness	a malfunction of the eyes or the optic nerves.
Cretinism	underactive thyroid in a child.
Deafness	a malfunction of the ears or auditory nerves.
Diabetes	underactive Islands of Langerhans - not enough insulin.
Dwarfism	underactive pituitary in childhood.
Giantism	overactive pituitary in childhood.
Near & far sightedness	wrong shaped eyes or the lense does not focus properly.

The disorders related to the glands of the body will be further investigated in the chapter on the endocrine system.

Genetic Diseases

A fourth type of noninfectious disease is genetic disease. This type cannot be contracted from someone who has it but it can be passed on to a person's children. Sometimes a chromosome in the nucleus of an egg or sperm cell is lost or damaged as the cell is formed. With the piece of DNA that is lost are the instructions for some function of the body.

These changes in DNA may occur in people who use drugs, drink alcohol and smoke cigarettes. X-rays and other energy sources, can cause genetic changes. Many people inherit a genetic disease from their parents.

Color blindness is a genetic disease that boys inherit more often than girls. HEMOPHILIA, bleeder's disease, is also more common in boys. In sickle cell anemia the instruction for the shape of the red blood cell is missing. The red cells should be round disks but instead are sickle shaped and do not carry the oxygen correctly (Figure13-5).

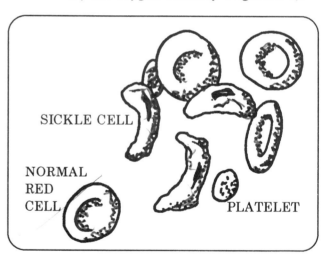

SICKLE CELL

NORMAL
RED
CELL

PLATELET

Figure 13-5 SICKLE CELLS

In sickle cell anemia many of the red blood cells are shaped incorrectly and do not carry oxygen as they should. This disease seems to be an advantage where malaria is common.

Sickle cell anemia tends to be more common among members of the Negroid Race. There are other genetic diseases that afflict different racial or ethnic groups. This fact is because these diseases are genetic and thus passed on in families.

INFECTIOUS DISEASES

A disease that may be contracted, or "caught" from another person is called INFECTIOUS. Infectious diseases are spread several ways:

1. **Droplets** - when sneezing without covering the mouth millions of droplets are ejected into the air. Of course, if you cover your mouth and sneeze but then do not wash your hands, you will spread the germs causing the disease onto everything you touch.

2. **Food** - contaminated food and food waste that is not properly handled will allow the growth of disease causing microbes.

3. **Contact** - a variety of diseases are spread by DIRECT CONTACT where a person touches another. Some are spread by INDIRECT CONTACT in which the germs are on the blankets or socks or the floors used by the diseased person.

4. **Cuts** - some diseases only infect you if your skin is cut or you have a PUNCTURE wound.

5. **Vectors** - when plants or animals carry a disease but do not die from it they can then transmit the disease causing organisms to a new HOST. The carrier, called a VECTOR, must be controlled in order to control the disease.

Plants may also suffer from infectious diseases (Figure 13-6) where wind is often the agent that spreads the disease. For now we will concentrate on a few of the many infectious diseases that affect people.

**Figure 13-6
PLANT
DISEASE**

Black Knot, Dibotryon morbosum, is a tree disease often found growing on black cherry trees, Prunus serotina.
Black knot, which looks like its name, is an infectious disease caused by a fungus.

DISEASE DEFENSES

There is a tremendous life and death battle going on right now. Millions of casualties are being transported to central locations in your lymph system for processing. This fight for life is raging inside of you twenty four hours a day. Your body would succumb to one of the billions of disease organisms that you contact each day if it did not have an active defense against disease!

Your skin, including the mucous membranes in the nose and throat are your 1st line of defense. The EPIDERMIS, when clean and uncut, prevents entry of PATHOGENS.

If the germs enter with your food, or through the lungs or a cut then the 2nd line of defense must take quick action to kill the invaders. The hydrochloric acid in gastric juice kills many of the microbes on ingested materials. In the rest of the body an ameboid army of white blood cells, called PHAGOCYTES, move out of the capillaries to engulf and destroy the invaders.

The germs that survive face a 3rd line of defense, ANTIBODIES, chemicals that stop the effect of the germs or help your phagocytes capture them. There are four types of antibodies.

1. **Antitoxins** are chemicals that cancel the effect of poisons made by the antigens (disease organisms). "Anti" means against and "toxin" means poison. Your body makes antitoxins to protect you from the chemical warfare of germs.

2. **Lysins** are chemicals that dissolve the membranes of the germ cells. Perhaps you have heard of Lysol, a disinfectant whose name has the same root as lysins.

3. **Opsonins** are chemicals that weaken pathogens so that the phagocytes have the advantage and can win the battle against the germ cells.

4. **Agglutinins** are chemicals that cause the microbes to clump together making it easier for the white blood cells to engulf them.

IMMUNITY is the ability of an organism to resist disease. Natural immunity is built into the chromosomes that were inherited when the organism's life began at fertilization. Acquired immunity is gained during a creature's lifetime when an animal comes in contact with a disease organism and the 3rd line of defense, antibodies, are activated. If the animal wins the battle and stays alive then it has active immunity which is a long term ability to resist a disease. When you get your "shots" the germ for the VACCINE has been weakened so that you are sure to win, and your body gains active immunity in the process. The next time you contact that pathogen your body is ready and can resist the disease. When necessary certain antibodies can be injected into the body. This creates passive immunity which lasts only a short time.

Viral Diseases

You probably don't appreciate having to go to the doctor to get your "shots". A shot, also called a vaccination, creates active acquired immunity in your body so that you don't get diseases that used to kill many junior high school aged pupils and their younger brothers and sisters.

Small pox

The first vaccine was made by Edward Jenner, an English doctor, in 1796. Jenner had noticed over several years that the milk maids who got cow pox did not get the stronger small pox disease. Jenner scratched the arm of a boy named James Phipps. Cow pox and small pox are spread by direct and indirect contact. The doctor put some of the pus from the cow pox into the scratch. James got cow pox, then got better. Now came the dangerous part, Jenner infected young Phipps with small pox. The often fatal disease could not get started in James Phipps' body because he had acquired immunity from the cow pox. At first Jenner's tremendous discovery was rejected by the Royal Society in England. Cartoons appeared in the newspapers showing people with cow's heads after Dr. Jenner vaccinated them. But the success of that first vaccine soon replaced ignorance and millions have been saved by vaccines since that special day in 1796.

Today we know that small pox is caused by a virus so small that more than one half million of them could fit on the head of a straight pin.

Rabies

Rabies is a gruesome viral disease spread by warm blooded animal vectors. Before 1885 a person bitten by a rabid animal would suffer a terribly painful illness that usually ended in death. Joseph Meister, a young French boy had been bitten. He was almost sure to die of rabies. Louis Pasteur, the scientist who had used the first man made vaccine to save the sheep of France from anthrax, was working on a rabies vaccine. Pasteur, called the father of bacteriology, had invented the process of Pasteurization of

milk. Now, should he chance using an unproven vaccine that could itself kill the boy if Pasteur's deductions were incorrect? Should he wait, and if the boy got rabies, see young Meister die of hydrophobia? Pasteur began the 14 vaccinations and Joseph survived.

A rabid dog's bite can be fatal. Your pets should be regularly vaccinated.

Yellow fever

The vector for yellow fever, the female <u>Aedes</u> mosquito, was identified by an American doctor, Walter Reed in 1900. A chemical, DDT, was used eventually to control the mosquito population and thousands of lives were saved. DDT is today blamed for polluting our environment.

Polio

It is still unclear how the polio virus is spread. Possibly it is transmitted by droplets. Without knowing everything about polio, Dr. Jonas Salk was still able to make a polio vaccine in 1953. The first mass vaccination was done by Salk on nearly 2 million school children in 1954. In 1961 Dr. Albert Sabin made a polio vaccine that could be swallowed instead of injected. You or some of your classmates would surely have been crippled by polio before reaching your present grade level if these vaccines were never developed.

AIDS

We explained earlier how your body has three lines of defense to fight off diseases. This natural defense is called the immune system. A new viral disease, AIDS causes the body's immune system to stop working correctly. AIDS is communicated by sexual contact or indirect contact with infected body fluids. Currently there is no cure for AIDS, which kills its host in 2 to 3 years after symptoms appear. To prevent contracting AIDS, a person must not use any drug addict's needles, and must practice chastity. Those who are married must be faithful to their spouse. Public health officials must be sure that the emergency blood supply is free of the AIDS virus.

Other Viral Diseases

Other viral diseases include colds, chicken pox, the flu, measles, warts, and the mumps. Some cancers may be caused by viral particles but more research must be done to prove this idea. Perhaps you could discover if viruses cause cancer!

Moneran Diseases

DPT

The DPT shot required before entering school is to prevent three diseases caused by members of Kingdom Monera. Diptheria is caused by a bacillus bacterium and spread by droplets. An antitoxin for diptheria was first developed in 1890 by Emil von Behring of Germany.

Pertussis is whooping cough and it is the P in the DPT shot.

Tetanus is also caused by a bacillus but this moneran is anaerobic. You recall that means able to live without oxygen gas. Cuts often have the tetanus bacillus on them but the oxygen in the air prevents it from growing. If you step on a rusty nail, or get some other puncture wound, then lockjaw, another name for tetanus, is a threat because the bacillus is deep in the wound.

Typhoid fever

Another moneran disease is typhoid fever, caused by _Salmonella typhi_. There was an outbreak of typhoid in New York State during the summer of 1989. Health officials think it may have been contaminated orange juice that caused the outbreak. Typhoid may be spread by animal vectors, unwashed hands or contaminated food.

Figure 13-7 shows the vectors that carry Lyme disease. Lyme is the name of the town in Connecticut where the disease was first recognized in 1976. The deer ticks contain a spirilli bacterium, _Borrelia burgdorferi_, that causes a rash and high fevers in humans. The spirilli are named after Dr. Willy Burgdorfer of the U.S because he identified them in the bodies of deer ticks.

Scarlet fever and tuberculosis are also caused by monerans.

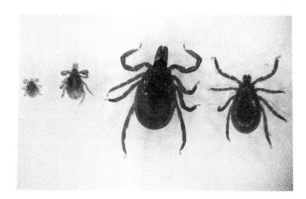

Figure 13-7 VECTORS (8 X)
Larva, nymph, female and male deer ticks, _Ixodes_ _dammini_, are disease vectors that transmit Lyme disease to humans .

Protistan Diseases

If we control the insect vector, the malaria germ it carries can also be controlled.

Malaria

For those who live in temperate and arctic climates, the disease MALARIA has never been a major problem. This disease is common where the _Anopheles_ sp. mosquito is abundant. The female _Anopheles_ is the vector that transmits _Plasmodium malariae_ from an infected person to another person. But that fact was not easily discovered. Malaria is associated with swamps and the belief was that something wrong with swamp air caused the alternating chills and fevers of malaria. The very name: mal - aria, means "bad air."

Former use of DDT and the drainage of swamps have helped reduce the vector population but malaria is still a major problem in tropical regions. Quinine, a chemical from the bark of a tree, is used to treat people with malaria.

Sleeping Sickness

Another tropical disease caused by a protist is African sleeping sickness. For this disease the tsetse (pronounced: teat sea) fly is the vector that spreads the pathogen, _Trypanosoma gambiense_.

Diarrhea

Closer to home, amebic diarrhea is a common complaint caused by one of the ameboid protistans, _Entamoeba histolytica_. This disease is spread mainly through water contaminated by sewage. The importance of the decay bacteria in helping to purify water at sewage treatment plants should be more appreciated! Washing the hands after using the toilet will prevent you from spreading diarrhea. To help keep you from getting diarrhea by contacting door handles contaminated with _Entamoeba_, remind your friends to wash their hands after using a toilet.

Fungal Diseases

Thrush

Thrush, or candidiasis, is caused by a yeast infection of _Candida albicans_. Thrush affects the tongue and is usually not serious if treated.

Ringworm

RINGWORM is a fungal disease that causes a circular spot that spreads outward and heals from the center. This pattern gives the disease its name. Several genera and many species of fungi can cause ringworm.

Athlete's Foot

Athlete's foot is caused when one of several fungi grows in the skin of the foot. The itching that results demands attention even if you don't remember the name of the fungus that causes it: Trichophytron mentagrophytes; among others!

Flatworm and Nematode Diseases

Tapeworm

The flatworm Diphyllobothrium latum has a name that seems long. However, the tapeworm itself can grow up to ten meters inside a human intestine. That is longer than the length of most classrooms! There can be as many as 4000 egg filled proglottids on one of these tapeworms.

Beef Tapeworm

Another parasitic member of the Phylum Platyhelminthes, the common beef tapeworm, was mentioned in the chapter on animals.

Hookworm and Porkworm

Hookworm and porkworm were two nematodes discussed in the chapter on Kingdom Animalia.

Pin worm

A nasty and uncomfortable infection of PIN WORM, Enterobius vermicularis, can be socially devastating due to a habit of the adult female worms. They move out through the anal opening, where they burst, releasing thousands of eggs each. At the same time their action causes severe itching. Though not life threatening you would want to get pin worm treated if you contracted it!

Prevention of nematode infestations is best accomplished by proper sewage treatment, the wearing of shoes and personal hygiene after using the toilet. The largest parasitic nematodes in humans, Ascaris lumbricoides, can release 200,000 eggs per day! Not getting infected in the first place is the best method of nematode control.

Plant Diseases

Most plants do not cause disease in the sense that we have been discussing disease here. Ingesting certain plants can certainly make a person sick or even kill them. Poison Ivy, Poison Oak, and Poison Sumac will all cause a rash but normally are not life threatening. In the case of an individual who has an allergic reaction, immediate help should be sought.

FIGHTING DISEASE

Antiseptics

The fight for life against pathogens involves more than vaccines. One of the greatest advances in fighting infections came in 1865 when Joseph Lister of England used an ANTISEPTIC to cleanse his medical tools and his hands before treating the next patient. No one realized, up to that point, that the doctors were causing many of the lethal infections in their own patients. You will recognize Lister's name in a mouthwash on the market today - Listerine, that is advertised as helping to kill the microbes causing bad breath.

Scientific Thinking

Just seventeen years after Lister's discovery, Robert Koch discovered the bacterium that causes tuberculosis, the very first germ proven to cause a human disease. The isolation of a germ, and proof that it causes the disease in question, is done by rules now known as Koch's Postulates.

1. Every case of the disease must have the germ present.

2. The microbe must be grown in a pure culture.

3. The pure pathogen must cause the disease in a healthy organism.

4. The germ must be reisolated, cultured and identified identical to the original.

Figure 13-8 KOCH'S POSTULATES

These rules are used every day in medical labs around the world as scientists continue to fight disease.

Antibiotics

In 1929 another step forward in the effort to save lives was made when Fleming (see the chapter on bacteria) first used penicillin. This was the first ANTIBIOTIC and is still prescribed today to control many infectious diseases. Other antibiotics, for example streptomycin and erythromycin, come from fungi as evidenced by the root word: mycota, that is part of their names.

Drugs

In 1935 a chemical made in a laboratory from a red dye, sulfanilamide, was discovered by Gerhard Domagk to kill some bacteria. Since then many drugs have been manufactured to help in the fight against disease.

You are the battlefield in a constant war! Now you should understand how you can assist your body in the fight for life. Many diseases can be avoided or prevented by knowledge and good habits. For others, like leprosy, called Hansen's disease (Figure 13-9), drugs are available to arrest the disease or prevent it. Some diseases are still not understood and the world needs a life scientist who will find the cause and the cure.

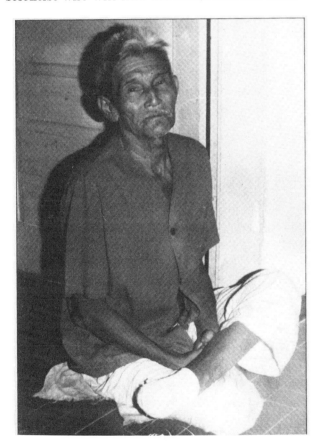

Figure 13-9 MUCH TO BE DONE

This 62 year old leper from Brazil cannot regain his fingers and toes but with medication he can rejoin his family. Leprosy, an ancient and feared infectious disease can be contained. You can help in the fight against disease. For more information contact your local health department or write to the Leprosy Relief Society at 35750 Moravian Drive, Fraser, Michigan, 48026.

CHAPTER 13 REVIEW

OBJECTIVES:

1. **Distinguish between two types of disease.**

2. **Know four types of non-infectious disease and an example of each.**

3. **List ways infectious diseases are spread.**

4. **Understand how the body fights disease.**

5. **Identify infectious diseases.**

6. **Appreciate the contributions made to our health by life scientists.**

PART I. Use full sentences to answer each of the questions below:

1. What are the two basic types of disease?
2. List four kinds of non-infectious diseases with an example of each.
3. What are five different ways that most infectious diseases may be spread?
4. What are the human body's three lines of defense against disease?
5. When, where and by whom was the first recorded antiseptic used?

PART II. Write a short paragraph of full sentences describing the first vaccination ever done.

PART III. In a neatly written paragraph, list Koch's Postulates.

PART IV. Define the following keywords from Chapter 13 - Disease. Set up your definitions as directed in Chapter 1.

antibiotics	indirect contact
antibodies	infectious
antiseptic	noninfectious
direct contact	pathogens
disease	phagocytes
droplets	puncture
epidermis	vaccine
host	vector
immunity	*"finis"*

PART V. Write each disease listed below then write an "I" or an "N" in the margin in front of each disease to identify the type:
I = infectious   N = noninfectious.

1. AIDS   6. MALARIA
2. ALLERGY   7. PIN WORM
3. BEEF TAPEWORM   8. RINGWORM
4. HEMOPHILIA   9. SCURVY
5. LUNG CANCER   10. TETANUS

PART VI. Write each sentence neatly using one of the keywords from Part IV and a disease from Part V to fill in the blanks. Words will be used only once, if at all.

1. __?__ is a fungus that attacks the __?__.
2. Whenever a person has a __?__ wound __?__ is a possible problem.
3. Bleeder's disease, __?__, is __?__ and can not become an epidemic.
4. The female <u>Anopheles</u> mosquito is the __?__ that carries __?__.
5. In countries without meat inspection you could become the __?__ to a __?__!
6. The nematode disease __?__ is __?__ and may be spread by poor personal hygiene.
7. __?__, acquired immune deficiency syndrome, is spread by _?_ with infected body fluids.
8. An __?__ is when a person's system of __?__ overreacts.
9. __?__ is a fatal __?__ that often results from smoking cigarettes.
10. _?_, caused by a lack of ascorbic acid, cannot be prevented by a _?_ as can small pox.

PART VII. Match by writing the full term in column A, then in the margin in front of each question, write the best term from column B. You may use a term from column B more than once.

Column A	Column B
1. Using a friend's towel	A. Athlete's foot
2. Stepping on a rusty nail	B. Malaria
3. Getting bit by a mosquito	C. Common cold
4. Using food that is too old	D. Deficiency disease
5. Flies land on your food	
6. Drinking impure water	E. Tetanus
7. Refusing to drink milk	F. Typhoid
8. Not eating green vegetables	G. None of these
9. Shaking hands	
10. Sneezing without covering the mouth.	

PART VIII. Copy and complete the chart below:

SCIENTISTS FIGHT FOR LIFE		
NAME	DATE	NOTES ON DISEASE OR DISCOVERY
?#1.	1796	?#2.
?#3.	1865	First to use an antiseptic to clean his surgeons tools.
?#4.	1882	By his rules, he proved a certain bacterium causes tuberculosis.
?#5.	1885	?#6.
?#7.	?#8.	The first antitoxin was used to fight diptheria.
?#9.	1929	?#10.
Charles G. King	1932	?#11.
Gerhard Domagk	?#12.	?#13.
Jonas Salk	1953	?#14.
Willy Burgdorfer	?#15	Identifies the spirilli bacterium that causes Lyme disease.

PART IX. Match by writing the disease in column A followed by the term from Column B that is most closely associated with the disease. You will not use all of the terms in column B.

Column A	Column B
1. Anemia	A. ascorbic acid needed
2. Beriberi	B. vitamin B1 from grains needed.
3. Color blindness	C. carotene will help.
4. Diabetes	D. vitamin D in milk is needed.
5. Goiter	E. prevented by not smoking
6. Hemophilia	F. Fe is lacking in the diet.
7. Lung cancer	G. glucose is not controlled due to lack of insulin.
8. Malaria	H. Hemo- refers to the blood.
9. Night blindness	I. iodine is lacking in the diet.
10. Rickets	J. Jenner used a vaccine.
11. Scurvy	K. Koch's postulates.
12. Typhoid fever	L. Louis Pasteur saved a boy.
	M. mosquitoes are the vectors.
	N. not washing hands by food handlers.
	O. overactive pituitary in child.
	P. inherited by boys more than girls.

PART X. Write a short paragraph explaining the difference between natural and acquired immunity. Distinguish between the two types of acquired immunity: active and passive.

PART XI.

Fight Against Disease Report

Choose a scientist that made a contribution to our understanding of disease. Agree with your teacher on the topic and the due date for your report. Write a biographical report that includes:

1. **The correct heading and a title.**

2. **A table of contents.**

3. **When and where the scientist lived.**

4. **The major accomplishments of the life scientist whom you have chosen.**

5. **Obstacles the scientist overcame.**

6. **Two references other than this text. List the references at the end of the report in the format given by the instructor.**

BEWARE OF THESE INSECT VECTORS!

Pests that many people consider to be harmless actually can pose life-threatening risks. Fleas, ticks, chiggers, mosquitoes and ants, especially prevalent in the spring and summer months, are known disease carriers. The tiny deer tick, for example, can transmit Lyme disease. Lyme disease is a sometimes deadly disorder for wildlife, pets, and humans. This Moneran disease can trigger persistent fever, chills and headaches for weeks, and if left untreated may lead to death.

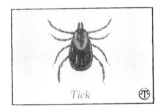

Tick

CHAPTER 14 - TESTING FOR NUTRIENTS

LIFE SCIENCE

ALL CREATURES GREAT AND SMALL

DOWN

1. The material that passes through a filter.

3. Living matter.

4. Instrument used to measure heat.

5. How hot or cold compared to a standard.

7. The substance that dissolves.

8. The substance that is present in the greater amount in a solution.

10. Able to dissolve.

11. The amount of heat needed to raise the temperature of one gram of water one degree Celsius.

Testing For Nutrients Crossword Puzzle

Use the keywords from this chapter to fill in the puzzle. See how many you know before reading the chapter! Complete the puzzle after completing this chapter.

Write in this book only if it belongs to you. You may wish to make a copy of this page.

ACROSS

2. The solid caught in a filter.

3. The solid formed when two liquids react chemically.

6. A brown solution used to test for starches.

9. Allows light through but cannot be seen through clearly.

12. A blue solution used to test for simple sugars.

13. Energy available for transfer.

CHAPTER 14
TESTING FOR NUTRIENTS
More Chemistry

Chemistry is the basis for many of the advances and discoveries in the life sciences. The fight against disease is very much a chemical war. The very life of your body is dependent on the chemical reaction of cellular respiration. Food chains begin with the chemistry of photosynthesis. The foods we eat are chemicals and our bodies are the test tubes and beakers in which we take apart food chemicals and react the pieces to make ourselves! In this chapter we will investigate several chemical tests that will identify foods as belonging to one of the five basic nutrient groups: carbohydrates, fats, proteins, vitamins & minerals and water. Some nutrients are SOLUBLE, some are not and will not dissolve in water. For example, corn starch and glucose are both white powders. If we have a mixture of them we could separate the mixture by adding water and filtering (see Figure 14-1). The starch would be the RESIDUE left in the filter paper. The glucose would be in the FILTRATE. By evaporation of the water we get the glucose back again.

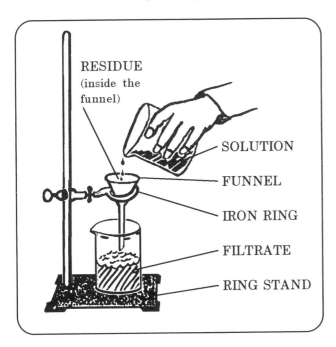

Figure 14-1 FILTERING APPARATUS

The ring stand is used to hold the iron ring, which holds the funnel. The solution that is being filtered must not be allowed to rise above the edge of the filter paper.

CARBOHYDRATES

White sugar is a carbohydrate, or at least, we said it was in the chapter on nutrition. A simple test may be done to illustrate that sucrose is made of carbon, hydrogen and oxygen. Place a small amount of white table sugar into a small beaker and saturate with concentrated sulfuric acid. The acid has a very strong ability to take water out of substances, for example: your clothes, skin or the sugar! For this reason you must use caution even when this test is performed as a demonstration.

After a few moments the beaker will get so hot it will be hard to hold. Some of the energy in the sugar's chemical bonds is being released. A definite TEMPERATURE change is one indication that a chemical reaction is occurring. Some of the odor you may notice is from burnt sugar and some is from sulfur compounds from the acid. Just a few moments more and water vapor, made from the hydrogens and oxygens in the white sugar and the acid, begins to escape. This leaves the carbon in the beaker. The carbon is black and greatly expanded compared to the original sugar. This mass of carbon must be washed to remove any sulfuric acid before it is handled (Fig. 14-2).

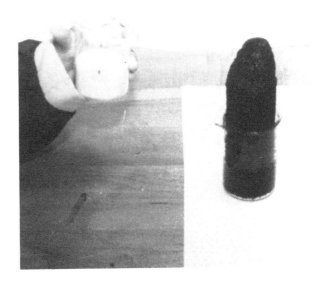

Figure 14-2 CARBON

The amount of white sugar shown on the left produced the amount of carbon on the right. The hydrogen and oxygen that were bonded to the carbon have escaped as water.

Calories

The HEAT given off is one way of measuring the energy content of foods. Fats have the most energy per gram. However, fats are hard for the body to use. Carbohydrates, more easily digested, are the main energy source for the body.

An experiment to determine the approximate calories in a food source may be done easily in any lab. Using a paper clip bent into a "stand", as shown in Figure 14-3, light a peanut under a test tube containing 10 grams (10 ml) of water.

Figure 14-3 MEASURING CALORIES

Safety equipment and proper lab behavior must be observed whenever an experiment is being carried out.

The centigrade temperature of the water has to be recorded first. After the peanut has burned record the highest temperature reached by the water. By using the definition of a CALORIE the energy released from the chemical bonds as the peanut oxidized can be calculated. For example, if the 10 g of H_2O was at 18.1 °C, then after burning the peanut the temperature was 18.7 °C. The total calories of heat released were **at least**:

HEAT = mass of H_2O x 1 cal/g-°C x temp. change

HEAT = 10 g of H_2O x 1 cal/g-°C x 0.6 °C
The units g and °C cancel to give:
HEAT = 10 x 1 x 0.6 calories

HEAT = 6 cal

Why did I emphasize **at least**? Because some of the heat could get away into the air and the test tube and the paper clip. In laboratories where the calories must be measured accurately and very carefully a CALORIMETER is used.

Figure 14-4 is a chart comparing the amount of energy in different foods.

Food Sample	Calories per 100 g	Main Nutrient Group	Main Vitamin Mineral
Almonds	630	Fat	A
Apples	60	Carbohydrate	C
Beans, dried	330	Carbohydrate	B1
Beef, lean	230	Protein	B2
Bread,	260	Carbohydrate	B1
Butter	730	Fat	A
Cashew	600	Fat	B2
Peanut	590	Fat	A
Tuna, in oil	200	Protein	Na, I
Water-melon	30	Water	C

Figure 14-4
CALORIC CONTENT OF FOODS

Starches

Starches (polysaccharides) are one of the two major groups of carbohydrates. The test for starch is simple. Place a drop of LUGOL'S SOLUTION, which contains iodine, onto the sample being tested. Lugol's solution is brown. If you use pure starch it is white. Starch does not dissolve very well in water. If the spot of iodine turns blue-black then starch is present! Look back at Figure 14-4. Do you think that peanuts will test positive for starch? Don't be too hasty in deciding! The chart only indicates the main nutrient group in peanuts. Most foods contain more than one nutrient group.

Simple Sugars

Monosaccharides are the sugars with only one sugar ring. Digestion turns much of the starch, and some of the fat into glucose, a simple sugar. Fruits already contain fructose, another simple sugar, when you ingest them. To test for simple sugar: put the food sample into a test tube and cover it with blue BENEDICT'S SOLUTION. If you use pure sugar it is white but its solution is clear. Heat this mixture for approximately three minutes. Figure 14-5 will allow you to interpret your result.

Color after heating	Amount of simple sugar
BLUE	none
GREEN	very little
YELLOW	fair amount
ORANGE-RED to BRICK RED	lots of simple sugar present

Figure 14-5 SIMPLE SUGAR TEST

When a food is carefully and gently heated with Benedict's solution a color change indicates the presence of simple sugars.

What color will result when sucrose, table sugar, is tested? Think carefully before you answer, table sugar is a disaccharide!

FATS

Fats and oils are mainly used by the body for long term storage of energy and for insulation. They are also used to lubricate. Cholesterol, a fatty sterol, can be a problem in the heart and arteries of people with excess fat in their diet!

To test for fats simply rub the food sample on a piece of unglazed paper (heat from a lamp will help). Newsprint from a newspaper will work if no paper towels or napkins are available. Fats and oils usually leave a TRANSLUCENT spot that will not evaporate over night. The windows in most bathrooms are translucent, allowing light to come through, but not clearly. Water will make a spot but it will quickly dry up.

PROTEINS

Both tests described here should be done by an instructor. Egg white is a good sample to demonstrate the presence of protein. Place equal amounts of egg white and water into a test tube and shake the test tube. Add an equal amount of 10% sodium hydroxide solution (NaOH) and stir. Add 3 drops of 3% copper sulfate solution ($CuSO_4$). Violet or a pink violet color is positive for proteoses and peptones from protein.

A second test requires just as much caution. Add the food sample to a small amount of concentrated nitric acid, boil, pour off the acid and rinse with water. Now cover the sample with ammonium hydroxide (NH_4OH). An orange color indicates protein is present.

Proteins from milk, eggs, and meat are sources of amino acids in your diet. Proteins are digested into amino acids. Amino acids are used to build and repair cells and tom make PROTOPLASM.

VITAMINS AND MINERALS

The body uses small amounts of vitamins and minerals for control of chemical reactions (metabolic regulation). Several minerals are easy to test for. Adding starch to a solution can indicate if iodine is present, the starch turns blue-black.

Chlorine may be detected by adding a few drops of silver nitrate solution ($AgNO_3$) to the sample. A white solid, called a PRECIPITATE, forms when chlorine is present.

WATER

Water is not a source of energy for the body. It provides no minerals or vitamins needed for bones and enzymes. Water is not used to get amino acids needed for skin, hair and muscles. The water in your body is a SOLVENT in which the chemicals of life dissolve and react. Each dissolved chemical is a SOLUTE. Water is the most abundant compound in the body (Fig. 14-6).

Using a balance determine the mass of a food sample before and after drying. The precent of its mass that was water may now be determined. Subtract the dry from the fresh mass. This is the mass of water. Divide the mass of water by the fresh mass. Multiply by 100 to make your answer a percent. See the sample on the next page.

Blue cobalt chloride paper ($CoCl_2$) turns white in the presence of water vapor.

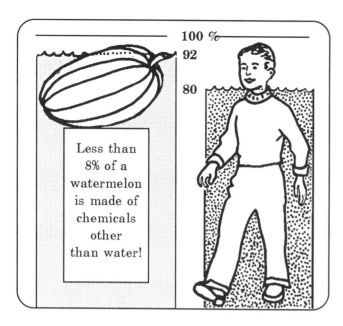

Figure 14-6 PERCENT WATER

The human body is approximately 80 percent water. Watermelon is more than 92 percent water! All creatures great or small need H_2O.

The following sample problem will illustrate how to determine a percent. A percent of anything is the amount of that thing divided by the total amount and then multiplied by 100.

% THING = $\dfrac{\text{AMOUNT OF THE THING}}{\text{TOTAL AMOUNT}}$ X 100

If a piece of fresh, juicy watermelon has a mass of 10.0 g and after total drying has a mass of only 0.7 grams then **follow these steps to determine the percent water :**

1. Subtract the dry mass from the fresh mass.

10.0 g - 0.7 g = 9.3 g

This computation gives the mass of the water originally in the sample.

2. Divide the mass of water by the fresh mass.

9.3 g / 10.0 g = .93

3. Multipy by 100 to change the decimal to a percent. Write the answer with a % sign.

.93 X 100 = 93 %

CHAPTER 14 REVIEW

OBJECTIVES
1. **Understand the function each nutrient group serves in the body.**
2. **Ability to test for each nutrient group.**

PART I. Define the 14 keywords from chapter 14 TESTING FOR NUTRIENTS.

PART II. Diagram and label the filtering set up.

PART III. Using full sentences, explain how to test for each of the following nutrients. Include the correct name of any apparatus or solutions, and the meaning of any color changes.
1. Glucose
2. Cellulose
3. Fat
4. Protein
5. Chlorine
6. Water

PART IV. Fill in the missing parts of the chart

Heat (cal) = mass (g) x 1 $\frac{\text{calorie}}{\text{gram-}^\circ\text{C}}$ x temp. change

	HEAT (cal)	MASS (grams)	INITIAL TEMP	FINAL TEMP.	TEMP. CHANGE
Ex.	below	10 g	12 ºC	14 ºC	see below
A	#2 ?	5 g	6 ºC	7 ºC	#1 ?
B	#4 ?	100 g	40 ºC	43 ºC	#3 ?
C	#6 ?	3 g	15 ºC	#5 ?	2 C
D	4 cal	2 g	#8 ?	10 ºC	#7 ?
E	50 cal	#10 ?	10 ºC	35 ºC	#9 ?

Ex. First determine the change in temperature
Temp. Change = Final Temp. - Initial Temp.
Temperature change = 14 ºC - 12 ºC
Temperature change = 2 ºC
Now use the formula above for heat
Heat = 10 g **x** 1 cal/g-ºC **x** 2 ºC
Note: g & ºC cancel
Heat = 20 calories

PART V. Solve:
1. If a watermelon slice has a mass of 25 grams, and after drying has a mass of 2 grams, what is the percent water in the melon?
2. If a pupil gets three wrong out of 20 questions, what is that pupil's percent correct?
3. What mass of a 40 kg person is water (use 80%)?

MIDWAY REVIEW

The following questions touch on the major topics. You must study all of your notes, homeworks, labs, and quizzes to do your best.

PART I. KEYWORDS

Study the keywords from each chapter.
1. After you have studied ask someone to quiz you orally on each word. They should read the definition and you correctly spell the word.
2. Ask them to please mark each word you correctly spell.
3. Restudy any of the words missed and repeat steps 1-3 until you know them all.
4. Now have someone quiz you by giving you the word and you explain the definition. Repeat steps 1-3 until you really know the definitions.

PART II. INSTRUMENTS

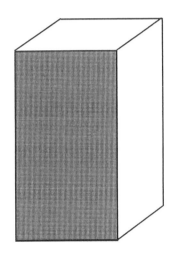

PART II - 2. BOX

1. List 6 parts of a book and briefly explain each.

2. Measure the length, width and height of the BOX above, then determine the area of the shaded face and the volume of the box.

3. Convert: 5 m to cm; 847 ml to l; 8 cc to ml.

4. List three reasons why collections are made.

5. Sketch and label: a thermometer, pan balance, and a microscope.

6. List the rules to follow when using the bunsen burner.

PART III. CELLS

1. Correctly spell the name of each element: C, H, O, N, S, P, I, Na, Cl, Fe, Cu, K, Mg, Ca, Zn.
2. Write the formula for: water, carbon dioxide, oxygen gas, glucose, and table salt.
3. Sketch and label a plant cell.
4. Sketch and label an animal cell.
5. List the parts of a cell and give the main function of each part.
6. Explain osmosis.

PART IV. CLASSIFICATION

1. List the seven taxons in order from largest to smallest.
2. List the five Kingdoms.
3. Name three basic shapes of bacteria.
4. Sketch and label: Ameba, Paramecium, and Euglena
5. Sketch and label a mushroom.
6. List and give examples of the two higher phyla of plants.
7. List three classes of Phylum Tracheophyta with examples.
8. Name the two subclasses of Angiosperms and give four differences of plants in the two subclasses.
9. List the nine main phyla in the Animal Kingdom and an example of each.
10. Identify the main characteristics of the seven classes in phylum chordata.

PART V. NUTRITION AND DISEASE

1. Write the equation for cellular respiration.
2. Write the equation for photosynthesis.
3. List the five major nutrient groups.
4. Explain how to test for: starch, monosaccharides, water, and chlorine.
5. Name five deficiency diseases and the vitamin or mineral needed to prevent it.
6. Identify four different kinds of noninfectious disease and give an example for each.
7. Name five ways infectious diseases may be transmitted.
8. Make a chart listing viral, moneran, protistan, fungal and animal groups with two examples of diseases caused by each group.
9. Identify who, what, when, where for each name: Jenner, Lister, Pasteur, Koch, von Behring, Reed, Fleming, Domagk, and Salk.

CHAPTER 15 - INTRODUCTION TO SYSTEMS

LIFE SCIENCE

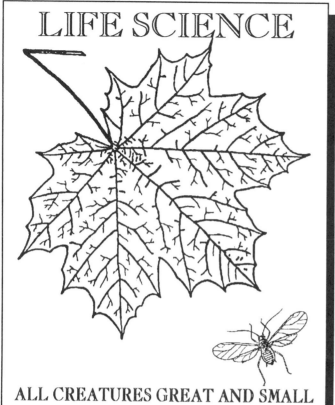

ALL CREATURES GREAT AND SMALL

DOWN

1. The inside of the skull.

2. The part of the body inside the ribcage.

5. All the systems of an organism taken together.

Introduction To Systems Crossword Puzzle

Use the keywords from this chapter to fill in the puzzle. See how many you know before reading the chapter! Complete the puzzle after completing this chapter.

Write in this book only if it belongs to you. You may wish to make a copy of this page.

ACROSS

3. A collection of sensory organs and a mass of nerve tissue.

4. Arms and legs.

6. The part of the body containing most of the digestive system.

7. Chest and abdomen.

CHAPTER 15
INTRODUCTION TO SYSTEMS

Imagine the tremendous forces that the hand and arm of Lynn Nolan Ryan underwent when he pitched a baseball 162.3 km/hr on August 20 of 1974. Ryan's hand went from zero to more than 100 mph then stopped again in a split second!

Consider a man, Calvin Phillips, just 67 cm (2ft 2 1/2 in.) tall at 19 years of age! Zeng Jinlian, a young Chinese girl, was 247 cm tall (8ft 1 in.) at 17 years of age! Calvin would just barely reach the abdomen of the typical Junior High girl pictured in Figure 15-2.

Your life began as a single cell the size of a small pin head, just 9 months later you were a complex organism of billions of cells all working together to cry and kick!

The human body is amazing. It is amazing in what it can do, the variety of shapes and sizes it comes in and the organization it displays. The human machine is a collection of parts and pieces that go together in some wonderful way to allow us to taste, see, move, feel, hear, think, grow, and remember. As we study "the plumbing" so to speak, it is important to realize that all of the parts of our bodies work together. Each part has its function that contributes to the life of the whole organism.

Cells to Systems

Every living thing is made of cells. Inside the cells are smaller organelles, the mitochondria, golgi bodies and all the rest. Cells of the same shape form a tissue where the cells all do the same function. Your epidermis is made of cells that protect the rest of your tissues. The muscle tissue in your arm is made of skeletal muscle cells all designed to contract and extend.

A group of tissues that work together to perform a single function is an organ. Your stomach, an organ of the digestive system, consists of muscle, nerves, epithelial, glandular and circulatory tissues. These tissues work together to hold and digest the food you eat. Along with your mouth, esophagus, the small and large intestines and an assortment of other organs, the stomach makes up one of the systems of your body. The systems carry out the life functions for an organism. In Figure 15-1 each system is matched with a life function.

SYSTEM	LIFE FUNCTION
Skeletal	Irritability
Muscular	Irritability
Digestive	Nutrition
Circulatory	Transport
Respiratory	Respiration
Excretory	Excretion
Endocrine	Synthesis
Nervous	Irritability
Reproductive	Reproduction

The life function of growth is carried out at the cellular level in all of the systems.

Figure 15-1
LIFE FUNCTIONS AND SYSTEMS

The life functions may be matched up to the systems in the human body.

Regions of the Body

The BODY consists of four basic regions.
1. The HEAD, a collection of sensory organs and a mass of nerve tissue. The head includes the skull or CRANIAL CAVITY.
2. The CHEST CAVITY, a hollow region protected by the ribs that contains lungs and heart.
3. The ABDOMINAL CAVITY, containing most of the digestive system. The chest and the abdomen together are called the TORSO.
4. The LIMBS are also called arms and legs. See Figure 15-2.

**Figure 15-2
REGIONS OF
THE BODY**

The chest and abdomen put together may be called the torso. The arms and legs are often called limbs.

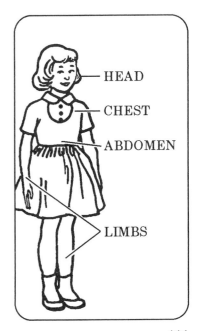

HEAD

CHEST

ABDOMEN

LIMBS

CHAPTER 15 REVIEW

OBJECTIVES:

1. Understand the organization of complex organisms.

2. Associate each life function with a system of the body.

3. Identify four regions of the body.

PART I. Use the following terms to answer each sentence. Neatly write out a full sentence as your answer.

ORGANELLE   CELL   TISSUE
ORGAN   SYSTEM   ORGANISM

1. Which term includes all the others?
2. Which term is the unit of structure and function of living things?
3. Which is a group of organs working together to carry out a life function?
4. Epidermis, nerves, and muscles are examples of which term?
5. The mouth, esophagus, stomach, intestines and associated organs all together are an example of which term?

PART II. List each of the eight life functions except growth and write the name of a system of the body that carries out that function?

PART III. Draw an outline of a human body and label each major region of the body. Include a title.

PART IV. Match each term with a diagram. Some of the diagrams may be used more than once.

TERM   DIAGRAM

1. Molecule   A.

2. Organelles   B.

3. Cell   C.

4. Tissue

5. Organ   D.

7. System

8. Organism   E.

                        F.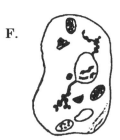

                        G.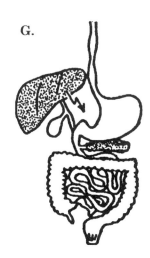

CHAPTER 16 – THE SKELETAL AND MUSCULAR SYSTEMS

LIFE SCIENCE

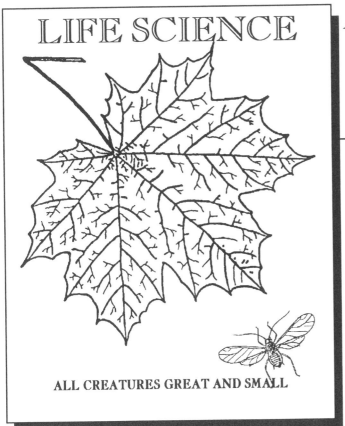

ALL CREATURES GREAT AND SMALL

DOWN

2. Term for muscles not controlled by the conscious mind.

3. The soft center of long bones.

4. Bands on some voluntary muscles.

7. Tissue that connects bone to bone.

9. Rubbery connective tissue.

The Skeletal and Muscular Systems Crossword Puzzle

Use the keywords from this chapter to fill in the puzzle.
See how many you know before reading the chapter!
Complete the puzzle after completing this chapter.
Write in this book only if it belongs to you.

ACROSS

1. Literally "near the bone."

5. Support cells containing calcium.

6. Term for muscles controlled by the conscious mind.

8. Fat cells.

10. Referring to the heart.

11. Immovable, ball and socket, hinge and gliding are four types.

12. Tissue that connects muscles to other muscles or to bone.

CHAPTER 16
THE SKELETAL AND MUSCULAR SYSTEMS

"Make no bones about it!" You need your skeleton for more than life science class!

The 206 bones of the human body (Figure 16-6) are more than just supports on which to hang muscles and organs. Support is the most obvious function of our internal skeletal system but there are four other important functions as well.

The skeleton protects vital organs. For example the skull protects the brain (Figure 16-1).

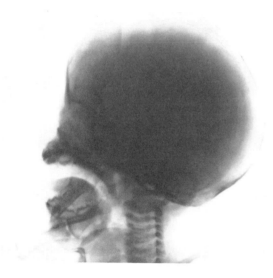

Figure 16-1 INTERNAL SKELETON

This X-ray photograph of a three month old girl's neck and skull shows the vertebrae of the neck which protect the dorsal nerve bundle called the spinal cord. The skull protects the brain.

The skeleton provides storage of minerals.

The moveable bones are levers for attachment of the muscles (Figure 16-2).

The longest human bone is the femur, or upper leg bone. The femur and other long bones manufacture blood cells.

While a bone is alive it has a skin like covering, the PERIOSTEUM. The soft center of the long bones, MARROW, is where your red and white blood cells are made.

The skeletal system includes several kinds of connective tissue other than BONE. Cartilage is a rubber like tissue that acts as a shock absorber between bones. CARTILAGE is used for

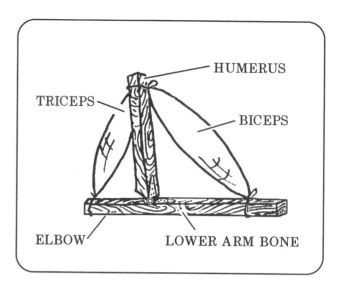

Figure 16-2 BONES ARE LEVERS

The knee, elbow and fingers have hinge joints so that the muscles can use the bones as levers.

support in the ears and nose where some flexibilty is required.

A LIGAMENT is a thin, tough and fibrous connective tissue that connects bone to bone. A TENDON, also string like, is the connective tissue that attaches a muscle to a bone, or one muscle to another. Touch the underside of your knee while holding your foot up to feel 2 tendons.

One other type of connective tissue is not usually associated with bones, cartilage, ligaments, and tendons. Fat is deposited in ADIPOSE CELLS, a type of connective tissue that provides more insulation than support (see Figure 16-3).

Figure 16-3 shows a hinge JOINT in the knee. Similar joints are in the elbows and fingers. A hinge joint, like the hinge on a door, allows movement in only one plane.

The hip and shoulder have a ball and socket joint. See Figure 16-4 on the next page. The ball and socket allows more movement than the hinge or gliding joints. The stick shift in many standard cars is a ball and socket.

Your wrists, ankles and backbone move by means of a gliding joint. The gliding joint allows a limited amount of twisting movement.

A fourth type of joint is immovable, such as the solid joints in the skull. You can observe an immovable joint in Figure 16-1. In a baby only three months old that joint is supposed to be open. After the brain grows the joint grows together. Elena, the girl in the X-ray, had to have surgery to open up that immovable joint.

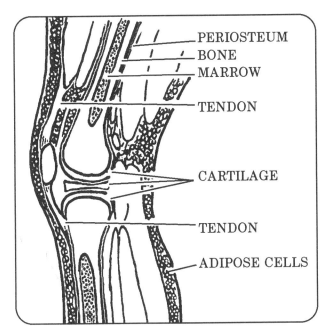

Figure 16-3 TISSUES IN THE
SKELETAL SYSTEM

Bones are complex organs made of many tissues. Bones are alive and blood vessels must bring in food and oxygen and remove wastes.

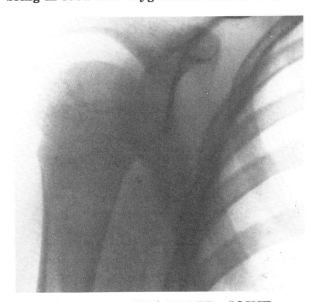

Figure 16-4 SHOULDER JOINT

The ball on the upper arm bone, the humerus, fits into the socket of the shoulder blade. This allows a great range of movement for the arm.

Here's a question you can sit on and think about for a while: what is the largest muscle in the body? There are over 600 to choose from. You can sit on it because the answer is the gluteus maximus or buttock muscle.

When we "make a muscle" we tighten our biceps as shown in the model in Figure 16-2.

When you think of muscles, if you picture Arnold Schwarzenneger, you are thinking of skeletal muscles. This type of tissue has cells with more than one nucleus. Skeletal muscle cells are marked with STRIATIONS when viewed under a microscope (Figure 16-5). The importance of skeletal muscles is their ability to contract.

The muscles attached to your skeleton are in pairs. When one contracts the opposing muscle must extend. You can move your skeletal muscles when you want to, thus they are sometimes called VOLUNTARY muscles. These skeletal muscles of the body perform the life function of irritability. Without a skeleton to provide support you would be like a giant ameba, changing shape but unable to move in any definite direction!

There are two other types of muscle tissue which are part of other body systems. CARDIAC muscle is also striated but is not voluntary. Cardiac muscle also has many nuclei in one cell. These heart muscle cells are shaped like many letter "H's" connected together (see Figure 16-5). Your heart began beating somewhere around 18 days after your life began at fertilization. By the time you were born your cardiac muscle had already worked non-stop for over eight months!

Smooth muscle in the digestive system and in glands and blood vessels does not have striations (Figure 16-4). Your body controls these muscles without your conscious effort. Smooth muscle, because it contracts and relaxes regularly, not just when you want it to, is INVOLUNTARY muscle.

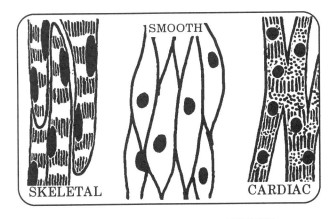

Figure 16-5 MUSCLE TISSUE

Skeletal muscle is the tissue that makes up the muscular system of the body. The other two kinds of muscle cells are in organs of other systems of the body.

115

Figure 16-6 THE HUMAN SKELETON

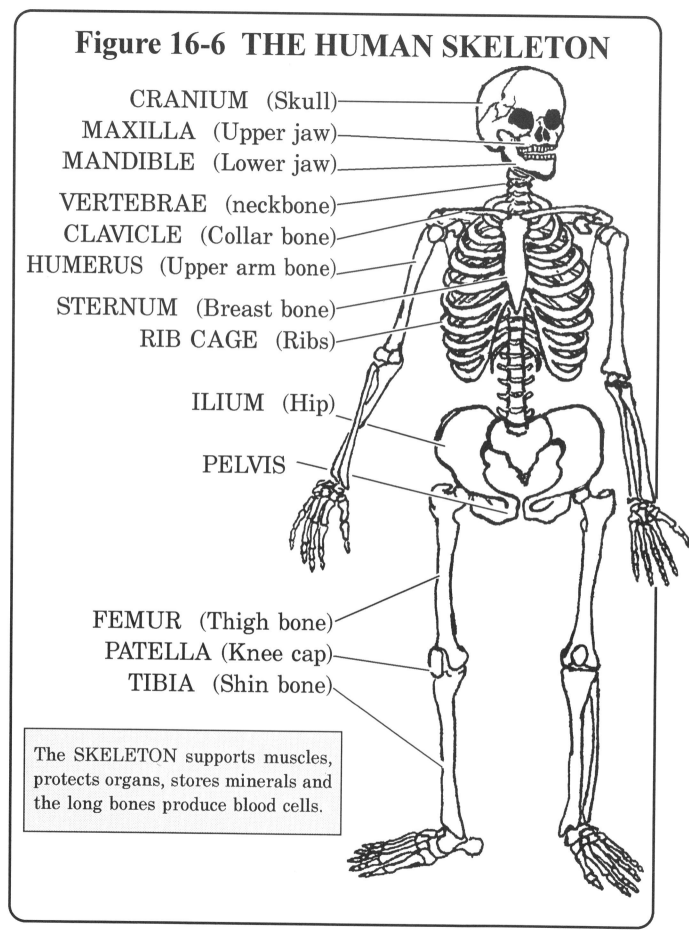

CRANIUM (Skull)

MAXILLA (Upper jaw)

MANDIBLE (Lower jaw)

VERTEBRAE (neckbone)

CLAVICLE (Collar bone)

HUMERUS (Upper arm bone)

STERNUM (Breast bone)

RIB CAGE (Ribs)

ILIUM (Hip)

PELVIS

FEMUR (Thigh bone)

PATELLA (Knee cap)

TIBIA (Shin bone)

The SKELETON supports muscles, protects organs, stores minerals and the long bones produce blood cells.

CHAPTER 16 REVIEW

OBJECTIVES:

1. Understand the functions of the skeletal and muscular systems.

2. Identify the kinds of connective tissue.

3. Distinguish and diagram three types of muscle cells.

PART I. Define the 12 Keywords in Chapter 16 - The Skeletal and Muscular Systems.

PART II. Neatly write each phrase below. Then in the margin in front identify the term as most closely related to involuntary (I) or voluntary (V).

1. Heartbeat   6. Intestinal contractions
2. Raising your hand 7. Tapping your finger
3. Hiccups   8. Growing
4. Crossing the street 9. Digesting food
5. Opening the door   10. Going to school!

PART III. Write each sentence using one of the Keywords to fill in the blank.
1. The ball and socket __?__ allows the most movement.
2. The __?__ inside the ear allows bending without breaking.
3. Both skeletal and cardiac muscles have __?__.
4. Smooth muscle is __?__, contracting without a conscious thought.
5. An overweight individual has extra __?__.
6. "H" shaped cells with striations and many nuclei are found in __?__ muscle.
7. The upper and lower leg bones are connected by __?__.
8. The "rubber band" like material you can feel behind your knee is a __?__ that connects the thigh muscle to the lower leg.
9. Red and white blood cells are produced in the __?__.
10. Calcium salts cause __?__ cells to be hard and rigid.

PART IV. Diagram and label a knee joint.

PART V. Diagram and label three kinds of muscle cells.

PART VI. Write the name of each part of the skeleton labelled below.

PART VII. For each part in number VI above give a function that the part carries out for the body.

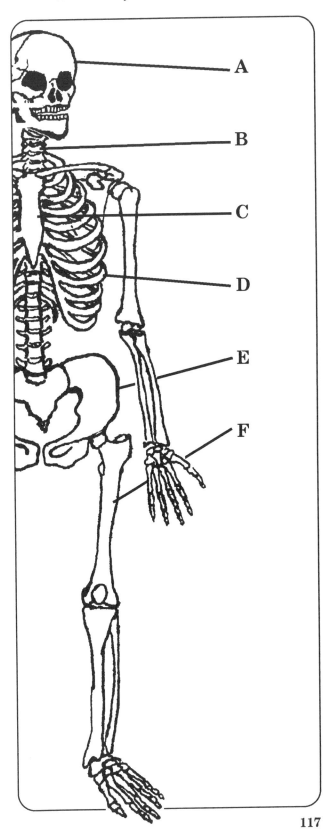

CHAPTER 17 - THE DIGESTIVE SYSTEM

LIFE SCIENCE

ALL CREATURES GREAT AND SMALL

2. An organ that mixes food , for several hours, with gastric juice.
4. A lymph vessel that absorbs fatty acids.
6. An organ that stores bile.
7. An enzyme in gastric juice that begins the digestion of proteins.
9. The part of the digestive tract where water is absorbed.
10. A muscular organ in the mouth.
11. The storage organ for solid wastes.
12. Finger-like projections of the wall of the small intestine.
14. Bumps on the tongue that detect sweet, salt, sour and bitter.
15. An enzyme in saliva that begins the digestion of starches.
16. An organ that makes glucagon.
17. A type of digestion in which the food is simply made smaller.
18. The "food tube."
22. A tiny projection of the wall of the small intestine.

The Digestive System Crossword Puzzle

Use the keywords from this chapter to fill in the puzzle.
See how many you know before reading the chapter!
Complete the puzzle after completing this chapter.

ACROSS

1. Chisel-like front teeth.
3. A large flat tooth for grinding.
5. The valve that closes the stomach.
8. The longest organ, in which digestion is completed.
13. A type of digestion that changes the food into simpler chemicals.
15. The opening through which solid wastes are excreted.
19. A large organ that makes bile.
20. A tooth with two points.
21. Rhythmic movements of the digestive tract.
23. Food passing through a membrane.
24. Also called a canine tooth.
25. A solution in the mouth.

CHAPTER 17
THE DIGESTIVE SYSTEM

After the last chapter and all that talk about bones I hope you can stomach a discussion of the digestive system (see Figure 17-7 and 17-8 at the end of this chapter)! The organs that break down complex foods, so that your body can use the pieces, are a long tube right through your middle! You need the products of digestion for energy (the glucose), for growth and repair (the amino acids), and for metabolic regulation (elements).

TONGUE

Digestion begins in the mouth. The TONGUE is a muscular organ covered with sensory bumps called TASTE BUDS (figure 17-1). Taste serves to prevent an organism from eating certain foods. It can also cause some people to eat too much of certain foods! The tongue moves food between the teeth and into the pharynx. Proper speech depends on the tongue as well.

Figure 17-1
TASTE BUDS

The taste buds on the tongue detect four sensations: sweet on the tip, salt & sour, sides, and on the back, bitter.

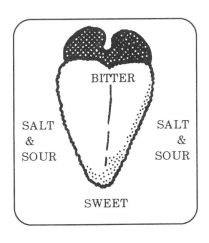

TEETH

The <u>MECHANICAL DIGESTION</u> of food begins with the teeth. Mechanical digestion is simply making the food into smaller pieces of the same material. Cutting up a piece of meat is mechanical digestion! The 32 teeth in an adult come in four styles.

INCISOR teeth are flat and wide like a chisel. Rabbits, squirrels (Figure 17-2), and beavers have very pronounced incisors. Horses (Figure 17-2) have good incisors used to bite off grass. Cows must tear the grass since they have no incisors at all!

The CUSPID, or canine teeth are prominant in cats, dogs, and the Count Dracula of horror movie

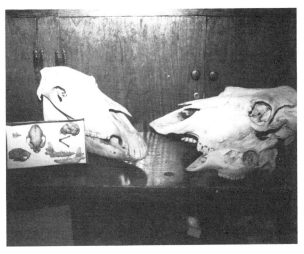

Figure 17-2 TEETH

Depending on what an animal eats, some types of teeth may be extra large, or small, or missing altogether.

fame. On either side of your four incisors should be a cuspid. Though not as pointed as those of many carnivores, you can feel the point with your finger. Cuspids are for ripping meat.

People with healthy teeth have 8 BICUSPID teeth, two each side, top and bottom. Cuspid means "point" and a canine tooth (cuspid) has one point. Now you know what a bicuspid tooth is - a tooth with two points used to grind food.

A MOLAR tooth is large and quite flat. You can probably see two molars on each side, on the top and bottom, of your mouth. Your last molars, called wisdom teeth will come in during the late teens or early twenties. Molar teeth mechanically crush even hard foods into many tiny pieces with lots of surface area (Figure 17-3)

Figure 17-3
HUMAN
TEETH

I = incisor
C = cuspid
B = bicuspid
M = molar

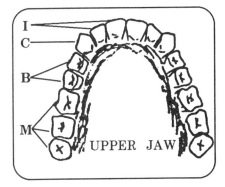

Each kind of tooth has a special shape for a special function. There are 20 teeth in a set of baby teeth. A full set of adult teeth should have 32 teeth total (top and bottom together).

CHEMICAL DIGESTION

The increased surface area of tiny bits of food is why you should chew your food well. Surface area is needed for CHEMICAL DIGESTION. In chemical digestion, foods are changed into different chemicals. For example, the starch in a cracker is crunched up by your teeth. Since it is still starch, so far, the cracker is only mechanically digested.

The SALIVA, a liquid secreted by the salivary glands in the walls of the mouth, contains salivary AMYLASE. Amylase is one of those enzymes we discussed as examples of proteins. The amylase changes the starch of the cracker into sugar. Big molecules of starch are broken into the smaller molecules of sugar. This is chemical digestion! Fats and proteins must wait until later for their chemical digestion to begin.

When the tongue pushes the food mixed with saliva to the back of the throat the food enters the ESOPHAGUS. This food tube is shaped like a soft hose. The food is pushed by waves of contractions called PERISTALSIS. You are not able to control peristalsis consciously because the esophagus is made of involuntary, smooth muscle tissue lined with special epidermal cells.

STOMACH

The STOMACH, shaped like a short, wide letter "J", is also made of smooth muscle tissue. It churns your food without your thinking to tell it to. The inside of the stomach is folded into many wrinkles lined with glandular epithelial tissue. These special epidermal cells make gastric juice. The stomach holds food for two to five hours. The exit of the stomach is controlled by the PYLORUS, a donut shaped valve. A summary of chemical digestion in the stomach is in Fig. 17-4.

The lining of the stomach secretes gastric juice which contains the compounds needed for chemical digestion to continue. Note that chemical digestion of proteins begins in the stomach when PEPSIN and hydrochloric acid (HCl) begin changing the proteins into amino acids. The HCl in the stomach can cause acid indigestion in some people. In others the stomach lining gets a hole in it, an ulcer, and the acid burns the smooth muscle of the stomach.

COMPOUND	EFFECT
Water (H_2O)	A solvent to dissolve chemicals allowing reactions to occur.
Hydrochloric acid (HCl)	Kills many microbes and provides the proper pH for pepsin to work.
Pepsin	An enzyme that begins the chemical digestion of proteins in meats.
Rennin	An enzyme that curdles milk proteins and begins their digestion.

Figure 17-4 DIGESTION IN THE STOMACH

SMALL INTESTINE

When the pylorus opens up the partially digested food enters the SMALL INTESTINE to begin final digestion. Don't confuse "small" with short, your small intestine could stretch from the front to the back of most classrooms with some left over! It is approximately 28 feet long in Average Arnold and other adults.

There are several digestive organs that the food never goes through. The LIVER, largest organ in your body is made of glandular tissue. It produces BILE. The bile is saved up in a small "balloon shaped" GALL BLADDER. Then, as the food passes through, the bile is squirted through the bile duct into the beginning of the small intestine. The PANCREAS makes pancreatic juice which enters the intestine with the bile. The small intestine, made of smooth muscle cells is lined by glandular epithelial cells and villi. This special lining of the intestine makes intestinal juices. Digestion in the small intestine is summarized in Figure 17-5. Note that chemical digestion of fat begins in the small intestine. Final digestion of carbohydrates, proteins and fats is completed in the small intestine.

Roughage, material that cannot be digested, is important in a diet to keep the smooth muscles of the intestinal wall in good condition.

120

COMPOUND	EFFECT	FINAL PRODUCTS
From the Liver:		
Bile	Bile is an emulsifying agent, it breaks fat up into tiny globules.	----------
Pancreatic juice:		
Amylase	Acts on starches.	----------
Trypsin	Acts on proteins.	Proteins make amino acids.
Lipase	Acts on lipids (fats).	Fats become fatty acids and glycerol.
Intestinal juice:		
Maltase	Acts on maltose.	Starches and sugars become glucose.
Sucrase	Acts on sucrose.	Glucose.

Figure 17-5 INTESTINAL DIGESTION

ABSORPTION

Once digestion is complete the small intestine carries out ABSORPTION. A clean piece of the inside of a small intestine looks almost like velvet, soft and fuzzy. Under a microscope tiny finger like projections become visible. They appear a lot like root hairs in shape and they serve the same function: to increase surface area for absorption. To do the same job without villi the small intestine would have to be many kilometers long instead of 8 to 9 meters!

VILLI (Figure 17-6) contain capillaries, tiny blood vessels, that absorb the glucose and amino acids as they pass through the thin walls of each VILLUS. Inside each villus there is a LACTEAL, a small lymph vessel, that absorbs the fatty acids and glycerol. These end products of fat digestion go into the blood through the thoracic duct in the chest.

LARGE INTESTINE

The LARGE INTESTINE is only about 1/6 the length of the small intestine, but it is fatter. The function of the large intestine is to absorb and recycle much of the water in the fecal material. The fecal material is all of the contents of the large intestine.

There are mutualistic bacteria that use the organic molecules in the large intestine's contents as a food source. We learned that mutualism benefits both organisms. What do these intestinal bacteria do for you? They make vitamin B and vitamin K!

The final remains of undigested food, enzymes and bacteria form the stool inside the RECTUM. The stool is eliminated through the ANUS. See Figures 17-7 and 17-8 of the human and the frog digestive systems on the next page.

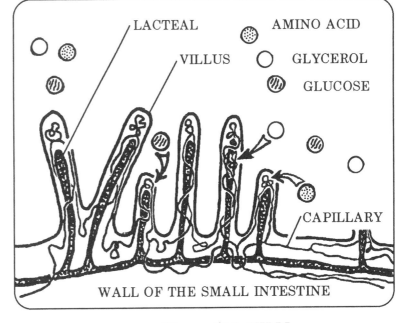

Figure 17-6 VILLI

The final products of digestion are absorbed through the villi: glucose and amino acids into the capillaries, fatty acids and glycerol into the lacteals.

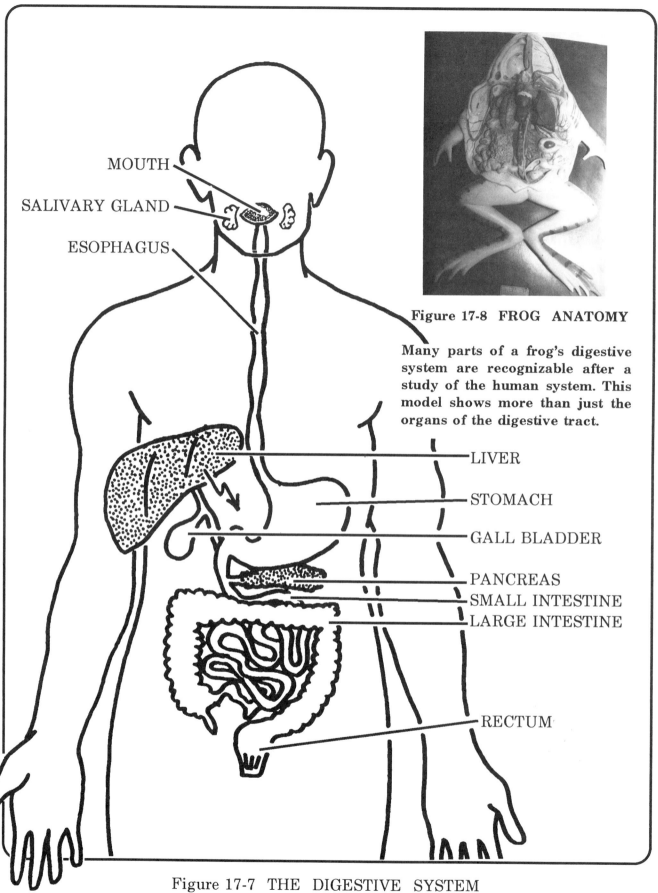

MOUTH

SALIVARY GLAND

ESOPHAGUS

Figure 17-8 FROG ANATOMY

Many parts of a frog's digestive system are recognizable after a study of the human system. This model shows more than just the organs of the digestive tract.

LIVER

STOMACH

GALL BLADDER

PANCREAS
SMALL INTESTINE
LARGE INTESTINE

RECTUM

Figure 17-7 THE DIGESTIVE SYSTEM
The human digestive system is similar to that of all the chordates.

CHAPTER 17 REVIEW

OBJECTIVES

1. **Distinguish between mechanical and chemical digestion.**
2. **Know the parts and functions of the digestive system.**
3. **Identify the location and end product in digestion of carbohydrates, proteins and fats.**

PART I. Explain in full sentences the difference between mechanical and chemical digestion.

PART II. Diagram and label the parts of the human digestive system.

PART III. Define the 26 Keywords from Chapter 17 - Digestion.

PART IV. Use a Keyword from this chapter to fill in each blank. Neatly write out the full sentence as your answer.

1. A __?__, like a root hair, increases surface area for absorption
2. The __?__ is sometimes called a canine tooth.
3. __?__ is the enzyme that initiates the chemical digestion of starches in the mouth.
4. Hydrochloric acid must be present for __?__ to begin the chemical digestion of proteins in the stomach.
5. Chemical digestion of fats begins after __?__ emulsifies them in the small intestine.
6. Food is moved through the digestive system by rhythmic motions called __?__.
7. A __?__ inside each villus absorbs the fatty acids and glycerol from fat digestion.
8. The __?__, largest organ in the body, makes bile.
9. The __?__ stores bile.
10. The __?__ is a tube of smooth muscle tissue that connects the mouth and stomach.
11. Food cannot move out of the stomach until the __?__ opens up.
12. Your __?__ is needed to move food back to the pharynx!
13. Water is reabsorbed in the __?__.
14. Amylase, trypsin and lipase are made in the __?__ and added to food in the intestine.
15. The stool is formed in the __?__ before elimination through the anus.

PART V. Describe and explain an experiment that demonstrates that chemical digestion begins in the mouth. Include: a control, the name of the food before digestion, the name of the food after digestion, the name of the indicator reagent and the color change that indicates which food is present.

PART VI. Make the following chart on a separate sheet of paper and fill in each part:

Process / Food	Where Digestion Begins	Digestive Juice Involved	Enzyme Involved	Final Product
Carbohydrate	1.	2.	3.	4.
Fat	5.	6.	7.	8.
Protein	9.	10.	11.	12.

CHART: SUMMARY OF DIGESTION

PART VII. List the four main kinds of teeth, and their functions. Be able to locate them on a diagram.

PART VIII. Use a full sentence to answer each question.
1. What is the thick muscle in the mouth?
2. What are the bumps on the muscle in #1 called?
3. What are the four basic tastes?
4. Where are the nerves located for detecting each taste?
5. How many teeth does an adult human have?
6. What is the longest and most important organ of the digestive tract?
7. What are digested foods used for by the body?
8. What are the movements of the digestive tract called?
9. What are inside villi?
10. How long does food remain in the stomach?
11. What is the name of the valve (ring muscle) between the stomach and the small intestine? What is its function?
12. Name two chemicals made by bacteria in the large intestine that are used by the body.

PART IX. List at least six different enzymes and tell where each is made and what kind of food it helps to break down.

CHAPTER 18 - THE CIRCULATORY SYSTEM

LIFE SCIENCE

ALL CREATURES GREAT AND SMALL

DOWN

1. Large vein from the upper body.

2. The "wall" that divides the heart.

3. The organ that pumps blood.

5. Blood vessels with valves.

7. Veins from the lungs to the heart.

8. An upper chamber of the heart.

9. The liquid part of the blood.

12. A red, iron protein in the blood.

13. Microscopic blood vessels.

15. Disk shaped cells with hemoglobin.

16. A lower chamber of the heart.

17. Tube leading away from the heart.

The Circulatory System Crossword Puzzle
Use the keywords from this chapter to fill in the puzzle.
See how many you know before reading the chapter!
Complete the puzzle after completing this chapter.

ACROSS

4. Vessel from heart to lungs.

6. Partial cell that begins clotting.

7. Referring to the lungs.

10. Blood cells that destroy germs.

11. A protein that helps blood clot.

14. The main vein from the lower body

17. The largest artery.

18. Referring to the body.

CHAPTER 18
THE CIRCULATORY SYSTEM

Having spent some time digesting the material in the last chapter, let us now get straight to the heart of the circulatory system. The job of moving materials throughout every part of the human body is accomplished with arteries, capillaries, veins and the heart.

THE HEART

The HEART is the most important organ of the circulatory system. See Figures 18-1 and 18-2. It is rare for an individual to survive more than a few minutes once their heart stops beating.

Average Adam's heart began its work more than eight months before Adam was born! The human heart begins beating eighteen days after conception and continues pumping day and night, year after year, until the person dies. In Average Arnold, Adam's dad, the heart contracts 70 to 72 times per minute. It pumps approximately 6,000 liters a day!

The message that tells the heart to beat is from the sino-atrial node, a small spot in the wall of the heart. This node is activated by a flow of sodium ions through the cell membranes. The sino-atrial node is called the pacemaker because it causes the rhythmic beat of the heart.

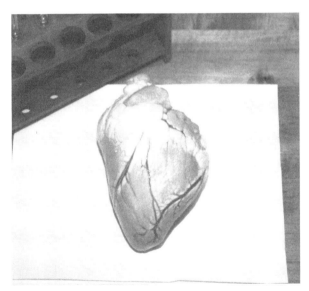

Figure 18-1 A CALF HEART

This heart is larger than a person's heart. Your heart is about the size of your fist. The white areas are fat tissue.

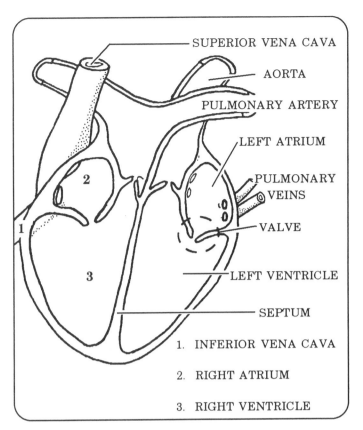

- SUPERIOR VENA CAVA
- AORTA
- PULMONARY ARTERY
- LEFT ATRIUM
- PULMONARY VEINS
- VALVE
- LEFT VENTRICLE
- SEPTUM

1. INFERIOR VENA CAVA
2. RIGHT ATRIUM
3. RIGHT VENTRICLE

Figure 18-2 HEART LONGISECTION

The V in ventricle points downward. The A in atrium points upward. When determining the left or right side you must think of the heart as your own.

In 1628 William Harvey of England published a book in which he described the circulation of the blood correctly. The Chinese had learned of the true circulation of the blood nearly 700 years before Harvey's "discovery", but their knowledge was not known to Europeans.

SYSTEMIC CIRCULATION

Starting in the left ATRIUM, oxygen rich blood moves through a one way valve into the heart's left ventricle. The strongest chamber of the heart, the left VENTRICLE pumps the bright red blood through another valve into the AORTA. The aorta, largest of the arteries, branches into many smaller arteries. Each ARTERY is a thick walled, muscular blood vessel that carries blood away from the heart. Remember "a in artery for away". The reason arteries are thick walled is because they must withstand the blood pressure exerted by each muscular contraction of the powerful left ventricle.

The arteries finally branch into vessels so

small that the blood cells must line up single file to get through. Harvey knew that the blood made a circle but he never saw the capillaries. In 1660, Marcello Malpighi of Italy described capillaries and Harvey's work was completed. Each microscopic blood vessel is a CAPILLARY. No part in the body is more than two or three cells from a capillary. A great number of capillaries are in the villi where lots of glucose diffuses into the liquid part of the blood. As the oxygen rich blood in the arteries moves through the capillaries the red blood cells give up their oxygen and glucose to the surrounding lymph fluid, which surrounds each cell. Carbon dioxide, a waste from respiration, is carried away from the cells (Figure 18-3).

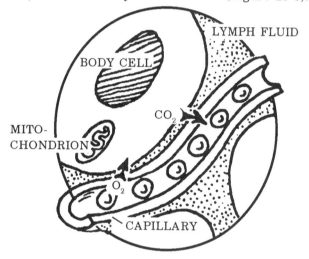

Figure 18-3 CELLULAR RESPIRATION

By diffusion oxygen molecules move into the cells and are used to burn glucose. Carbon dioxide, built up in the cell, moves into the capillaries.

It has been estimated that the millions, even billions, of capillaries in one adult's body have a combined surface area almost equal to that of one and one half regulation basketball courts!

The capillaries join together to form veins. Each VEIN has valves to prevent the back flow of blood. Remember the "v in veins is for valves". Since the pressure is less on the vein side of the capillaries, the veins are thin walled. The veins keep joining together until there are just two of them. One is the SUPERIOR VENA CAVA, or vein from the upper cavity, and the other is the INFERIOR VENA CAVA. Both empty their oxygen poor "blue blood" into the right atrium. You can figure the meaning of inferior vena cava knowing that inferior means below, or lower.

The blood has made a full circle from the heart out to all the systems of the body and back again. However the blood is now on the opposite side of the SEPTUM that divides the heart into two halves. But SYSTEMIC CIRCULATION, the flow of blood around through the systems, is only half the story of circulation!

PULMONARY CIRCULATION

The blood in the right atrium, is loaded with carbon dioxide. Before the heart sends that blood out to the systems again the blood must exchange the carbon dioxide for oxygen in the lungs. The right atrium squeezes the oxygen poor blood through a valve into the right ventricle. You will notice in Figure 18-2 that the right ventricle opens through a valve into the PULMONARY ARTERY. The right ventricle is smaller than the left because it only has to pump blood to the lungs and back. Both atria are much smaller than the ventricles because they only pump the blood through a valve into the ventricles. The pulmonary artery branches into two, one for each lung. Inside the lungs the arteries branch into capillaries that surround each air sac (Figure 18-4). Here, at the air sacs, the carbon dioxide diffuses out of the blood and oxygen diffuses in. The blood turns bright red.

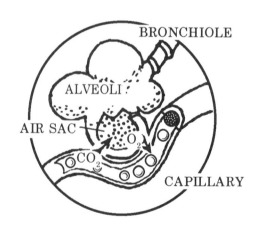

Figure 18-4 EXTERNAL RESPIRATION

That precious gas, oxygen, enters the blood through thin walled capillaries in the air sacs of the lungs. Hemoglobin, the protein that gives red blood cells their color, holds the oxygen molecules.

126

The oxygen rich "red blood" flows through the pulmonary veins back to the left atrium. That completes the circle of blood through the lungs, PULMONARY CIRCULATION. The blood then starts over in the systemic circulation.

Each PULMONARY VEIN is special because it is a vein with oxygen rich, red blood in it. Of all the veins in the body only pulmonary veins carry red, oxygen rich blood. Of all the arteries in the body only the pulmonary arteries carry oxygen poor, blue blood! Remember: all arteries have "a" for carrying blood away from the heart. All veins have a "v" for valves that point back to the heart. The arteries and veins for pulmonary circulation are switched only in the kind of blood they carry.

BLOOD TISSUE

The blood that flows through your veins is a very special mixture of many chemicals and cells (See Figure 18-5).

1. Plasma is the liquid part of the blood. PLASMA dissolves many substances needed by the cells. Gases, enzymes, food and salt are all transported in the plasma. Waste products from cells are also transported dissolved in the plasma.

2. Red cells are made in your bone marrow. When mature a tiny RED CELL no longer has a nucleus. It contains HEMOGLOBIN, the iron protein needed to carry oxygen. You will recall that a deficiency of iron causes a form of anemia. Sickle cell anemia, a genetic disorder, can cause a person to lack energy and feel weak.

Red cells are the most numerous cells in the body. It is estimated that 1/3 of the 75 trillion cells in the human body are red cells. That is quite a few cells. How many? If Average Arnold lives to be 72 years old, there are more red blood cells in him now than there are seconds in 1000 of his lifetimes!

3. White blood cells are made inside the bone marrow. A WHITE CELL is a soldier cell that fights microbes. We included the white blood cells in our discussion of the body's second line of defense against disease. Too many white blood cells is itself a disease! Leuco is Greek for white, and too many white cells is called leukemia.

4. Platelets are cell fragments. Each colorless PLATELET can help in clotting the blood. The platelets and a protein, FIBRINOGEN form the clot that stops the bleeding from a cut. Do you remember the name of bleeder's disease, where a person's blood does not clot correctly?

BLOOD TYPES

Not everyone's blood is the same. There are four basic types of human blood called A, B, AB, and O. Type AB people can receive a transfusion from anyone. Type O people can donate blood to anyone, but may only receive O type blood.

The main function of the circulatory system is transport. The transporting of food, wastes and chemicals is necessary every second of every day that an organism is alive! A second function of the blood is to help with an organism's immunity to disease. The circulatory system is intertwined into every other system. Even the cardiac muscle cells of the heart need arteries, capillaries and veins! If you do not remember what cardiac muscle looks like go back to the chapter on the muscular system! The special pulmonary circulation indicates how closely the circulatory and respiratory systems are connected.

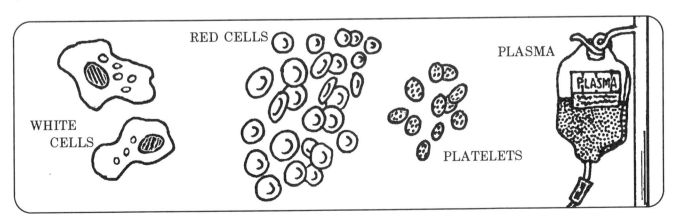

Figure 18-5 BLOOD TISSUE

The parts of the blood all work together to transport materials, that makes blood a tissue.

CHAPTER 18 REVIEW

OBJECTIVES:

1. **Know the functions and the parts of the human circulatory system.**

2. **Diagram and label the heart.**

3. **Understand the path of blood circulation.**

PART I. Define the 20 Keywords from Chapter 18 THE CIRCULATORY SYSTEM.

PART II. Diagram and label the heart.

PART III. If a statement below is false, change the *italicized* word to make it true. Neatly write out each statement once it is true.

1. Waste material from a cell diffuses through the lymph into *capillaries*.
2. O_2 is carried by hemoglobin in the *platelets*.
3. The "blue blood" returns to the heart through *arteries*.
4. The *veins* have valves.

Part III continued:
5. From the inferior vena cava the blood enters the right *ventricle*.
6. The right *ventricle* pumps blood to the lungs.
7. Pulmonary *veins* contain oxygen rich, red blood.
8. The left *ventricle* is the strongest chamber of the heart.
9. The large artery that curves out of the top of the heart is the *superior vena cava*.
10. Each artery is *thick* walled and muscular.
11. *Platelet* is the liquid part of the blood.
12. *Red* blood cells fight disease organisms.
13. *Hemoglobin* is a blood protein needed for clotting.
14. Systemic circulation takes blood to the *lungs*.
15. Cardiac muscle is *smooth* and has many nuclei in one branched cell.

PART IV. Write a short paragraph explaining systemic circulation.

PART V. Write a short paragraph explaining pulmonary circulation.

PART VI. Copy and complete the chart below:

The Circulatory System

Part	Description	Function
1. _____	2. _____	Dissolve and carry enzymes, gases and salts.
3. _____	Colorless fragments of cells.	4. _____
White cells.	5. _____	6. _____
7. _____	Disk shaped with no nuclei.	8. _____
9. _____	10. _____	Vessels through which blood returns to the heart.
11. _____	Thick walled, no valves, tube.	12. _____
13. _____	Muscular, about fist size.	14. _____
15. _____	Thin walled very tiny vessels.	To allow diffusion of materials into and out of the blood.

CHAPTER 19 - THE RESPIRATORY SYSTEM

LIFE SCIENCE

ALL CREATURES GREAT AND SMALL

DOWN

1. Thin membranes that cause sounds when vibrated.

3. The process of breathing in.

4. Spasms of the diaphragm.

6. The openings in the nose.

8. Combining oxygen with glucose.

10. To breathe in.

11. Air sacs.

14. The wind pipe.

The Respiratory System Crossword Puzzle

Use the keywords from this chapter to fill in the puzzle.
See how many you know before reading the chapter!
Complete the puzzle after completing this chapter.

Write in this book only if it belongs to you.

ACROSS

2. Tubes inside the lungs.

5. A sheet of muscle between the chest and abdominal cavities.

7. A flap that covers the trachea.

9. The process of breathing out.

12. A branch of the trachea.

13. The voice box.

15. The region where the nose, mouth andesophagus all connect.

16. A sticky secretion.

17. To breathe out.

CHAPTER 19
THE RESPIRATORY SYSTEM

I will admit that the opening lines of the last chapters don't exactly "take your breath away!" However, this system is "breath taking!"

The function of the human respiratory system is to exchange gases (see Figure 19-1 on the next page). It also helps regulate body temperature.

RESPIRATORY TRACT

The NOSTRILS and mouth take in air. Breathing through the nose is good for 2 reasons.

1. The hairs and the MUCUS lining of the nose filter the air.

2. The nasal passages warm the air before it reaches the delicate inside of the lungs.

The nose and mouth also moisten the air before it reaches the lungs.

The air then moves into the PHARYNX, the space at the back of the nose and throat, which is connected to the esophagus and the wind pipe.

The wind pipe, or TRACHEA, is in front of the food tube (Figure 19-1). The inventor of the human machine put a special flap, called the EPIGLOTTIS, over the opening of the trachea to keep food out (Figure 19-1). If you have ever had "food go down the wrong pipe" you know that taking a breath and swallowing at the same time doesn't work. That makes you cough and choke until the piece of food comes up instead of going down into the lungs.

The trachea has rings of cartilage that keep the wind pipe open. You may feel the cartilage rings in your own throat by placing your fingers just above the collar bone and sliding them up and down. The inside of the trachea is lined with ciliated epithelial tissue. These cells have mucus and cilia that trap dust and move it upward.

The lump in your throat is commonly called the Adam's apple, or if you prefer, the Harriet's apple! The proper name for this voice box is the LARYNX (Figure 19-1). Inside the larynx are the VOCAL CORDS. Somewhat like two rubberbands, the edges of the two vocal cords vibrate when air is forced past them. This creates sounds formed into words by the tongue, teeth and lips.

The trachea divides into two main branches, the bronchi, one for each lung. Inside the lungs each BRONCHUS divides into many smaller BRONCHIAL TUBES and these divide into tiny

bronchioles. The bronchioles end in clusters of air sacs that look like microscopic bunches of grapes (Figure 19-1). These clusters of air sacs, where some of the oxygen in the air moves into the blood, are called ALVEOLI. At the same time carbon dioxide in the blood moves into the sacs.

Each lung contains an unbelievable number of air sacs. Their total surface area is estimated to be approximately 140 sq. meters. That is, if all the air sacs in one set of adult lungs were flattened out they could cover the floors of two of Average Adam's classrooms. If people used their skin for respiration, as worms do, we would need the skin on 100 people to be able to breathe! Also, we would have to stay slimy with mucus.

The lungs are spongy because they contain so many alveoli, capillaries and air. They are enclosed in a double protective layer called the pleura. Under the lungs is a smooth, dome shaped muscle, the DIAPHRAGM (die a fram) needed for breathing (Figure 19-2).

Some animals like the blue gill, use gills instead of lungs. The ameba, and other protists, respire through their cell membranes.

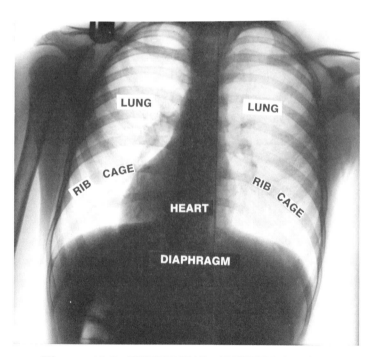

Figure 19-2 EXTERNAL RESPIRATION

The lungs, ribs and diaphragm are visible in this X-ray of a young boy. When the diaphragm contracts it moves downward and creates a vacuum in the chest cavity. Air rushes into the lungs to fill the vacuum. The X-ray is looking from the back.

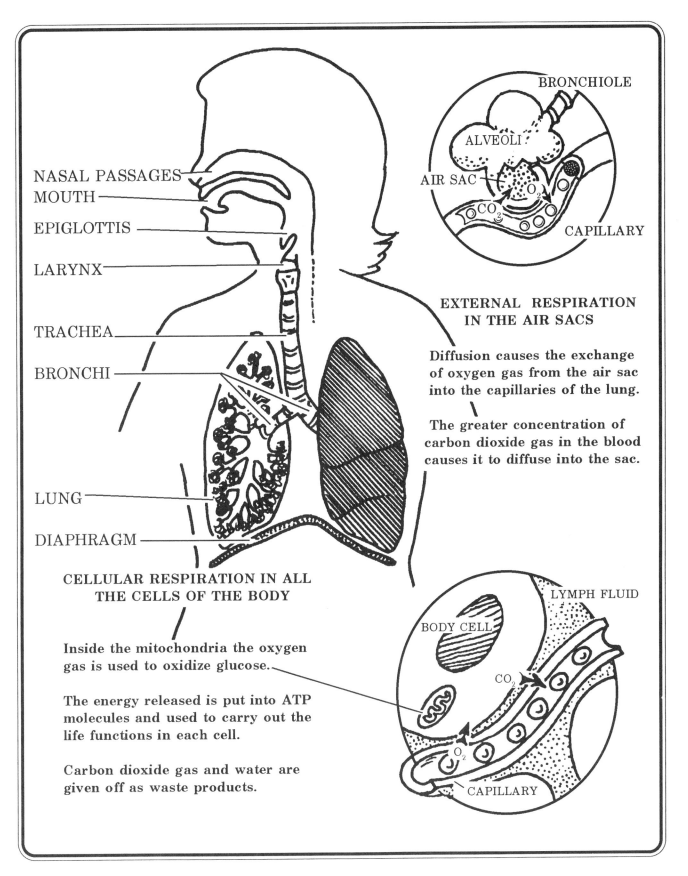

NASAL PASSAGES

MOUTH

EPIGLOTTIS

LARYNX

TRACHEA

BRONCHI

LUNG

DIAPHRAGM

BRONCHIOLE

ALVEOLI

AIR SAC

O_2

CO_2

CAPILLARY

EXTERNAL RESPIRATION IN THE AIR SACS

Diffusion causes the exchange of oxygen gas from the air sac into the capillaries of the lung.

The greater concentration of carbon dioxide gas in the blood causes it to diffuse into the sac.

CELLULAR RESPIRATION IN ALL THE CELLS OF THE BODY

Inside the mitochondria the oxygen gas is used to oxidize glucose.

The energy released is put into ATP molecules and used to carry out the life functions in each cell.

Carbon dioxide gas and water are given off as waste products.

LYMPH FLUID

BODY CELL

CO_2

O_2

CAPILLARY

Figure 19 -1 THE RESPIRATORY SYSTEM

Moist membranes close to a supply of oxygen are needed for respiration.

EXTERNAL RESPIRATION

We actually do not breathe in. Our bodies have no means of pulling the air in! To INHALE the muscles between the ribs contract lifting the rib cage. At the same time the diaphragm contracts which makes it move lower. These motions cause the chest cavity to get larger. Air, due to the air pressure outside of the body, rushes into the lungs to fill up the empty space. The process of breathing in is INSPIRATION.

To EXHALE the rib muscles and diaphragm relax. The ribs drop downward and the chest cavity gets smaller. The air is forced out of the lungs (Fig. 19-3). The process of breathing out is EXPIRATION. Recall "ex", as in exit, means out.

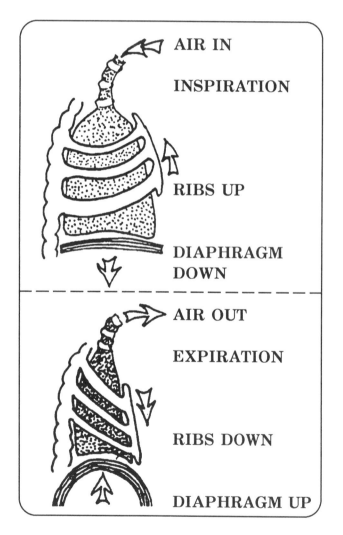

Figure 19-3 BREATHING
Inhaling occurs when the rib muscles and diaphragm contract, and the chest cavity gets larger. Air forces its way into the lungs. Exhaling requires a relaxation of the rib muscles and diaphragm.

Breathing is partly voluntary, but not completely voluntary. When individuals hold their breath, their cells still use up oxygen and make carbon dioxide waste. As more and more carbon dioxide moves from the cells into the blood, nerves in the walls of the arteries send messages to the brain. Ready or not, the brain then sends messages to the diaphragm and the rib muscles to contract.

Sometimes the diaphragm has spasms that most people call HICCUPS.

While in the lungs the air is slightly changed. By diffusion oxygen moves from the air sacs, where there is more, to the capillaries, where the concentration is less. The hemoglobin grabs the oxygen molecules. Water vapor evaporates from the moist surfaces of the alveoli into the air. Carbon dioxide is more concentrated in the capillaries. As a result carbon dioxide moves out of the capillaries and into the air (Figure 19-1). The rest of the breath-taking story of respiration occurs at every cell, those right in the air sac wall all the way to those in the little toe.

CELLULAR RESPIRATION

At the cells the exchange of gases follows the same idea as in the lungs. Each gas diffuses from where there is more to where there is less.

The oxygen is released by the hemoglobin in the red cells and diffuses out of the capillary and through the lymph fluid into the cell. Inside the mighty mitochondria, oxidation of glucose releases the energy needed by the cell to stay alive.

In this case carbon dioxide has built up inside the cell due to OXIDATION of glucose. The carbon dioxide gas diffuses out of the cell, through the lymph fluid and into the capillary. That waste is eliminated, by way of the circulatory system, through the respiratory system. Excretion of waste is the next chapter, but the systems of the body are so closely connected that we have already discussed part of that topic!

CHAPTER 19 REVIEW

Chapter 19 review

OBJECTIVES:

1. **Diagram and label the respiratory tract.**
2. **Know the parts and the functions of the respiratory tract.**
3. **Trace the path of gases through the body.**
4. **Distinguish between external and cellular respiration.**

PART I. Diagram & label the respiratory system.

PART II. Answer the following questions with a brief, but complete, sentence.
1. List the functions of a respiratory system.
2. What gas is required by every living cell in the human body?
3. What gas must be eliminated from every cell?
4. Describe an ideal respiratory surface.
5. In fish what organ is used for respiration?
6. What is the respiratory surface in worms?
7. What part of an ameba is used for respiration?
8. Describe alveoli, include what is inside and outside of each air sac.
9. What is external respiration?
10. What is cellular respiration?

PART III. Define the 17 Keywords in Chapter 19 The Respiratory System.

PART IV. Use a Keyword to fill in each blank, write a complete sentence as your answer.
1. Inside the larynx are two __?__.
2. When you breathe through the __?__ the air is cleaned and warmed.
3. To inhale, the __?__ and rib muscles must contract.
4. The tar and smoke from cigarettes clogs up the __?__ at the ends of the bronchioles so that breathing becomes difficult.
5. The lung is connected to the trachea by a _?_.
6. __?__ is sticky and moist to trap dust and germs that enter the respiratory system.
7. During __?__ the diaphragm relaxes and the rib cage is lowered to force air out of the lungs.
8. Even unborn babies get the __?__ when their diaphragm contracts with spasms.
9. The __?__ prevents food from entering the trachea.
10. Oxygen is needed in each cell for __?__ in which energy is released.

PART V. Rearrange the following ten statements into the correct order **starting with inspiration.** You may have to refer to the previous chapter. Write neatly.
1. O_2 is used in the cell.
2. O_2 diffuses into the blood.
3. The diaphragm contracts.
4. The blood leaves the right ventricle.
5. The blood leaves the left ventricle.
6. The diaphragm relaxes.
7. Blue O_2 poor blood flows in arteries.
8. Red O_2 rich blood flows in the arteries.
9. Hemoglobin holds onto oxygen.
10. Oxygen diffuses out of the blood.

PART VI. If false, change the *italicized* word to make the statement true. Neatly write each full statement once it is true.
1. The function of the human *circulatory* system is to exchange gases.
2. The nose and mouth warm and *dry* the air before it reaches the lungs.
3. The *larynx* is the space at the back of the nose and mouth.
4. The epiglottis prevents food from entering the *trachea.*
5. Vibrations of the *bronchial tubes* cause sounds for speech.
6. The *esophagus* directly connects the pharynx to the bronchi.
7. The *trachea* has rings of cartilage to keep it open.
8. The bronchioles end in *alveoli.*
9. Like root hairs and villi the *bronchi* greatly increase the surface area of an organ.
10. When too much carbon dioxide is in the blood the brain tells the *hiccups* to contract.
11. Pulmonary circulation brings blood to the *lungs.*
12. The process of oxygen moving from the blood into the cells for use in oxidation is called *cellular* respiration.
13. Waste carbon dioxide moves from the cells to the lymph fluid and into the blood by *absorption.*
14. The veins and diaphragm are made of *cardiac* muscle.
15. *Digestion* occurs when the rib muscles and the diaphragm relax.

PART VII. Write a short paragragh discussing how the skeletal, muscular, circulatory and respiratory systems are interrelated..

CHAPTER 20 - THE EXCRETORY SYSTEM

LIFE SCIENCE

ALL CREATURES GREAT AND SMALL

DOWN

1. Tubes connecting the kidneys to the bladder.

2. The long, thin part of a nephron where reabsorption occurs.

3. Parts of the kidneys that filter.

4. The outer dead layer of skin.

6. Coiled tubes that make sweat.

7. Solid matter in the rectum.

10. A nitrogenous waste.

11. A tube from the bladder to the outside.

The Excretory System Crossword Puzzle

Use the keywords from this chapter to fill in the puzzle.
See how many you know before reading the chapter!
Complete the puzzle after completing this chapter.

ACROSS

1. All the parts that handle urine.

5. Small openings.

8. The living layer of skin.

9. The knot of capillaries in the nephron where filtration occurs.

11. A mixture of nitrogenous wastes, water and other soluble wastes.

12. An organ that stores urine.

13. The separation of solutions by diffusion.

Write in this book only if it belongs to you.
You may wish to make a copy of this page.

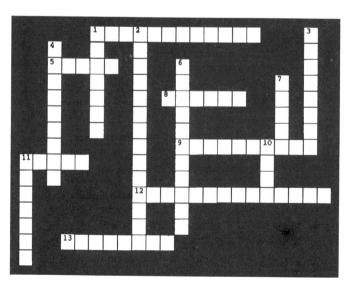

CHAPTER 20
THE EXCRETORY SYSTEM

It appears the opening line of the last several chapters has been a *waste* so, for this chapter, we'll *eliminate* it!

The function of the human excretory system is to eliminate wastes from the body. Just as our rivers, lakes and fields can become polluted by the build up of wastes, our cells can become polluted and die if wastes are not constantly removed.

LUNGS

We discussed in the chapter on the respiratory system how **carbon dioxide** and **water vapor** diffuse from the blood into the air sacs. Each time a person exhales these wastes are eliminated through the **mouth** and **nostrils**. If CO_2 cannot be removed the organism dies of asphyxiation.

LARGE INTESTINE

In the chapter on the digestive system we learned that the large intestine reabsorbs water from the **solid wastes** left from digestion. The STOOL is formed in the rectum and eliminated through the **anus**.

LIVER

The largest organ in the body is actually a waste treatment center. Its importance is indicated by the fact that nearly one third of the blood goes through the liver on each contraction of the heart.

In addition to making bile for emulsifying fats, the liver converts **ammonia** from the blood into UREA. Ammonia (NH_3) is a toxic waste produced when the human body uses certain **amino acids**. Urea is a colorless nitrogen compound that the kidneys can filter from the blood.

The spleen helps in the removal of worn out red cells from the body. The liver recycles the amino acids in worn out red blood cells and makes other waste chemicals in the body into a form the skin or kidneys can handle. The parts and pieces that are no longer usable are sent through the **bile duct** into the intestine. The liver is still under study and is not understood completely.

KIDNEYS

The circulatory system transports wastes from the cells and from the liver to the kidneys in the lower back. The two 10 cm long kidneys are like the filter on a pool, taking out materials and allowing the purified liquid to pass through. But the kidneys are complex and critically important organs (See Figure 20-1). A person cannot live if both of their kidneys fail, unless they use an artificial kidney.

Kidneys in all of the vertebrates serve the same function, excretion of **nitrogenous wastes** and **water.**

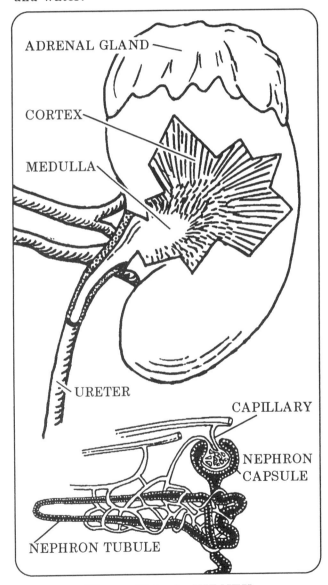

Figure 20-1 A KIDNEY

The outer part of the kidney is the cortex. The middle region is the medulla. The nephrons start in the cortex and empty the urine into the medulla of the kidney.

When people's kidneys fail to work properly they may undergo DIALYSIS at a medical center. The dialysis machine is an artificial kidney that allows diffusion of nitrogenous wastes from the blood through cellophane menbranes. In the cortex of a healthy human kidney this diffusion takes place in any one of approximately 1 million NEPHRONS. The end of each nephron holds a knot of capillaries called the GLOMERULUS. The capillaries are closely intertwined with the nephron capsules so that **water**, **salts**, **amino acids** and **glucose** can diffuse out of the blood. The blood becomes thicker and some of the water is then actively put back into the blood by the NEPHRON TUBULES.

Each nephron tubule leads to the medulla of the kidney where the URINE is collected. The urine is then passed through the two URETERS to the URINARY BLADDER. The bladder empties through the one URETHRA. Use the a to remember you have **a** urethr**a** but two ureters (Figure 20-2). Urine exits through the **urethra**.

A summary of the excretory action carried out in the URINARY TRACT is included in Fig. 20-3.

Part	Action
nephron capsule	filtration
nephron tubule	reabsorption
the two ureters	transport
urinary bladder	storage
the one urethra	excretion

Figure 20-3
URINARY TRACT SUMMARY

The urine is an excellent indicator of a body's condition in terms of health. Too much, or not enough, glucose and vitamins can be detected by testing the urine. Alcohol and drug abusers can be detected by urine tests, hopefully before they cause accidents that harm innocent people. A woman can determine if she is carrying an unborn child by another urine test.

SKIN

The outermost layer of skin is composed of closely packed dead cells, the EPIDERMIS. This layer protects the tissue underneath. The epidermis has many PORES that open into the dermis where SWEAT GLANDS are located. Capillaries are all through the DERMIS and concentrated around each sweat gland. Skin allows the human body to excrete excess **heat**, **water**, **salts** and **nitrogen wastes** not excreted in the urine.

Excess heat is eliminated when the capillaries open up wide and allow more blood through. This action is what makes a person look reddish when they are too hot. Sweat that evaporates from the skin also lowers the body's temperature.

The water, salts and nitrogen wastes taken from the blood by the sweat glands are excreted onto the surface through **pores** in the skin (Figure 20-4). Regular washing of the skin is important to keep these pores open.

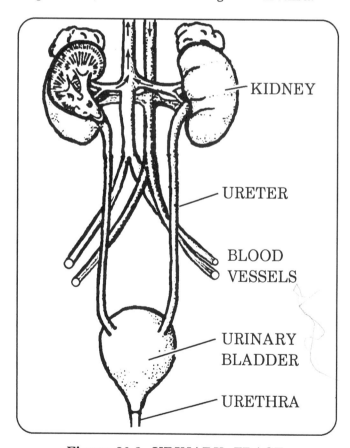

KIDNEY

URETER

BLOOD VESSELS

URINARY BLADDER

URETHRA

Figure 20-2 URINARY TRACT

The organs of the excretory system that deal with urine are the urinary tract. Urine is formed in the kidneys from amino acid wastes. Excess vitamins and drugs are also in urine.

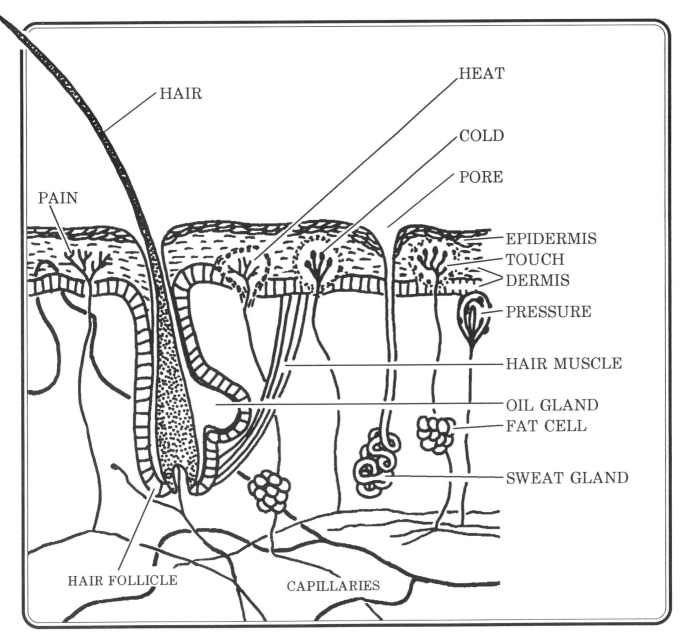

Figure 20-4 CROSS SECTION OF HUMAN SKIN

The skin is a complex organ that serves the excretory and the nervous systems.

The five kinds of nerve endings are discussed in the chapter on the nervous system.

Note that the pressure sensors are deeper in the skin than the endings for pain, heat, cold and touch.

Heat escapes through the skin.

Salts, dissolved in water, are excreted through the pores that lead to the sweat glands.

CHAPTER 20 REVIEW

OBJECTIVES:

1. Identify the parts and functions of the human excretory system.

2. Know how each type of waste product is eliminated.

3. Appreciate the need for excretion.

PART I. Copy and complete the chart below.

TITLE: THE __1__ SYSTEM

Part of the Excretory System	Wastes that are excreted	Opening for elimination
2._____	CO_2 and H_2O	3._____ 4._____
Large Intestine	5._____	6._____
7._____	8._____ 9._____	Bile duct or capillaries
10._____	11._____ 12._____ 13._____ and glucose	urethra
14._____	heat, water salts, and nitrogen wastes	15._____

PART II. Diagram and label the kidney.

PART III. Diagram and label the parts of the human urinary tract.

PART IV. Diagram and label the skin.

PART V. Define the 15 Keywords in Chapter 20 - The Excretory System.

PART VI. Neatly write each sentence filling in the blank using a Keyword from PART V.

1. Inside the kidney are millions of __?__ that filter the blood.

2. __?__ occurs naturally in healthy kidneys.

3. Water is reabsorbed into the capillaries that wrap around the __?__.

4. Perspiration is formed in the __?__.

5. Perspiration is excreted through __?__ in the skin.

6. The sweat glands are in the __?__.

7. The pores are in the __?__.

8. Testing a patient's __?__ can often indicate if the person is healthy.

9. The colorless nitrogen compound __?__ is formed in the liver from ammonia.

10. The __?__ connect each kidney to the urinary bladder.

PART VII. Write a concise paragraph explaining the excretion of carbon dioxide. Include:

1. How CO_2 is made inside the body;

2. Where CO_2 is made;

3. How CO_2 gets to the organ that excretes it;

4. The organ of excretion for CO_2;

5. The openings through which CO_2 leaves the body;

6. What happens if the CO_2 is not eliminated from the body.

CHAPTER 21 - THE ENDOCRINE SYSTEM

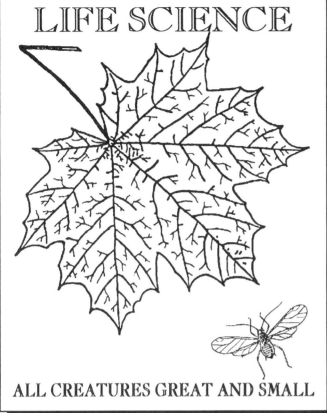

LIFE SCIENCE

ALL CREATURES GREAT AND SMALL

DOWN

1. The master gland in the head.

2. Hormone that controls the release of glucose from the liver.

4. A disease when too much glucose is in the blood due to a lack of insulin.

5. A hormone for emergencies.

7. Hormone that controls metabolism.

8. All the ductless glands.

10. A chemical messenger.

The Endocrine System Crossword Puzzle

Use the keywords from this chapter to fill in the puzzle.
See how many you know before reading the chapter!
Complete the puzzle after completing this chapter.

ACROSS

3. Glands on the kidneys.

6. The growth hormone.

9. Hormone that controls the amount of catilage at the joints.

11. A gland located in the neck.

12. Insulin is made here.

13. Iodine is needed to prevent this.

14. Hormone to control the use of glucose in the body.

CHAPTER 21
THE ENDOCRINE SYSTEM

If you get the *message* in this chapter you should be able to keep your blood pressure under *control*.

The human ENDOCRINE SYSTEM is a group of ductless glands that produce chemical messengers. A duct is a tube. The salivary glands empty saliva into the mouth through salivary ducts. The gall bladder releases bile through the bile duct. Endocrine glands have no ducts. The chemicals are produced in special glandular cells and are secreted directly into the blood. Within a matter of seconds these chemical messengers, called HORMONES, cause great changes in breathing, heart beat and capillary size. Some hormones act slowly over many years. The function of the endocrine system, and its hormones, is to coordinate and control body growth and metabolism.

That's a mouthful. What is meant by coordinate and control body metabolism is best explained by several examples. If a baby's left leg grew to adult size first, then the left arm, etc.; the baby would be a bit awkward! If a tiger's body grew to adult size first, then its head and brain; you would have a very playful several hundred pounds of muscle, sinew, and claws (Figure 21-1). The endocrine glands help coordinate growth.

Figure 21-1
WITHOUT AN ENDOCRINE SYSTEM

Without the hormones produced by ductless endocrine glands an organism's growth and metabolism would not be coordinated.

When you run a race and need lots of energy, you first need lots of oxygen and glucose. The rate of respiration must keep up with your race pace. The glucose coming out of temporary storage in the liver must speed up. When you stop running, these processes must slow down. The endocrine glands help control metabolism.

PITUITARY GLAND

The "master gland" that controls many of the other endocrine glands is located at the base of the brain. It is the PITUITARY GLAND, which is fastened to the hypothalamus of the brain. Many of the hormones of the pituitary gland are made in the hypothalamus.

ACTH is a nickname for a pituitary hormone that tells the adrenal glands to secrete their hormones. The **A** in **ACTH** is for **A**drenal glands.

TSH is the hormone from the pituitary gland that controls the thyroid gland. The name **TSH** means "Thyroid Stimulating Hormone". There are other hormones in the pituitary that control various other glands. That is why the pituitary is nicknamed the master gland.

The pituitary gland also secretes the growth hormone TETHELIN. In some adults an overactive pituitary gland causes acromegaly.

In a child, if the pituitary gland does not produce enough tethelin the child will not grow properly. He or she will be a dwarf. If the pituitary is overactive a giant will result. Pauline Musters, a girl from the Netherlands was the shortest dwarf recorded. Pauline was 59 cm tall when she died at age 19. Today injections of growth hormone can often save a child from a life in circuses and a premature death. The tallest giant recorded was an American boy, Robert Wadlow of Illinios. One of history's most famous giants of all time was Charlemagne, emperor of the Holy Roman Empire.

THYROID GLAND

The THYROID GLAND is shaped like a bow tie. It is located just where a bow tie would be, below the larynx on the front of the trachea. This was the gland we mentioned needs iodine. The iodine is part of the hormone THYROXIN. If the diet lacks iodine then the thyroid gland can't make enough thyroxin. The body reacts as if the thyroid gland is not big enough and the thyroid grows larger. The lack of iodine causes a greatly enlarged thyroid gland in the neck called SIMPLE GOITER.

Most people have a normal diet and a normal thyroid. The thyroxin produced controls the rate of metabolism. Do you remember what metabolism is? Metabolism is the sum of all life activities. The thyroxin is necessary in proper amounts for normal physical and mental development. An underactive thyroid gland causes cretinism in children; their development is not normal.

PARATHYROID GLANDS

Imbedded inside the back of the thyroid gland are the parathyroid glands. The hormone secreted by the parathyroid gland is easy to remember: parathormone. Its name is a combination of the words **parath**yroid and **hormone**. Parathormone controls the body's use of calcium and phosphate compounds. You already know that the calcium is needed for bones and teeth. The phosphates are needed for the nerves.

THYMUS GLANDS

The thymus glands in the center of the chest may help a child's immune system. The thymus gland is still not completely understood.

PANCREAS

Inside the pancreas are small spots of different tissue. To a researcher looking through a microscope these spots appear like islands in the sea of pancreatic cells. These important spots of tissue, called ISLANDS OF LANGERHANS, are part of the endocrine system. I'll bet you can figure out the name of the scientist who discovered them! Another name for the Islands of Langerhans could be "sugar islands" because the hormones that control glucose in the body are made here.

GLUCAGON is the hormone that controls the release of glucose from its temporary storage in the liver. INSULIN regulates the use of the glucose in the cells. Since glucose is the source of energy for each living cell, insulin is needed for life itself.

When the pancreas does not work properly or is damaged and the Islands of Langerhans cannot make insulin, DIABETES results. Daily injections of insulin can allow a diabetic to live for many years. Today experimental computer chip Islands of Langerhans are being put under the skin of some diabetics. The computer chips release insulin into the blood automatically when needed. This new arrangement allows diabetics to live without daily injections.

ADRENAL GLANDS

On top of the kidneys are the ADRENAL GLANDS, sometimes called the glands of combat (See Figure 20-1, page 135). The hormone made by the outer part of the adrenal glands, called the cortex, is CORTISONE. Cortisone regulates sugar metabolism and salt balance in the body.

But it is the ADRENALIN from the adrenal medulla that gives the adrenal glands their nickname: glands of combat. Another name for the homone adrenalin is epinephrine

Adrenalin is dumped into the blood stream whenever you get into a fight or a fright. The adrenalin causes the heart to beat faster. That moves the blood faster so the cells get oxygen and glucose at a more rapid pace. To get more oxygen you must also breathe more rapidly and adrenalin speeds up the respiratory rate. It also causes an increase of glucose in the blood. Once all that happens you are ready to rough it or run!

SEX GLANDS

The gonads are the endocrine glands particular to each sex. In a male, the testes, located in the scrotum, produce the hormone testosterone. The testosterone causes the beard and other secondary male characteristics to develop. In a female, the ovaries in the lower abdomen secrete estrogen which causes the secondary female characteristics to develop.

The major glands in the human endocrine system are illustrated in Figure 21-2. The complex job of getting billions of cells to grow and change in an orderly fashion is done by the endocrine system. Without it your body would be a wreck. Most giants and dwarfs die very young. Their lives are sadly dominated by their size, either great or small.

Modern medicine has helped some victims of endocrine disorders through injections of hormones or dietary improvements. There is still plenty to be learned about how the human body, with all its systems, works together in a healthy individual. Life scientists are needed who will study and learn and eventually discover the still unknown secrets of the endocrine system

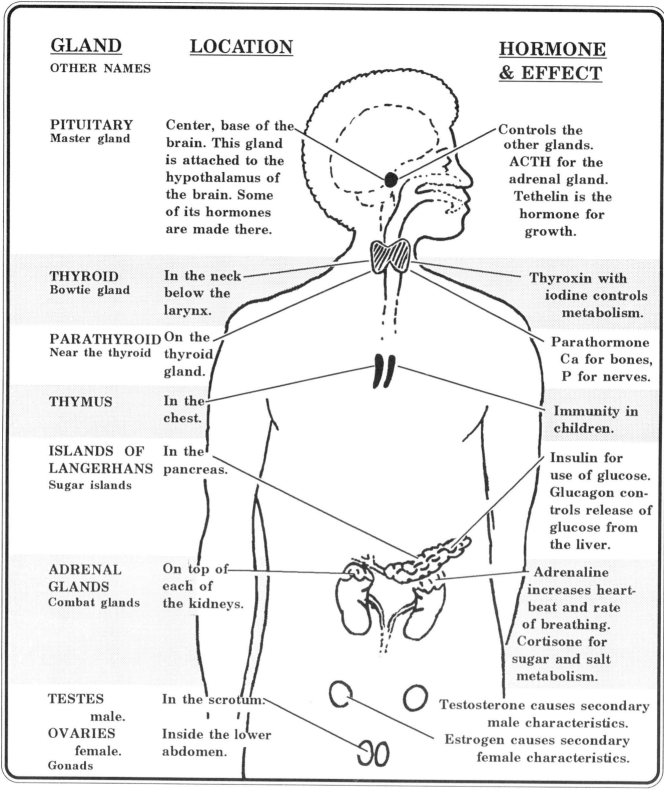

GLAND OTHER NAMES	LOCATION	HORMONE & EFFECT
PITUITARY Master gland	Center, base of the brain. This gland is attached to the hypothalamus of the brain. Some of its hormones are made there.	Controls the other glands. ACTH for the adrenal gland. Tethelin is the hormone for growth.
THYROID Bowtie gland	In the neck below the larynx.	Thyroxin with iodine controls metabolism.
PARATHYROID Near the thyroid	On the thyroid gland.	Parathormone Ca for bones, P for nerves.
THYMUS	In the chest.	Immunity in children.
ISLANDS OF LANGERHANS Sugar islands	In the pancreas.	Insulin for use of glucose. Glucagon controls release of glucose from the liver.
ADRENAL GLANDS Combat glands	On top of each of the kidneys.	Adrenaline increases heartbeat and rate of breathing. Cortisone for sugar and salt metabolism.
TESTES male. OVARIES female. Gonads	In the scrotum. Inside the lower abdomen.	Testosterone causes secondary male characteristics. Estrogen causes secondary female characteristics.

Figure 21 - 2 THE ENDOCRINE SYSTEM

The hormones produced by the ductless glands are the chemical messengers of the brain. They allow the brain to control the systems of the body in relationship to each other. Your hormones help to change your child's body into an adult body.

CHAPTER 21 REVIEW

OBJECTIVES:

1. **Understand how the endocrine system controls body functions.**

2. **Know the major glands and hormones of the endocrine system.**

3. **Describe the effects of hormones and the results of their absence or excess.**

PART I. Give two examples of glands that are not endocrine glands.

PART II. What is the most important difference between endocrine glands and other glands of the body?

PART III. Choose your answers for the next questions from the glands listed below:

Pituitary Gland Thyroid Gland Pancreas
Adrenal Gland Parathyroid Glands Gonads

1. Often called the "master gland."
2. Butterfly shaped gland located in the neck.
3. Requires the mineral iodine in order to work properly.
4. Secretes thyroxin.
5. Secretes the growth hormone.
6. Controls the rate at which our body uses calcium.
7. If this gland doesn't work properly, diabetes can result.
8. This gland secretes cortisone.
9. Secretes a hormone that causes glucose to be stored in the liver as glycogen.
10. Located at the base of the brain.
11. Located on top of the kidneys.
12. The sex glands (ovaries and testes).
13. Secretes a hormone that causes glycogen in the liver to be changed back into glucose in the blood.
14. A digestive gland and an endocrine gland.
15. Often called the "glands of combat."
16. Goiter and cretinism are two conditions that can result when this gland does not work properly.

PART IV. Define the 14 Keywords in Chapter 21 The Endocrine System.

PART V. List and locate at least five endocrine glands.

PART VI. Write a report on a dwarf or a giant. Have your topic approved by your instructor. Be sure to outline your topic, do a rough copy and include:

1. A title page;

2. The cause of the person's condition;

3. Where and how long the person lived;

4. What the person did for a living;

5. Quotations and footnotes as instructed;

6. Glossary of important terms; and

7. References.

PART VII. Make a chart listing at least five endocrine system related **diseases**. Include the **cause** of the disease and the **hormone** involved.

CHAPTER 22 - THE NERVOUS SYSTEM

LIFE SCIENCE

ALL CREATURES GREAT AND SMALL

DOWN

2. Chemicals that carry an impulse across the synapse.

4. The part of the brain that controls balance.

5. Bumps on the brain.

7. "Tree branch" like parts of neurons.

8. A nerve message.

10. Part of a sensory organ that receives input.

11. The brain stem.

13. The large, main part of a neuron.

The Nervous System Crossword Puzzle

ACROSS

1. A nerve cell that sends impulses in to the brain.

3. Muscles or glands that act.

6. Nerve cells that carry impulses out from the brain.

9. A neuron between other neurons, that puts impulses together.

12. The largest part of the human brain.

14. A single cell in a nerve.

15. The long thin part of a neuron.

16. The gap between the ends of the neurons.

Use the keywords from this chapter to fill in the puzzle. See how many you know before reading the chapter! Complete the puzzle after completing this chapter.

CHAPTER 22
THE NERVOUS SYSTEM

PART A: PARTS OF THE
NERVOUS SYSTEM

If the opening lines of the past chapters got on your "nerves" then I know you won't "mind" that this is the last chapter in which you will "see" or "hear" one of them.

The nervous system consists of all the cells of the body that can detect, send, or store information for later transmission. The functions of the nervous system are many. These functions are carried out with special organs and cells as outlined in Figure 22-1.

FUNCTION	PART
1. Control involuntary actions.	The medulla, part of the brain.
2. Control balance.	The cerebellum, part of the brain.
3. Data input.	The five sense organs.
4. Reflex actions.	The spinal cord in the backbone.
5. Transmission of messages.	The outer nerve cells & spinal cord.
6. Memory.	The cerebrum, part of the brain.
7. Control voluntary actions.	The cerebrum, part of the brain.
8. Thinking	The cerebrum,

Figure 22-1
FUNCTIONS OF THE NERVOUS SYSTEM

NEURONS

The basic unit of the nervous system is the NEURON. Neurons are similar to the wires and circuits in a radio or television. The neurons carry electrical messages. One difference from wires is: neurons will transmit an IMPULSE in one direction only (Figure 22-2). In general, there are three types of neurons.

1. SENSORY NEURONS are the nerve cells that receive data from the organism's environment. Sensory neurons transmit a signal to the spinal cord or brain. The sensory neurons are very concentrated in the sense organs: the eyes, ears, nose, tongue and skin. Each organ: eye, ear, nose, tongue and skin, has its own sensory neurons called RECEPTORS. Receptors are different shapes for receiving different information.

2. ASSOCIATIVE NEURONS are the nerve cells that connect the sensory neurons to the motor neurons. They are "associated" with both the input of information and the sending out of commands to body parts. Associative neurons are concentrated in the spinal cord and brain. These neurons are the nerve cells that form ideas.

3. MOTOR NEURONS are the nerve cells that carry impulses to the body's "motors", the muscles and glands. Since the muscles and glands can cause an effect they are termed EFFECTORS. Paralysis occurs when motor neurons are cut or stop working properly. Motor neurons are all through the body.

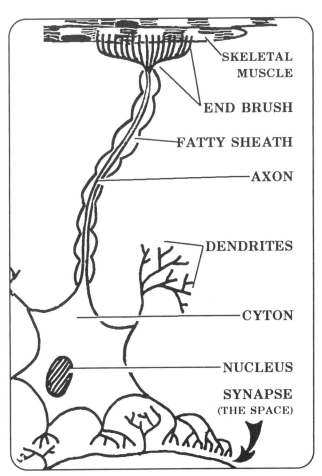

Figure 22-2 A MOTOR NEURON

At one end the motor neuron receives an impulse from an associative neuron. The other end transmits the message to a muscle.

The three kinds of neurons don't actually touch each other. They have tree-branched like parts called DENDRITES that come very close to, but don't touch another nerve cell.

The electrical nerve impulse is changed into a chemical message at the end of the dendrites. The nerve chemical, a NEUROTRANSMITTER, moves across the SYNAPSE and an impulse is initiated in the other nerve cell. Pain killer drugs, like aspirin, work because they stop the neurotransmitter from crossing the synapse.

Impulses move from the dendrite to the cell body, or CYTON, then along the AXON. The axon is the long thin part of a nerve cell that is covered with a fatty sheath, like a wire with the plastic insulation around it. At the far end of the neuron is the end brush where the message is distributed.

THE BRAIN

The brain and spinal cord are the center of all nervous activity in the body. Together they are called the central nervous sytem. The brain, a great mass of nerve cells, has three main regions which are protected by the skull.

The CEREBRUM is the largest part of the brain. The outer part of the cerebrum is mostly grayish cytons, or cell bodies, while the inner part is white due to the fatty sheaths of the axons. The "gray matter" is divided into left and right hemispheres. It is covered with winding bumps that are called CONVOLUTIONS (Figure 22-3). The cerebrum controls thinking and problem solving as well as sight, speech, and voluntary movement.

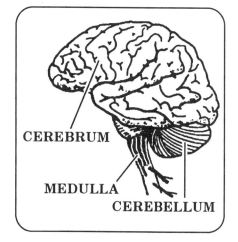

Figure 22-3

THE
BRAIN

CEREBRUM

MEDULLA

CEREBELLUM

Each part of the brain has specific functions. The largest part, the cerebrum, has special areas that control speech, sight, voluntary movement, thinking and memory.

The CEREBELLUM in the lower rear of the cranial cavity controls coordination and balance. The Latin word "bellum" means war or contest. To win a fight or contest the combatant's coordination and balance must be very good. Use the old word bellum in cerebellum to associate this part of the brain with the coordination and balance needed by a warrior (Figure 22-4).

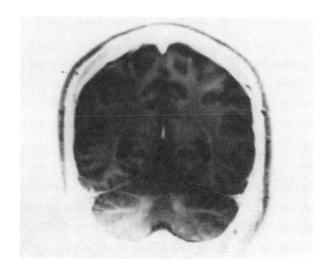

Figure 22-4 BRAIN LONGISECTION

This CAT scan image shows the left and right hemispheres of the cerebrum. Underneath is the cerebellum. This image was made without opening up the patient.

The MEDULLA oblongata is sometimes called the brain stem. The medulla is the control center for the smooth, involuntary muscles of the human digestive system. The medulla controls the heart beat for the circulatory system and breathing rate in the respiratory system.

THE SPINAL CORD

The spinal cord is a long bundle of associative neurons and the axons of many sensory and motor neurons. The spinal cord is protected by the bony vertebrae in the spinal column. Many reflex actions take place through impulses sent from the spinal cord. This bundle of neurons is the brain's connection to the torso and limbs.

There are 31 pairs of nerve bundles that go out through spaces between the vertebrae to all the muscles and glands in the body. These side nerves include the sensory neurons' axons bringing data into the central nervous system. All of these side nerves together are the peripheral nervous system.

LIFE SCIENCE All Creatures Great And Small

PART B: THE FIVE SENSES

It is impossible for anyone with all of their senses to imagine the thoughts and frustrations of someone whose eyes, or ears, or both don't function properly! The story of Helen Keller, who was both blind and deaf at birth, and her teacher can help people appreciate their senses. Senses are the means by which the brain gets its data.

THE EYES

The eyes contain the sensory neurons that detect light energy. ROD CELLS are designed for black and white vision in dim light. CONE CELLS are for color vision. Remember the "C" in cone is for color. Both rods and cones cover the back of the inside of each eye. This tissue of rods and cones is called the RETINA.

There is a tiny "blind spot" on each retina where it is fastened to the OPTIC NERVE (Figure 22-5). Close one eye and stare at a distant object. Hold a pencil, eraser end up, about 15 cm in front of your open eye. Slowly move the pencil back and forth, up and down. Keep staring straight ahead and you will see the end of the pencil disappear at a certain point. At that point the light rays from the pencil end are falling on the blind spot where there are no rods or cones.

Why did you have to close one eye? the brain puts the impulses received from both optic nerves together to make one image. Each eye fills in the blind spot from the other eye. Two eyes are also needed for depth perception. Anyone with a patch or only one eye must be extremely cautious when driving a car!

Figure 22-5

OPTIC NERVES

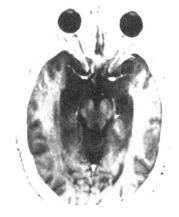

This section of the author's head makes it possible to see the optic nerves connecting the eyes to the brain. The left and right hemispheres of the cerebrum may be clearly distinguished.

BLINDNESS results when the sense of sight is destroyed by damage to the eye. The CONVEX LENS, the retina, the optic nerve and the part of the brain that handles the optic impulses must all work properly (Figure 22-6). Louis Braille of France invented a way of writing with bumps so that a blind person can read.

The figure shows the sclera, or white of the eye; the aqueous humor, a fluid between the CORNEA and lens; and the vitreous humor, a thicker fluid inside the eye. The IRIS, the colored part of the eye, adjusts the size of the pupil.

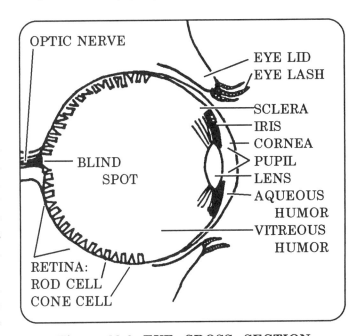

Figure 22-6 EYE CROSS SECTION

Like an expensive camera the human eye has an automatic focus and light control, a lens and a photosensitive surface. The eye lid is a "lens cover" to protect the delicate cornea. You blink once every 2 to 10 seconds to lubricate the eye.

People who are NEARSIGHTED have eyes in which the light is focused before it gets to their eye's retina. By the time the light is to the retina it is out of focus. This can happen if the lens of the eye is too thick or if the eye is oblong in shape. Nearsightedness can be corrected by placing a concave lens in front of the eye to bend the light rays apart before they pass through the cornea and pupil into the eye (Figure 22-7).

FARSIGHTEDNESS is the opposite problem. The light reaches the retina before it comes into focus. A convex lens can bend the light rays closer together and the eye's own convex lens can focus the light on the retina for clear vision.

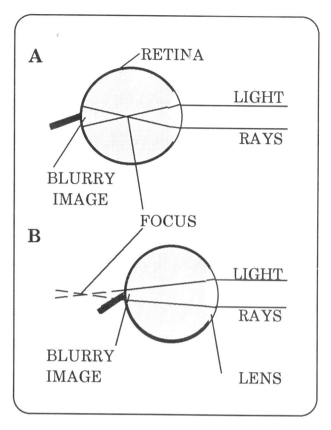

Figure 22-7 EYE CONDITIONS

Nearsightedness (A) is a condition in which the light rays are focused too near the lens. In a farsighted eye (B) the light is focused too far from the lens.

THE EARS

Most people consider sight their most important sense. The ability to hear is a close second. You learned to speak because you could hear others speaking. DEAFNESS is the inability to hear. Many people who are deaf are also mute. Their MUTENESS, the inability to speak, is very often a result of not being able to hear others or oneself speaking. To hear a car horn beep a warning, to hear "time for supper!", to hear your favorite song are all trite everyday events. The delicate pair of instruments that allow a person to hear are, on the other hand, intricate and interesting (Figure 22-8). In addition to hearing, the ear is necessary for the body to keep its balance.

The outer ear is the ear lobe, or pinna, supported by cartilage and the ear canal and ear drum. Sound waves in the air are gathered by the ear lobe and directed by the ear canal to the ear drum. Just as the vocal cords in the larynx vibrate to produce sounds. The sound waves in the air cause the ear drum to vibrate.

The middle ear contains three tiny bones, the hammer, anvil and stirrup, named because of

Figure 22-8 THE EAR
(See below)
Cochlea is from the Latin word for snail. It is inside the snail shaped cochlea that sound vibrations are changed into nerve impulses.

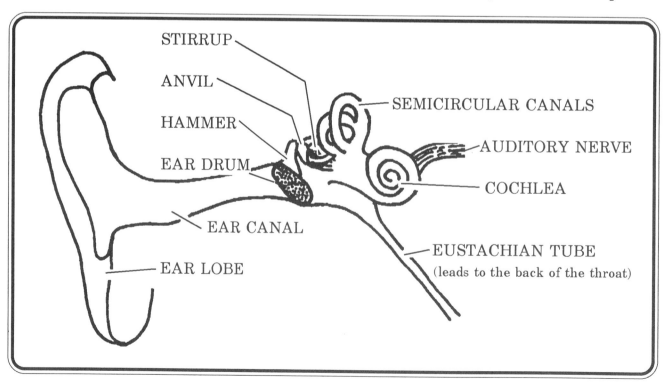

shapes. The stirrup is the smallest of the body's 206 bones. These three bones transfer the vibrations from the ear drum to the cochlea in the inner ear. The EUSTACHIAN TUBE is a tube that connects the ear to the pharynx. When your ears "pop" going up a hill in a car you need to get some of the air behind the eardrum out. By swallowing with your mouth open the extra air behind the eardrum goes through the eustachian tube and your ears feel normal again. If you rapidly go down the other side of the mountain you must swallow to force air through the eustachian tube into the ear behind the eardrum.

The inner ear contains the COCHLEA, so named due to its snail shape. The liquid inside the cochlea vibrates and causes the nerve endings to "fire". The impulses travel along the AUDITORY NERVE to the brain and you hear! For those who cannot hear there is a system of sign language used to communicate with their family and friends (Figure 22-9).

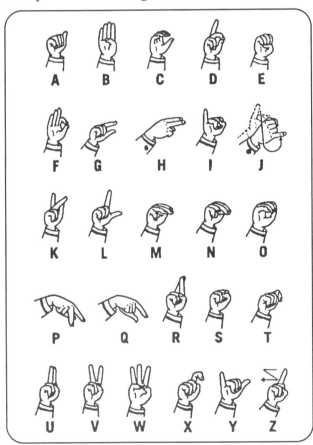

Figure 22-9 SIGN LANGUAGE

To obtain a computer program that illustrates many of the signs used by the deaf contact: SIGNFRIEND, Fran O'Gorman, Glenmere Ave, Florida, NY, 10921.

The SEMICIRCULAR CANALS are three loops in the inner ear that also contain fluid and nerve endings. When your head moves, the fluid in the semicircular canals moves and nerve impulses are sent to the cerebellum. The cerebellum sends messages to muscles that must adjust so that your body stays balanced. By spinning around rapidly several times and then stopping you can set the fluid inside the canals in motion. Even though you've stopped, the fluid is still moving and the nerves are still sending their messages. The brain thinks your body is still spinning and you experience dizziness.

THE NOSE

The sense of smell is located in the nose. The sensitive ends of the OLFACTORY NERVE detect odors in the air. The pleasant odor of most foods is required to make the food have its characteristic taste. If students hold their noses and someone puts a small piece of apple or potato on their tongue, the pieces taste the same. Without the sense of smell the flavor of foods is greatly reduced.

THE TONGUE

We discussed the sense of taste when we investigated digestion. If you can't recall the areas of the tongue that detect the tastes: sweet, salt, sour and bitter, refer back to that chapter.

Acids cause the sour taste. Salt ions cause the salty taste. Many different organic compounds cause the sweet taste sensation, sugar among them. The bitter taste is caused by organic compounds called alkaloids. If the bitter taste is too strong you reject the food. This is a protective function since many poisons are alkaloids!

THE SKIN

The sense of touch is located in the skin. The skin diagram in the section on the human excretory system (Figure 20-5) illustrates the five different kinds of receptors in the skin.

Touch receptors are closer to the surface than pressure receptors. Touch and pressure receptors are important for the body in maintaining muscle equilibrium. They also allow the human hand to pick up a baby without hurting it. On the other hand, a person can wield a sledge hammer!

There are also pain, heat and cold receptors. These special sensory nerve endings send important data to the central nervous system that allows the body to protect itself from excessive damage.

With the skin we've covered the entire body and its sense organs!

CHAPTER 22 REVIEW

OBJECTIVES:

1. **List the functions of the nervous system.**
2. **Diagram a nerve cell and the brain.**
3. **Distinguish three types of neurons.**
4. **Understand the functions of each part of the nervous system.**
5. **Define Keywords.**
6. **Diagram the eye and the ear.**
7. **Identify two eye conditions and how they can be corrected.**
8. **Know the five senses organs.**

PART I. List the part of the body involved and eight functions of the nervous system.

PART II. Diagram and label a neuron.

PART III. Define the 16 Keywords in **Part A** of Chapter 22 - The Nervous System.

PART IV. Neatly write each term below. In the margin in front of each term, write a letter (A, M or S) to identify the type of neuron that is most closely associated with the term. Use:
A = associative   **M** = motor   **S** = sensory

1. Brings messages from the brain to a muscle.
2. Concentrated in the sense organs.
3. Mostly in the brain.
4. Transmit messages from the eye to the brain.
5. Carry the impulses that cause a gland to secrete a hormone.
6. Located between the other 2 kinds of neurons.
7. A neuron that is connected to receptors.
8. A neuron that is connected to an effector.
9. Paralysis results when the nerves are cut.
10. These nerves form ideas.

PART V. Make a chart showing the three main parts of the human brain and the functions each part controls.

PART VI. Define the 17 Keywords from **Part B** of Chapter 22 - The Nervous System.

PART VII. List the five sense organs, the name of the sense, and any special nerves or parts associated with each sense.

PART VIII. Diagram and label the human eye.

PART IX. Write a short paragraph distinguishing between nearsightedness and farsightedness. Be sure to use at least six of the following terms:

concave lens	farsightedness	receptors
cone cells	iris	retina
convex lens	nearsightedness	rod cells
cornea	optic nerve	sensory neuron

PART X. Diagram and label the parts of the ear.

PART XI. Write each full sentence neatly using a Keyword from Chapter 22 (33 words in all) to fill in the blanks. Use a Keyword only once. You will not use all of the Keywords.

1. __?__ is an inability to hear.
2. __?__ is an inability to see.
3. The __?__ connects the eye to the brain.
4. The rods and cones together make up the _?_.
5. _?_ are the branch shaped parts of a neuron.
6. The __?__ is the snail shaped part of the ear.
7. People who are color blind may have a problem with their __?__.
8. The number of _?_, bumps, on the cerebrum may indicate how smart a person is.
9. The nerve message crosses the __?__ by means of a neurotransmitter.
10. Taste buds are __?__ that can sense sweet, salt, sour or bitter.
11. Damage to the brain's __?__ could cause a loss of balance and coordination.
12. Thinking out the answers to these questions occurs in your __?__.
13. The __?__ is also called the brain stem.
14. Air pressure behind the ear drum is changed when air moves through the __?__.
15. A person is __?__ when their eye focuses the light too far from the lens.
16. A person's eye color is determined by the color of their __?__.
17. The aroma of a hot apple pie causes the __?__ to send impulses to the brain.
18. The fluid in the __?__ moves when you move and impulses are sent to the cerebellum.
19. Like the terms auditorium, audition, and audiosystem, the __?__ has to do with hearing.
20. Some nerve cells are the longest cells because of the __?__ enclosed in the fatty sheath.

PART XII. A. Report on the Braille system invented by Louis Braille of France.
B. Research and report on the American System of Sign Language for the Deaf.

CHAPTER 23 - PLANT GROWTH

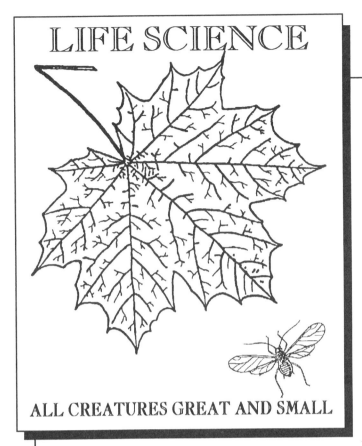

LIFE SCIENCE

ALL CREATURES GREAT AND SMALL

DOWN

1. A plant response to light.
2. All the petals of a flower.
4. The process of starting to grow.
5. The moment the sperm unites with an egg to create a new organism.
6. The female part of a flower.
11. Splitting into two, new organisms.
12. Sperm or egg cells.
14. A plant response to gravity.
16. Type of reproduction in which the offspring are genetically alike.
18. The cell formed by fertilization.
19. __?__ pollination: the pollen from one flower fertilizes another.
21. Type of reproduction in which two cells join to make a new organism.

Plant Growth Crossword Puzzle

Use the keywords from this chapter to fill in the puzzle.
See how many you know before reading the chapter!
Complete the puzzle after completing this chapter.

ACROSS

3. Asexual reproduction in yeast.
7. A tiny, new organism, still developing.
8. A plant response to touch.
9. The process of making spores.
10. Transfer of pollen to the stigma.
13. Scattering of seeds is called seed __?__.
15. Using part of a plant to make another plant.
17. Pollination when the pollen fertilizes the same flower.
20. Plant hormones.
22. A plant response to water.
23. Plant responses to stimuli.
24. The filament and anther together.

Copyright 1995 by Michael J. Spear

CHAPTER 23 PLANT GROWTH
Response and Reproduction

RESPONSE

Plants, unlike the animals, have no muscular and nervous systems. For plants to react to their environment they must change the water pressure in cells or grow in a new direction. AUXINS are special plant hormones that cause plant cells to grow more or less, depending on the cells. The amount of auxins in a cell depends on gravity, the amount of sunlight and many other environmental factors. A plant TROPISM is a response to various environmental factors caused by the different concentrations of auxins in cells.

PHOTOTROPISM is a "light response" in plants. Sunlight causes the auxin in cells to break down. The shaded side of a plant stem has a greater concentration of auxin. The cells on the shaded side grow longer than the sunny cells. This unequal growth causes the plant to grow toward the light (Figure 23-1).

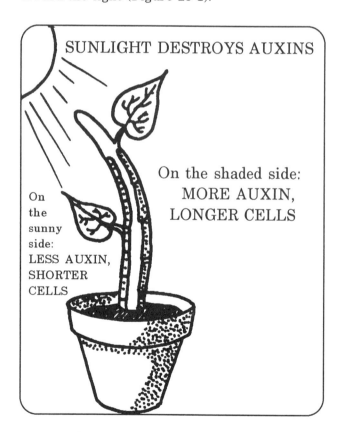

SUNLIGHT DESTROYS AUXINS

On the sunny side: LESS AUXIN, SHORTER CELLS

On the shaded side: MORE AUXIN, LONGER CELLS

Figure 23-1 PHOTOTROPISM

The stem cells with more auxin are on the shaded side. When they grow longer the plant bends toward the light.

GEOTROPISM is a plant response to gravity. The word part geo means "earth", and geotropism is movement toward or away from the earth. The earth's gravity causes the concentration of auxin in a stem that has tipped over to be greatest on the down side (Figure 23-2). The greater concentration of auxin in the lower stem cells causes them to grow longer and the stem grows upward.

Figure 23-2 GEOTROPISM IN PLANTS

This thistle plant tipped over. The part of the stem that was already mature could not change. The growing stem grew upward because gravity pulled the auxin down.

Many of the fungi also respond to gravity. The fungi produce spores for reproduction. The spores must fall out of pores or from between the gills. In order to reproduce, the fungus must grow with the correct surface facing downward. In Figure 23-3 the front edge is turned sideways. This occurred when the tree fell over.

Figure 23-3

GEOTROPISM IN FUNGI

This shell fungus grew on a dead tree. When the tree fell over the fungus reoriented itself to gravity. This is a geotropism!

The cells in the roots respond to auxins opposite the way stem cells respond. In a root more auxin causes less growth. The down side of a root has a greater concentration of auxin and the cells don't grow as much as those on the top side. The root curves downward (Figure 23-4). If the root is exposed at the surface, sunlight destroys the auxin in the top of the root. The upper cells grow faster and longer. The root bends downward.

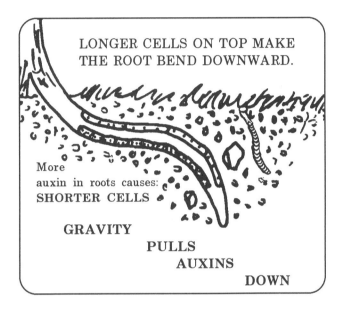

LONGER CELLS ON TOP MAKE THE ROOT BEND DOWNWARD.

More auxin in roots causes: SHORTER CELLS

GRAVITY PULLS AUXINS DOWN

Figure 23-4 GEOTROPISM IN ROOTS

The effect of auxin on root cells is opposite that of stems. The greater concentration of auxin in root cells inhibits growth and the roots grow downward.

HYDROTROPISM is a plant response to water. This can be a problem where there are water or drain pipes that are cracked. The plant roots grow toward and into the leaking pipes!

A THIGMOTROPISM is a plant response to touch. The sensitive plant, <u>Mimosa</u> <u>pudica</u>, is a good example of a plant that responds rapidly to touch. The venus fly trap captures its prey by thigmotropism. Another familiar example of thigmotropism is the tendril of a bean plant or other climbing plant. The tendrils wrap around whatever they touch .

A CHEMOTROPISM is a plant response to chemicals. The roots of plants may grow toward some chemicals but away from others. This topic would be interesting to investigate with an experiment of your own. Bean plants are good subjects for tropism experiments. You can buy the dried seeds in a grocery market.

REPRODUCTION

Of all the life functions, reproduction is the only one an individual can live without. However, the species cannot survive if some of its individuals do not reproduce. There are basically two kinds of reproduction.

Asexual Reproduction

ASEXUAL REPRODUCTION involves only one parent. The offspring produced during asexual reproduction are genetically the same as that one parent. This means that the offspring will have all the same characteristics as the parent. It is asexual reproduction that allows a farmer or scientist to grow some kinds of seedless plants. It also ensures that a certain trait will be passed on. With asexual reproduction, hybrids can be made that do not occur in nature. It produces plants more quickly than sexual reproduction.

BINARY FISSION is the "splitting into two" of a cell. First the cell copies all of the instructions in its nucleus. There is more about that in the next chapter. Then the mother cell divides its cytoplasm and nuclear material equally into two daughter cells. We mentioned in the section on classification that binary fission is how many bacteria, algae, and protists, reproduce (Figure 23-5). See Figure 8-7 if you cannot name the protist shown below.

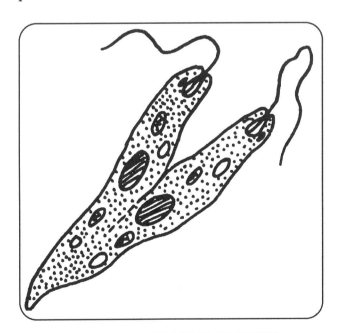

Figure 23-5 BINARY FISSION

The two daughter cells are exactly alike in terms of DNA. They are both genetically the same as the original parent cell.

BUDDING is similar to binary fission. The cell's nuclear material makes a copy of itself. However, in budding the cytoplasm is not divided equally. The mother cell is larger and the daughter cell is smaller. Both cells have all the same chromosome information as in every case of asexual reproduction (Figure 23-6). Yeast cells, like those sold in food stores, reproduce by budding. Some of the less complex animals also reproduce asexually by budding, for example, hydra.

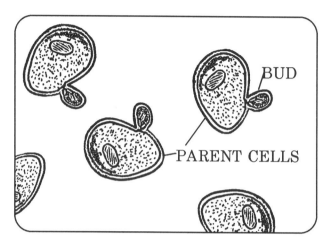

Figure 23-6 BUDDING

Yeast cells, used in making bread and wine, reproduce asexually by budding.

Fungi and some plants reproduce asexually by SPORULATION. Figure 23-7 shows the fruiting body of a mushroom turned upside down. The purpose of this part of a fungus is to produce spores that can produce new organisms in other locations. Each spore contains the same genetic information as the parent organism.

Figure 23-7

SPORULATION

Fungi, and ferns, reproduce by means of spores. The gills on the underside of a fungal cap are where the spores are produced.

There are a great many different methods of VEGETATIVE PROPAGATION. All of them are types of asexual reproduction in which part of a plant (vegetable) is used to grow a new plant (propagation). Some plants, geraniums are a good example, can be cut and the cut stems kept alive until they form roots. Then the **cuttings** may be planted. In others the cut part is attached to a plant that is already growing. This **grafting** allows farmers to grow seedless orange trees.

Runners are special horizontal stems that "run" along the surface and put down roots (See Figure 23-8). If the runner is later cut, there will be two of the strawberry, or other, plants.

Figure 23-8 RUNNERS
Runners are a type of asexual reproduction by vegetative propagation. The runners of these wild strawberry plants are visible over the rocks (see the arrows in the photo).

Similar to runners, plants like raspberries may have stems that bend down to touch the ground. The stem takes root and can be cut to make two plants. This is called **layering**. Both plants will be genetically the same; as in all the other types of asexual reproduction.

Two of the most familiar methods of asexual reproduction are **bulbs** and **tubers** (refer back to Figure 10-26). An onion bulb and a potato tuber are both special plant stems that we discussed in the chapter on plants. You should be familiar with the inside of an onion. The part you eat is actually a compressed stem and thick leaves. The "eyes" of a potato are actually new stems that can grow if given a chance. You should not eat the green parts of a potato plant. Bulbs and tubers yield plants genetically like the parent plant.

Sexual Reproduction

There is one very important difference between asexual and sexual reproduction. The information in the nucleus is combined from two parent cells in SEXUAL REPRODUCTION. Some fungi, called conjugation fungi, exchange nuclear material in a type of sexual reproduction. The new fungus is not exactly like the parent. This variety produces some individuals who are better able to live and survive under a given set of conditions. So then, the most important advantage of sexual reproduction is the variation in the offspring.

The more complex plants use FERTILIZATION by two GAMETES. The gametes are the special cells formed just for reproduction. The male cell is a sperm cell and the female cell is an egg cell.

In the most advanced plants, angiosperms, the flower is a specialized organ for reproduction. Any flower that has the parts to make both sperm and egg cells is a complete flower (Figure 23-9). Some flowers, called incomplete, can only produce sperm cells, others only make egg cells.

Most flowers have a swollen base that is called the receptacle. It holds the other parts. The sepals protect the flower bud before it opens. All the sepals together are called the calyx. The brightest and most obvious part of many flowers are the petals. Showy petals are found on flowers that need insects to pollinate them. The COROLLA, all the petals together, form bright patterns that certain insects fly toward. The corolla is like a target that attracts pollinators.

The Stamen

In studying the flower in Figure 23-9 note that the STAMEN is all of the parts needed to produce sperm cells. The filament is long and thin, just what "filament" means! The anther is the correct "anther" to give when asked where the pollen is formed. The pollen contains the sperm cell. These parts make up "Stanley Stamen," the male part of a flower. Remember the word men in sta**men** to associate the stamen with the male parts.

The Pistil

The central region of Figure 23-9 illustrates all the female parts of a flower, called the PISTIL. At the top is the sticky stigma whose function is to "grab a hold" of the pollen. The style is slender and connects the stigma to the ovule. Remember,

it is always in style to be slender. The enlarged part at the base of the pistil is the ovule. This is the part of a flower that becomes the fruit. Inside the ovule is the ovary which contains the egg nucleus. The ovary eventually becomes the seed. "Patty Pistil" is all of the female parts of the flower. A pistillate flower is an incomplete flower with only female parts: stigma, style, ovule and the ovary containing the egg cell.

Pollination

For sexual reproduction to occur the pollen in the anther must get to the sticky stigma on the style. The process of pollen getting from the anther to the stigma is called POLLINATION. Pollen from a flower reaches its own stigma in SELF POLLINATION. CROSS POLLINATION is when wind, water, insects or man cause pollen to reach a different flower's stigma (Fig. 23-10).

Figure 23-10
POLLINATION EXPERIMENT

The tops of all the tobacco plants have been covered to prevent self pollination. By such experiments a scientist can determine how to grow more vigorous plants. See page 170 to understand how tobacco depletes the soil.

155

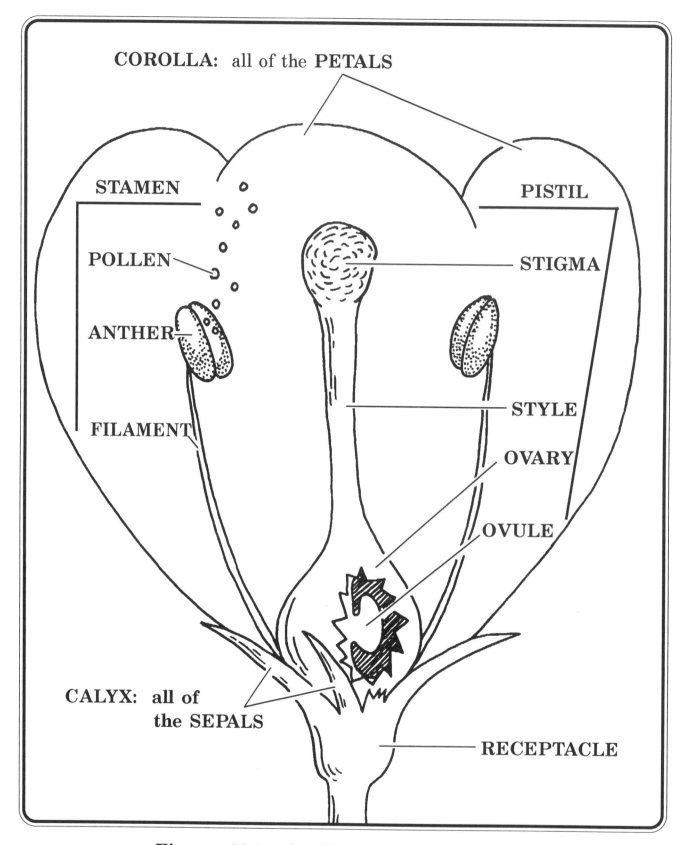

Figure 23-9 A COMPLETE FLOWER

This generalized flower has all the parts found in flowers and is called complete.
A flower with only the male parts is incomplete and is called a staminate flower.
A flower with only female parts is also incomplete and is called a pistilate flower.

Fertilization

It is only after pollination that fertilization can occur. FERTILIZATION is the process of fusion between two gametes. Fertilization is the most important part of sexual reproduction. At the moment of fertilization a new combination of DNA (chromosomes), for that species, is produced. A new, unique organism is formed.

In order for fertilization to occur in a flower the pollen grains stuck on the sticky stigma must grow down through the style. The pollen tube grows right through the ovule and into the ovary. When the sperm and egg nuclei join together, fertilization occurs and a new plant's life begins. That single cell formed during fertilization is the ZYGOTE. Even though it may be in a white flower the zygote could produce pink flowers when it matures. In other words, sexual reproduction has allowed gene variation. Because half the chemical instructions in the zygote came from the sperm in the pollen, the other half from the egg, the zygote is an individual!

The zygote will grow into an EMBRYO, or tiny organism. The ovary develops into the cotyledons and seed coat. The ovule becomes the fruit.

Seed Dispersal

The seeds inside the fruits of angiosperms and on the cones of gymnosperms are spread in several ways. The shape of a seed is related to its method of SEED DISPERSAL. Figure 23-11 illustrates seed shapes and agents of dispersal.

Germination

The tiny new plant inside its seed is alive but not actively growing. When the water and temperature become just right GERMINATION occurs. The seed swells, the seed coat splits open and the embryo uses the food in the cotyledons to grow vigorously. If it is on a fertile spot the embryo will take root and grow into a mature plant. Eventually it will produce flowers and the circle of life can begin again (See Figure 23-12 at right).

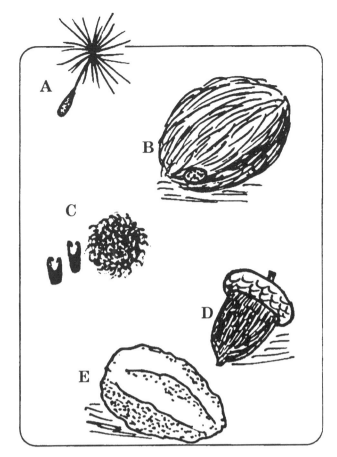

Figure 23-11 SEED DISPERSAL

Seeds with wings or parachutes (A) are spread by wind. The coconut (B) is designed to float on water. Some seeds (C) stick to animals. Others (D) are used by animals for food and are carried away and buried. Even gravity can pull fruits and nuts (E) downhill and thus spread that kind of plant.

Figure 23-12 GERMINATION
(See below)

Seeds will germinate if the environmental conditions are right for that species of seed.

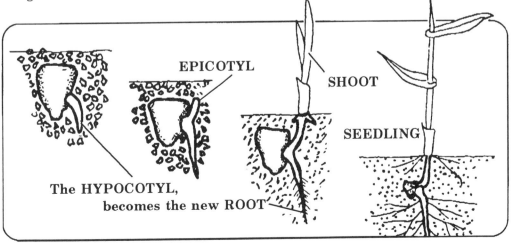

CHAPTER 23 REVIEW

OBJECTIVES:

1. **List five types of plant responses to their environment.**

2. **Know four types of asexual reproduction.**

3. **Diagram a flower.**

4. **Understand the processes involved in plant reproduction.**

PART I. List five different plant tropisms and the meaning of the root word in each term.

PART II. Write each statement below neatly. In the margin in front of each, identify the type of asexual reproduction with a:

B, F, S or V.

B = **B**udding   F = **B**inary **F**ission

S = **S**porulation   V = **V**egetative Propagation.

1. An ameba splits into two.

2. A large hydra forms a tiny hydra on its side.

3. A mushroom forms a cap.

4. Potato skins grow shoots and roots.

5. A yeast cell forms a tiny cell on the side.

6. Onions are planted from bulbs.

7. A seedless orange tree branch is grafted onto a normal orange tree.

8. A major method of reproduction for bacteria.

9. Horizontal shoots from strawberry plants take root.

10. Ferns form sori on the undersides of the fronds.

PART III. Diagram and label a complete flower.

PART IV. Define the 26 Keywords in Chapter 23 Plant Response and Reproduction.

PART V. Neatly write each sentence using one of the Keywords from Part IV to fill in the blanks. Use each Keyword only once.

1. Plants have __?__ which cause different cells to grow different amounts.
2. Due to the __?__ of a willow tree's roots the sewer pipe was clogged.
3. A small tree grows out from under a dark porch because of __?__.
4. Many algae reproduce by __?__, simply dividing into two.
5. Budding is a form of __?__ involving only one parent.
6. Grafting, layering and cuttings are all methods of __?__.
7. The __?__ of a flower attracts pollinators.
8. The filament and anther are parts of the __?__.
9. The __?__ is all the female parts of a flower.
10. Flowers are special organs for __?__ in which two cells unite.
11. The egg and sperm may be called __?__.
12. When the egg and sperm unite they form a __?__.
13. __?__ is when the pollen from one flower reaches the stigma of another.
14. Maple seeds have wings for __?__ by the wind.
15. If conditions are right __?__ occurs and the embryo grows into a mature plant.

PART VI. Neatly write the following terms in the correct order, start with "egg cell forms":

dispersal,   fertilization,   germination, pollination,   sperm forms,   zygote grows.

PART VII. Write a short paragraph explaining the major difference between asexual and sexual types of reproduction. Give at least one advantage of each type.

PART VIII. Write a report on the Shasta daisy. Include the name and nationality of the scientist who developed it; its scientific name and whether the Shasta daisy is a complete or incomplete flower.

CHAPTER 24 - ANIMAL BEHAVIOR

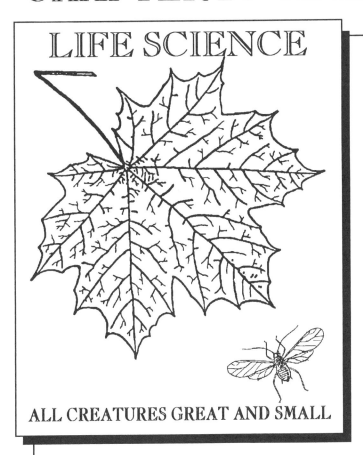

LIFE SCIENCE

ALL CREATURES GREAT AND SMALL

DOWN

1. Acronym for the stages of mitosis.

2. The female gamete.

3. Action of a muscle or gland.

4. Normal cell division.

6. Female organ that makes egg cells.

8. A reflex that involves the brain.

9. Type of reflex not requiring the brain.

11. Using learning to solve problems.

13. Special reproductive cells.

14. The male reproductive cell.

15. Using experiences to change responses.

16. The male gonads.

Animal Behavior Crossword Puzzle

Use the keywords from this chapter to fill in the puzzle.
See how many you know before reading the chapter!
Complete the puzzle after completing this chapter.

ACROSS

5. The study of how traits are passed on to the next generation.

7. A built in series of actions directed toward a single result.

10. Genes for 1 trait are the same.

11. Growing again a missing part.

12. Exchange of nuclear material.

14. A thing that activates neurons.

17. Special reduction cell division.

18. Two different genes for 1 trait.

Write in this book only if it belongs to you.
You may wish to make a copy of this page.

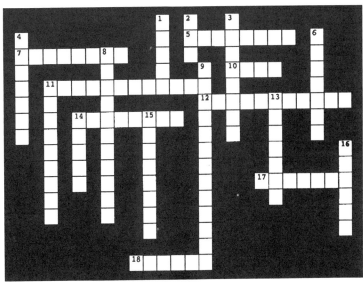

CHAPTER 24
ANIMAL BEHAVIOR
AND REPRODUCTION

BEHAVIOR

Much of the behavior exhibited by animals is built into the programming of their neurons before they are born. The simplest responses don't even require the brain.

This is reflected in the expression "to run around like a chicken with its head cut off". To stand, many movements, and scratchting are all actions that animals can carry out even if their brain has been destroyed. These relatively simple responses are centered in the spinal cord.

You also respond to certain situations, with the brain only learning about your response afterward. Pulling your finger away from a hot pot of potatoes is one of these quick responses. The human knee jerk is another example of a reflex.

There is another expression that someone reacts "in typical knee jerk fashion." This means that the person does not think about his or her response. For example, the instructor says "For homework tonight..." and immediately some students respond in "knee jerk fashion" with a groan. The real knee jerk response when the doctor strikes just below the knee cap is a reflex. The groaning is a more complex behavior.

Reflexes

Most simple reflexes are designed to protect the organism. When a girl in bare feet steps on a hot coal near a campfire, the pain receptors in her skin send a message along the sensory neuron to the spinal cord. The associative neurons in the spinal cord send out an impulse on a motor neuron that tells the muscles to move the foot, and do it fast! See Figure 24-1. The associative neurons also send impulses up the spinal cord so that the brain knows what has happened.

All this action takes just a fraction of a second. The hot coal in our example was the STIMULUS that initiated the reflex arc. Quickly pulling away the foot is the RESPONSE. This simple, quick response that does not require the brain is an UNCONDITIONED REFLEX (Figure 24-1).

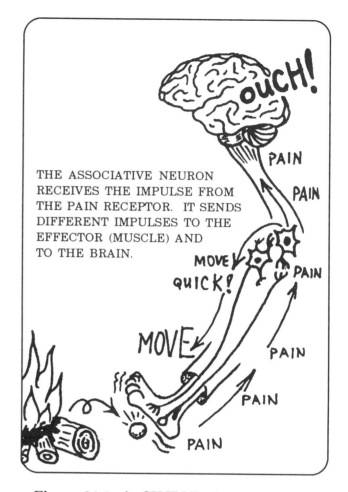

THE ASSOCIATIVE NEURON RECEIVES THE IMPULSE FROM THE PAIN RECEPTOR. IT SENDS DIFFERENT IMPULSES TO THE EFFECTOR (MUSCLE) AND TO THE BRAIN.

Figure 24-1 A SIMPLE REFLEX ARC

The stimulus causes an impulse that triggers an immediate response from the associative neurons in the spinal cord, without involving the brain. A reflex arc saves time when an organism responds to a stimulus.

A CONDITIONED REFLEX is a quick response to a stimulus but this reflex involves the brain. Our first understandings of reflexes came from work done by a Russian scientist, Ivan Pavlov (Figure 24-2). The normal secretion of saliva when food touches the tongue is a simple reflex. But Pavlov's dogs heard a bell each time they ate. After a short time, Pavlov could get the dogs to salivate just by ringing the bell! That is an example of a conditioned reflex.

People practice a musical instrument or a sport so that they build up a series of conditioned reflexes that allow quick responses to certain stimuli. Most students have played "Simon Says" in which the participant loses if he or she becomes conditioned to follow the leader's actions instead of doing what "Simon Says!"

Figure 24-2 PAVLOV'S DOG

Ivan Pavlov, surrounded by some students, is shown with one of the dogs from his classic conditioned reflexes experiment.

Instincts

Many built-in actions that animals carry out are a series of movements directed toward a specific end. When a robin builds its nest (see Figure 11-16 in chapter 11), it builds the same kind of nest that other robins build. Even if the bird under scrutiny never saw another robin build a nest, it still builds the same kind of nest! Such a series of built-in actions directed toward a specific end is called an INSTINCT. Instincts are what cause some birds to migrate, and some animals to hibernate. They even cause some people to respond to emergencies and help others.

Learning

Learning is a complex behavior just as instincts are. However, in LEARNING, past experience causes an organism to adjust its reponses to a stimulus. Fertile chicken eggs normally hatch in 21 days. A hen's instinct is to sit on the eggs in her nest to keep them at 39 ºC (just over 101 ºF) for that time period. If the eggs are removed the hen will often keep sitting on the

learn. Her instincts cause her to keep the empty nest warm even though her actions are no longer appropriate. Animals can learn to control instincts but it is in humans that learning is most important.

Learning takes many forms. It always involves basing future responses on past experiences. That is why learning is so important to a young person. The experiences and information learned in school will determine later responses. Experiments done in science class (Figure 24-3) give an alert student the opportunity to experience science in action. There is no better way to learn!

Figure 24-3

LEARNING

The student is carrying out a guided experiment that will add to his life's experiences. Learning will happen whenever a person changes his or her actions based on the sum total of past experiences. Learning makes life richer.

Learning about drug addiction does not require experimentation. Many who start don't stop until an overdose, AIDS, or a drug related accident stops them dead! However, those who have experienced addiction can explain the depression and horrors of getting "hooked" on drugs like alcohol. We can learn through others by listening and observing. We can learn through the experiences of others by reading and studying.

Reasoning

The highest type of thought related behavior is REASONING. Homo sapiens, - that's you and I, are supposed to be the best creatures at reasoning. Reasoning is using learning to solve a totally new problem. In order to reason one must have learned and remembered many previous experiences. In addition, the brain must then correlate, that is, put together, experiences. It must project any possible outcomes and devise a solution to the problem at hand. It seems reasonable to say that those pupils who learn their work today will be better able to solve the problems of life tomorrow, through the process of reasoning.

REPRODUCTION

Some of the animals, starfish and planaria (Fig. 11-4 in chapter 11) for example, are able to reproduce asexually through REGENERATION. Hydra, one of the coelenterates (Figure 11-3 in chapter 11) reproduces asexually by budding. However most animals, including the three listed above, reproduce sexually at sometime in their life cycle. You should recall from the previous chapter that sexual reproduction requires the joining of two cells to form a new combination of DNA. Because of sexual reproduction you are similar in many ways to each of your parents. But also because of sexual reproduction you are not exactly like either parent.

Inheritance

GENETICS, the study of how traits are passed on from one generation to the next was discovered in the 1800's to follow mathematical rules.

A Roman Catholic monk, Gregor Mendel is considered the "father of modern genetics." Mendel the monk lived in a monastery, Mendel the scientist spent years carefully noting down the traits of pea plants in the monastry garden. Mendel's Laws of heredity are accepted today as correct (Fig. 24-5).

Figure 24-4 GREGOR MENDEL

While growing peas in a monastery garden, Gregor Mendel discovered the mathematical rules of inheritance.

1. LAW OF DOMINANCE

One characteristic, called DOMINANT, can mask or cover another, which is RECESSIVE. In a hybrid offspring only the dominant character is visible.

2. LAW OF SEGREGATION

When two hybrid organisms are crossed the characteristics are sorted, some of the offspring will show the recessive trait.

Figure 24-5 MENDEL'S LAWS

In simple genetics problems, it is now possible to predict in percentages what kind of offspring there will be. For example, brown eyes are dominate over blue eyes. A brown eyed man could be PURE with the chromosomes from both of his parents calling for brown eyes. His wife could be HYBRID for brown eyes. She would have one chromosome that calls for brown but the other chromosome would have the instructions for blue eyes. Because the gene for brown is dominant, she has brown eyes. This is an example of the Law of Dominance. A Punnett square is used to determine what kind of offspring these parents could have:

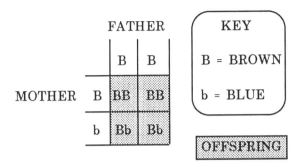

Because of dominance none of their children could have blue eyes. What would be the result if a hybrid man (brown eyes but carrying the gene for blue) married a hybrid woman? The father would have genes like this: **B b** ; and the mother's genes for eye color would also be: **B b**.

As we already stated: **sexual reproduction is the process that allows variation in a species, but also makes each offspring similar to its parents.**

Conjugation

A simple form of sexual reproduction is called CONJUGATION. In conjugation only some of the nuclear material in a cell is exchanged with another cell. The product is a single cell with a unique DNA complement, the zygote. In chapter 9 we classified one group of fungi, the zygomycota, just because they carry out conjugation and form zygotes. The name zygomycota means "zygote fungi." In chapter 10, Figure 10-4, conjugation by spirogyra is shown in the life cycle.

Now you must remember back to Chapter 8 - Protists, and what a paramecium looks like! What special feature did the paramecium have that the ameba and euglena did not? If necessary look back at Figure 8-6 in chapter 8. A paramecium has two nuclei! The macronucleus controls cell activities, as in other cells. The micronucleus is used by the paramecium to reproduce sexually by conjugation. Two paramecia line up side by side and exchange their micronuclei. A new combination of DNA is then made possible.

Fertilization

Fertilization is when a smaller motile SPERM cell fuses with a larger, nonmotile EGG cell. The egg is larger because it contains stored food for the new organism if fertilization occurs. In Chapter 21, The Endocrine System, it was explained that the male gonads are called the testes. The TESTES are the organs that produce sperm cells. OVARIES are the organs that contain and release egg cells. In plants the sperm cells are inside the pollen grains on the anther. The egg cells are in the ovary inside the ovule.

Some animals, as we discussed in chapter 11, have both testes and ovaries. The earthworm and hydra, for example, are hermaphroditic. Normally hermaphroditic animals cannot or do not fertilize themselves. The gonads mature at different times or are located so that the organism must fertilize another member of its own species. In many flowers, anthers and ovules mature at different times thus preventing self fertilization.

The sperm and egg cells are called GAMETES. This special name is because they only have half the usual number of chromosomes. Inside the testes and the ovaries a special kind of cell division, MEIOSIS, reduces the number of chromosomes. In a human muscle cell, or nerve cell, or skin cell, there are 46 chromosomes in the nucleus. In the nuclei of the gametes inside a human's gonads there are only 23 chromosomes. If fertilization occurs the male and female gametes join together. The unborn baby will have 46 chromosomes in each of his or her nuclei, 23 from one parent and 23 from his or her other parent. Species of creatures, great and small, each have a definite number of chromosomes, and half that number in their gametes.

In most fish and amphibians fertilization takes place externally in the water. Reptiles and birds lay eggs that were fertilized inside the female's body. In most mammals fertilization takes place in the fallopian tubes inside the mother. These are tubes that connect the ovaries to the uterus.

In humans, anytime two people have sexual intercourse there is the possibility of a new life beginning. That new life requires care, nurturing and attention if it is to grow and flourish. The lower vertebrates give almost no attention to their many offspring but the birds and mammals are characterized by their care of the young. Parenting is so important the United States has days for celebrating motherhood and fatherhood!

Growth

Once the egg is fertilized only food and time are required for the new person to grow and change through the continuum of life. The zygote becomes a blastula, then an embryo, fetus, newborn, infant, toddler, child, adult and senior citizen (Figure 24-6 and 24-7).

The most amazing growth occurs before birth. Appendix VIII outlines some of the significant events in the growth of a new person. Our understanding of how life begins was firmly established by Dr. Albert Liley, the "father of fetology". Dr. Liley did the first ever blood transfusion on an unborn baby.

For that single celled zygote to look like you it had to grow, just as you are growing now. Regular cell division, or MITOSIS, produces new cells. Each new cell has copies of the 46 chromosomes that were in the zygote. Figure 24-8 illustrates the process of cell division in all parts of the body. All parts except the gonads where meiosis reduces the chromosome number of the gametes.

To help remember the stages of mitosis use the word **IPMAT**.

Figure 24-7 INFANT

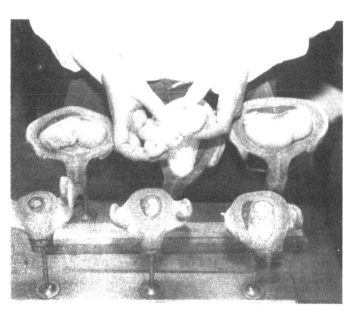

Figure 24-6 HUMAN LIFE

These scientifically accurate models show several of the stages in a human life. Beginning at the moment of conception the life functions are in clear evidence. Overcoming disease and avoiding accidents or purposeful destruction the new and unique person will mature through the rest of the stages of life and will reach old age.

Each person, great and small, was once an infant needing a mother's nurturing and care. Life is amazing and precious at every stage of development.

I: Interphase contains the word inter. Inter means "between" and interphase is when the cell is between divisions. During interphase the cell is working on growing larger, but, not dividing.
P: Prophase contains the prefix "pro-". Pro- often means first. What must happen first if a cell is to divide? First the chromosomes have to make a copy of themselves and the nuclear membrane must dissolve.
M: Metaphase begins with "M" for middle. The chromosomes and their newly made copies line up in the middle of the cell.
A: Anaphase begins with "a" for apart. The chromosomes move apart to each side of the cell.
T: Telophase begins with "t" for two. The cell with one set of chromosomes on each side divides into two. When mitosis is complete there are two cells with the normal number of chromosomes. Thousands of cells undergo mitosis daily in the human body.

The cytoplasm and organelles are also divided up between the two new daughter cells.

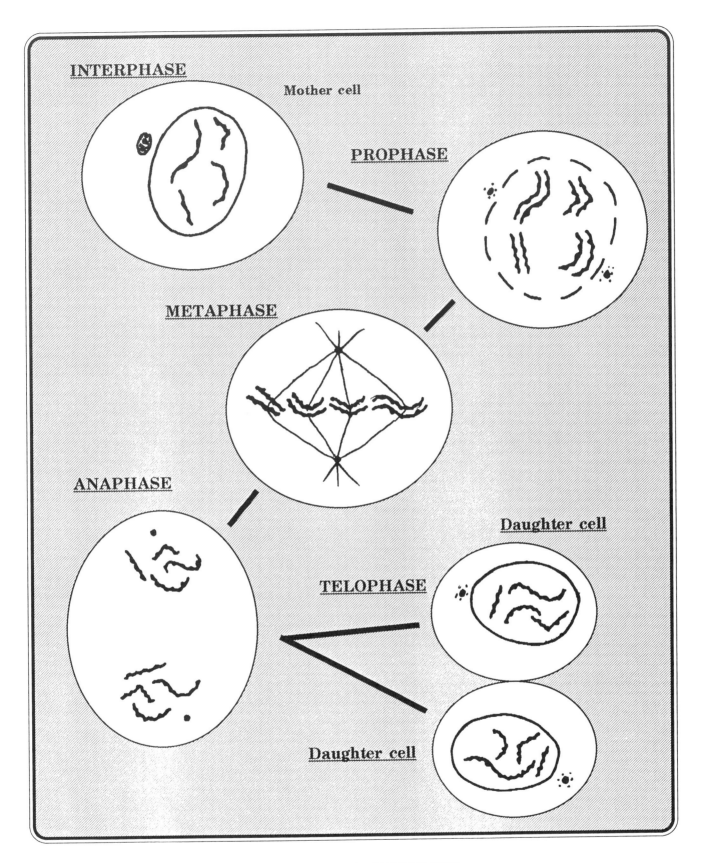

Figure 24-8 MITOSIS

The process of mitosis results in two daughter cells both of which contain the same set of the cell's instructions in the DNA of the chromosomes.

165

CHAPTER 24 REVIEW

OBJECTIVES:

1. Differentiate between four general kinds of behavior.

2. Understand a reflex arc.

3. Know Mendel's Laws of heredity.

4. Understand the process of fertilization.

5. List the stages of mitosis.

PART I. Define the 20 Keywords from Chapter 24 Animal Behavior and Reproduction.

PART II. Write each statement then identify which type of behavior is most closely associated with it. Write the appropriate letter in the margin in front of each statement.

C = Conditioned reflex
I = Instinct
L = Learning
R = Reasoning
U = Unconditioned reflex

1. A girl sits on a thorn and quickly jumps.
2. An oriole builds a hanging sack like nest.
3. Washing your hands often after learning how germs are spread.
4. After having detention a student no longer chews gum in class.
5. A frog estivates as its pond dries up during late summer.
6. Pavlov's dogs.
7. Playing Simon Says.
8. Solving a math problem.
9. Reading a book.
10. Honey bees building a honey comb.

PART III. Write a short paragraph explaining how a simple reflex occurs. Use these terms:

Associative Neuron	Response
Axon	Sensory Neuron
Effector	Spinal Cord
Motor Neuron	Stimulus
Receptor	Unconditioned Reflex

PART IV. Write a short report on the "father of genetics". Include the five W's: who, what, when, where, and why this person is important.

PART V. Write the following terms in order. Begin with the fertilized egg: adult, baby, blastula, child, embryo, fetus, zygote.

PART VI. Draw a labelled diagram of the five stages of mitosis. Show 3 chromosomes with different shapes in your initial cell.

PART VII. Neatly write each sentence filling in using one of the Keywords from PART I.

1. Pulling the hand away from a hot pan is an example of an __?__.
2. A moth builds its cocoon by __?__.
3. The __?__ for Pavlov's dogs to begin salivating was a bell.
4. __?__ from your mistakes is important.
5. A __?__ is any cell with only one half the normal number of chromosomes.
6. The __?__ cell is produced in the testes.
7. The __?__ cell is the larger gamete because it contains stored food.
8. A flower with both chromosomes for white blossoms is called __?__.
9. A person with brown eyes who also has the trait for blue eyes is a __?__.
10. By __?__ the one cell you once were has grown into billions of cells.

PART VIII. Draw a time line using Appendix VIII for your data.
1. Put the beginning of life at fertilization on the left side of a sheet of paper.
2. The sheet must be turned so that the longest of its dimensions is sideways.
3. Use one centimeter = 14 days. Change each time given in Appendix VIII into days. Note that one week = seven days. Use a ratio to change the number of days into cm.
   For example: ? cm = 21 days for our scale?
   $$\frac{1 \text{ cm}}{14 \text{ days}} = \frac{X}{21 \text{ days}}$$
   then cross multiply. Get help if needed!
4. Measure out and label the significant events in a new life.
5. End with birth on the right hand side of the sheet at 20 cm from the beginning.

CHAPTER 25 - ECOLOGY

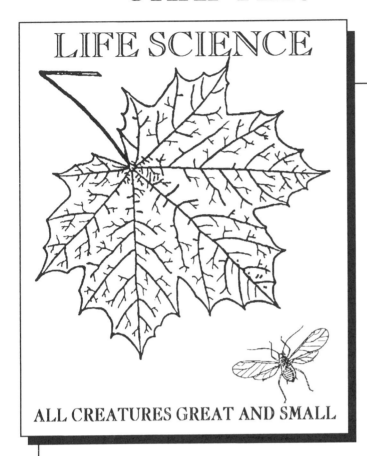

LIFE SCIENCE

ALL CREATURES GREAT AND SMALL

DOWN

1. The place where an organism lives.

2. A community of organisms and the abiotic factors they need.

3. Organisms that break down the molecules in dead organisms.

5. Organisms that eat consumers.

7. Living.

11. The study of natural relationships.

Ecology Crossword Puzzle

Use the keywords from this chapter to fill in the puzzle.
See how many you know before reading the chapter!
Complete the puzzle after completing this chapter.

ACROSS

4. Organisms that eat producers.

6. Nonliving.

8. Several of these, connected together, make a foodweb.

9. The "occupation" of an organism in the community.

10. Large ecosystems related to the climate of an area.

12. Green plants.

13. Many interlinked food chains.

CHAPTER 25 ECOLOGY
Use and Reuse

Longfellow's "Little Hiawatha" goes out into the forest to kill his first buck. As he stalks his deer the rabbits, birds and squirrels run out of the way. The "deer with antlers," feeding and drinking near a stream, senses danger. Instinctively it leaps, but Hiawatha's arrow sails true and the deer falls dead. Back at the Indian village old Nokokomis, the grandmother, makes a feast of the deer meat and a cloak from its hide. The bones of the deer are used to make needles, handles and ornaments.

Our "Average Adam" goes out into the stores on his first shopping trip alone. As he browses the air conditioners, electric lights and escalators run all day. The pizza vendor instinctively calls out to the average boy. Adam orders a large soda and two slices. Then he buys some things for his cousin. Back at the house Haphazard Harriet "munches out" on the artificially sweetened gum and tries on her new shorts. Shorts produced with fibers manufactured from oil. The plastic wrappers and paper bags go into the garbage.

A tremendous change has occured during the last two hundred years. A life in tune with nature was the normal way of life. For most of us that type of life style is gone. There is no going back. Of course we wouldn't want to go back to when you and your classmates would die or be disfigured by infectious diseases that today are rare. We wouldn't want to go back to when foods could not be easily preserved or transported. Nor would most of us want to go back to the outhouse on a cold winter's night! On the other hand Harriet should want streams clean enough to drink from. Adam should be able to walk down paths "flecked with leafy light and shadow".

Humans are interrelated with all creatures, great and small, and with the nonliving parts of the environment. Our habits and actions affect the BIOTIC and ABIOTIC things with which we share the earth. ECOLOGY is the study of the relationships between things.

Energy

The source of energy for almost every living thing is ultimately the sun. The human body is actually solar powered. Energy pours onto the earth everyday from the sun. Green plants, called PRODUCERS, use a small part of that energy to make food. Much of the energy is lost back to space or used as heat to power the weather. As animals, PRIMARY CONSUMERS, eat the green plants even more energy is lost. As other animals called SECONDARY CONSUMERS ingest the primary consumers even more energy is lost. Because the energy is less at each step there must be more producers than primary consumers. There must be even fewer secondary consumers. This fact is shown by the pyramid in Figure 25-1.

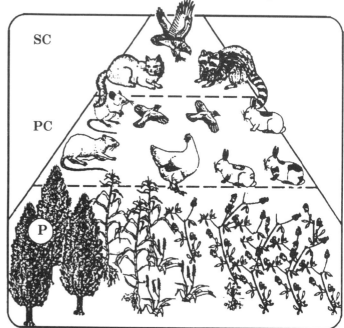

Figure 25-1 A FOOD PYRAMID
Energy is lost at each step. The secondary consumers (SC) at the top are limited by the number of primary consumers (PC). The consumers are limited by the mass of producers (P) at the bottom of the energy pyramid.

Cycles

The energy from the sun is on a one way trip. Energy is not reused. But the elements on earth are used and reused many times over.

Imagine if an atom could tell us where its been! The carbon atoms in the man made fibers of your clothes came from oil that millions of years ago was plants. Figures 25-2, 25-3 and 25-4 illustrate 3 of the most important cycles. The basic idea of cycles is one that humans must apply. The things we make and use must be recycled eventually. In nature DECOMPOSERS recycle nutrients and the elements. We explained in the fungi chapter that life can not go on without decomposers.

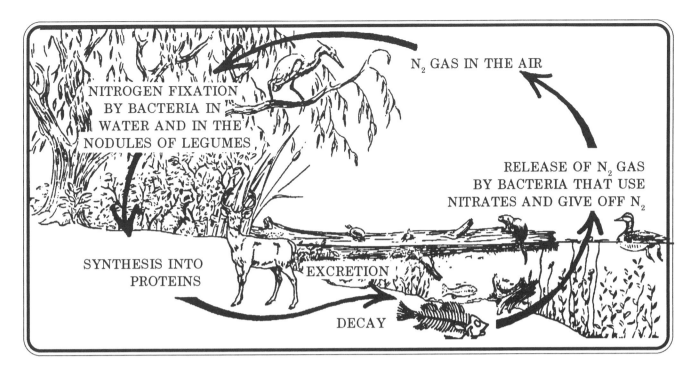

Figure 25-2 THE NITROGEN CYCLE

Nitrogen is in the proteins of living things. When the proteins are digested nitrogen wastes are produced. The wastes are decomposed and the nitrogen fixed into living things again.

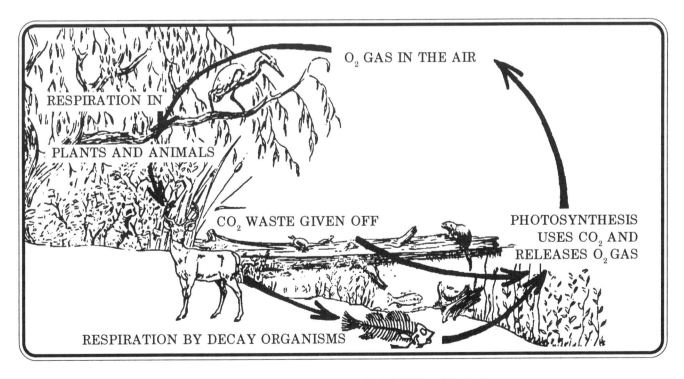

Figure 25-3 THE OXYGEN CYCLE

The process of respiration combines oxygen into water and carbon dioxide. This provides living bodies with energy. Photosynthesis releases the oxygen in water by using sunlight.

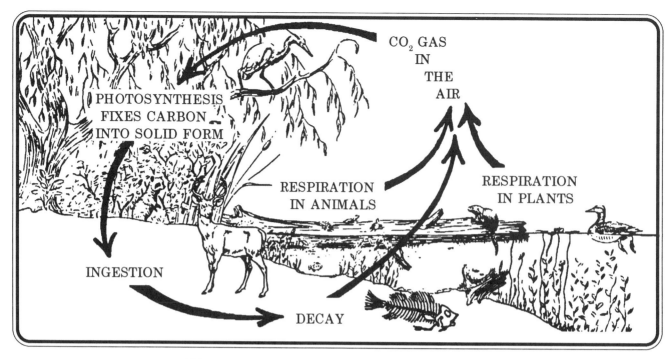

Figure 25-4 THE CARBON CYCLE

The process of photosynthesis in green plants fixes carbon from CO_2 gas into glucose. Respiration in every living thing returns the carbon to the atmosphere.

Nitrogen is the most abundant element in the air. However, most organisms cannot use nitrogen directly as the gas, N_2. Recall one of the important contributions of monerans was fixing nitrogen. The nitrogen fixing bacteria live in the root nodules of legumes. An outstanding example of using scientific knowledge to understand relationships between organisms is the work of George Washington Carver (Figure 25-5).

Carver was born in 1864 to slave parents near Diamond, Missouri. He struggled to get an education (a lesson in itself!) and later to carry out numerous experiments. Carver tried to convince poor farmers of the post Civil War South, to grow peanuts, Arachis hypogpea. Why peanuts? Everybody in the South grew cotton or tobacco. Both of those crops deplete the soil, especially the nitrates. Each year the farmers' crops grew less and less.

What George Washington Carver knew was that peanuts are a legume. If peanuts are grown on a cotton field then next year's cotton will grow better. The reason is that bacteria in the nodules of the peanut plant's roots fix free nitrogen gas into nitrates. But farmers could only grow peanuts if someone would buy them. Carver developed not just ten or twenty or even one hundred, but actually hundreds of uses for peanuts and

sweet potatoes and soybeans (another legume). This one man who struggled to learn has made life better for all of us.

His understanding of the need to return to the soil what is being taken out is a common practice today. The idea of rotating crops is an accepted standard farming practice that helps put food in your mouth and mine.

Figure 25-5

GEORGE WASHINGTON CARVER

Without the opportunity for a free education, and against great odds, George Washington Carver learned and experimented. His understanding led to ecologically sound farming practices still used today.

Food Chains

In our brief discussion of energy we listed four categories of living things. They are: producers, primary consumers, secondary consumers and the decomposers. An example of related organisms in each category will demonstrate a FOOD CHAIN. The bald eagle, Haliaeetus leucocephalus, is America's national bird (see the photos inside the back cover). Because the bald eagle feeds on other animals it is a secondary consumer. The fish and small birds and mammals that the eagle eats are primary consumers and the plants eaten by the primary consumers are the producers (Fig. 25-6). A favorite food of the bald eagle shown in the foldout is the sockeye salmon, Oncorhynchus nerka. The sockeye salmon eats plankton and many other small marine organisms.

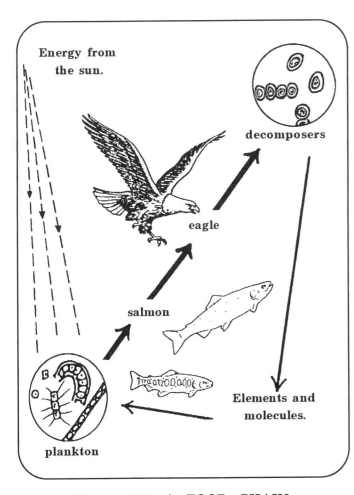

Figure 25-6 A FOOD CHAIN

Food chains always begin with green plants, the producers. Herbivores or omnivores eat the green plants. Then carnivores eat the herbivores. Finally the decomposers digest any of the others.

Actually a food chain simplifies the situation just a little too much. The plankton in Figure 25-6 may be eaten by any of numerous marine animals. The salmon, too, may be eaten by bears or people. If we try to draw a diagram that shows all the relationships, we would have a big web of lines connecting the organisms. A FOOD WEB is a group of food chains that are linked together.

Biomes

A HABITAT is the special place where an animal or plant lives. The bald eagle's habitat is a wild, remote forested area. Many organisms may also share the same habitat but in different niches. A NICHE is the occupation of an organism. A bald eagle's niche is secondary consumer.

Any habitat that includes all of the factors needed for it to continue in existence forms an ecosystem. The habitat is only one part of the larger ECOSYSTEM. An ecosystem can be as small as a fish tank or as big as a state. The earth's surface is divided into six very large ecosystems called biomes.

The BIOME that includes the bald eagle is the taiga. The **taiga** is the coniferous forest found near mountain tops and in the northern parts of North America, Europe and Asia. North of the taiga is a colder biome called the **tundra**. South of the taiga is the deciduous forest. Most of the eastern United States is a **deciduous forest** biome, this includes New York State.

In the foldout three other biomes are pictured. The golden eagle, Aquila chrysaetos, is shown in a **desert** biome. The bateleur eagle, Terathopius ecaudatus, feeds on snakes in a **grassland** biome. The Philippine eagle, Pithecophaga jefferyi, fills the secondary consumer niche in the hot **rain forest** biome. There are also various **fresh water** and **marine** biomes.

Because people have the ability to learn and to reason, human beings may be found in any of the biomes. Men and women can make clothing and shelters to keep themselves warm in the tundra. Medicines and buildings let people live in the swamps of rain forests. People live under the sea. Humans even live in outer space where no other living things have ever been found!

Mankind is different from other animals. People, you and I, have a special responsibility, a special niche, in the biosphere. The biosphere is just what its name means: the ball of life - that is, all the biomes of the earth taken together.

If we are to live up to our self appointed species name "sapiens", or wise ones, we must learn how to keep the relationships of the varied and complex biomes intact. A study of ecology points out that each organism affects all other parts of the one biosphere. Smog, acid rain and solid wastes are problems that strain the ecology of our habitats. They are problems we can solve.

Several decades ago the Hudson River, N.Y. was very polluted. Today with more people living in the Hudson River Valley, the River's waters are cleaner. There is still room for improvement but, with effort, we can make the changes necessary to put modern life in tune with nature.

The human foot print has as much right in the forest as the fox print or the deer track. But the fox and the deer are not named "sapiens". It is up to us, you and I, to conserve and manage the earth. An earth we share with all creatures great and small.

● ● ● ● ● ● ● ● ● ● ● ● ● ●

CHAPTER 25 REVIEW

OBJECTIVES

1. Understand the concept of food pyramid, food chain and food web.

2. Know three main material cycles.

3. List six biomes.

4. Appreciate the unique position of <u>Homo sapiens</u> in the biosphere.

PART I. Define the 13 Keywords in Chapter 25 - Ecology.

PART II. Write each statement below neatly. In the margin in front, identify the statement using: A = abiotic   B = biotic

1. A glass fish tank
2. Water in the aquarium
3. Amebas in the water
4. Gravel on the bottom
5. Elodea, a plant
6. A snail
7. A catfish
8. The filter
9. Tadpoles
10. A water beetle

PART III. Using a Keyword from Part I fill in. Write the sentence as your answer.

1. A bird eating a grasshopper that eats grass is an example of a __?__.
2. A cow's __?__ is that of a primary consumer.
3. N_2 gas is an __?__ factor in the environment.
4. Every food chain starts with __?__.
5. Herbivores may be the __?__ and eat plants.
6. The __?__ of the haircap moss is any moist shaded area in the forest.
7. All the plants, animals and nonliving factors in an area that go together is an __?__.
8. __?__ is the study of relationships.
9. The reason there are usually only a few eagles in an area is because eagles are __?__.
10. Cacti are producers in the desert __?__.

PART IV. Rearrange the following terms in order from smallest to largest: Biome, Habitat, Biosphere, Ecosystem, Organism.

PART V. For each set of organisms draw a food chain using arrows to show the direction of energy flow.

1. cow   grass   man
2. chicken   leafhopper   leaf
3. corn   mouse   snake
4. ants   apple   woodpecker
5. bass   spirogyra   tadpole

PART VI. Using the five food chains from Part V make one possible food web.

PART VII. Diagram and label the nitrogen cycle.

PART VIII. Diagram and label the oxygen cycle.

PART IX. Diagram and label the carbon cycle.

PART X. Make and complete a chart of the six biomes as shown:

BIOME	PLANT	ANIMAL
A. Tundra	Reindeer lichen	Caribou
B. __1__	__2__	__3__
C. __4__	__5__	__6__
D. __7__	__8__	__9__
E. __10__	__11__	__12__
F. __13__	__14__	__15__

PART XI. Write a report on George Washington Carver. Include the five W's: who, what, when, where and why he is important.

A Miniature Ecosystem

by Michael Andolina

For the naturalist it is a fascinating object of study. For the beginning or "armchair" ecologist it is a challenge. The alternative is a miniature ecosystem. This is a wholly self-sustaining, biologically balanced collection of natural elements which can be obtained from the nearest stream or pond. All you need is a net (mine was homemade) and a little luck. But *nothing artificial!*

Your nearby stream is teeming with life. If you are fortunate, you needn't go any farther to find an invaluable supply of materials for your new kind of fish collection.* The object of an ecosystem is to create a state of biological balance without the help of mechanical devices. No artificial pumps, food, or filters are necessary; just the right amount of sunlight, fish, plants, animals, temperature, and water are needed. Since your stream or pond itself is most probably in biological balance in its natural state, the best idea is to copy that model in your fish tank, but on a smaller scale. Let nature take care of the rest.

It is quite obvious that fish, as living organisms, require food and oxygen. So the first task is to insure an adequate supply of both. The key is the successful growth of plant-life in the tank. The plants will supply the oxygen to the fish through photosynthesis, and will be a source of food. Therefore, place your tank where it can receive adequate sunlight. Once the plants begin to grow, you can add the animal life. The fish (any arbitrary collection of minnows will do) give off carbon dioxide which the plants use in photosynthesis. If there are too many fish for the amount of plantlife, the fish will die from the resulting imbalance. A few plants will give enough oxygen for only a few fish. Don't overcrowd the tank. A ten gallon tank should not exceed ten fish, even in the most plentiful plant environment.

Now that the fish and plants are in oxygen and food balance, we need to deal with the waste and the cleaning of the tank. If you were fortunate in your pond sample, you may have caught some snails. These interesting little creatures will help clean the tank as they ingest tiny particles from the walls and floor of the tank. Remember, however, that they too must be considered as factors in the biological balance of the ecosystem. They too need the proper amounts of oxygen and food, so don't overcrowd the tank with snails.

Two more important factors in maintaining the success of the ecosystem are ph (acidity level) and temperature. As far as the ph factor is concerned, the only simple remedy is to periodically change the water and hope that your sample has a neutral ph value. Testing the water with litmus paper will indicate the acid and alkaline levels. The temperature level should be regulated to promote the growth of the plants. Of principal importance is maintaining the balance of the elements in the tank. If one element begins to dominate, the effects on the remaining elements will be immediately devastating.

If everything goes well, you will have a small aspect of nature's magic in your own home. Best assurance of success is an understanding of the interrelationships between organisms in the tank.

A. Materials: Ten gallon tank, clean water (from stream, pond, or well), clean soil, small sample of animal and plant life (including snails).

B. Method: Wash out tank to prevent undesirable bacteria. Bacteria are also important factors in maintaining balance. Certain strains of bacteria will aid in decomposing wastes and in supplying nitrogen necessary for plant growth, while others will directly attack and kill the fish. The safe way is to begin with a clean tank, clean water, and clean soil. It may be safe to assume that the water in the stream is clean. Of course if the stream has been tampered with by man, the balance may be upset. Part of the lesson of this experiment is to demonstrate the importance of the balance in a natural environment.

---

*Before removing anything from the water be sure to read Sections 272 and 273 of the New York State Fish and Game Law pertaining thereto.

JUNE-JULY, 1971
CON-37
This material excerpted from *The Conservationist*, the N.Y.S. Dept. of Environmental Conservation magazine.

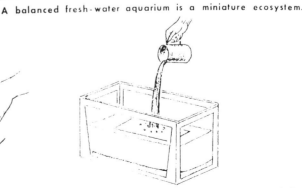

A balanced fresh-water aquarium is a miniature ecosystem.

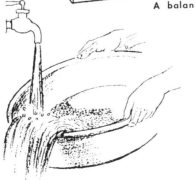

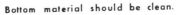

Bottom material should be clean.

Floating paper or cardboard helps prevent stirring of bottom material while tank is being filled.

APPENDIX I WORD ROOTS

ROOT WORD - MEANING	EXAMPLES
a or ab - not	abiotic, anaeobic
anti - against	antigen, antitoxin
aqua - water	aquarium, aquatic
audio - sound or hearing	auditory nerve
bi - two	binary fission, bilateral, biceps
bio - life	biology, biome, biosphere, biotic
cardiac - referring to the heart	cardiac muscle
cella - small room	cell, cellular
centi - 100	centimeter, century, cents
chromo - color	chromosome
cyano - dark blue	Cyanophyta
cyklos - circle	cyclosis, circular, cycle
deci - ten	decimeter, decimal, decade
derma - skin	epidermis, mesoderm
di - two	divide, dissect
epi - upon	epidermis
ex - out	exit, excretion, ectoderm
gastro - referring to stomach	gastric juice, gastrointestinal
geo - earth	geotropism, geography
glottis - tongue	glottis, epiglottis
grade - graduation or step	graduations, centigrade
in - in	inhale, ingest, inspiration
macro - big	macronucleus
marine - ocean	marine, submarine
meter - to measure	metric, meter, thermometer
micro - small	micro-organism, microscope
milli - 1000	millimeter, milliliter, mile
multi - many	multicellular
ology - the study of	biology, ornithology
photo - light	photosynthesis, phototropism
pulmo - referring to the lung	pulmonary circulation
re - to do again	reproduce, review
semi - partly	semipermeable
soma - body	chromosome
sub - under	submarine, subcutaneous
synthesis - to make	synthesis, photosynthesis
trans - across	transport, train
vaccinus - cow	vaccine, vaccination
video - see	vision, video

APPENDIX II MEASUREMENT

Mass (g)

The pan balance is used to measure mass in the units grams.
A mass of 1 gram is approximately the mass of a medium sized paper clip.
Do not confuse mass with weight.
Mass is the amount of matter present.
Weight is a measure of the force of gravity on a object.
1000 grams equals 1 kilogram which is approximately 2.2 pounds (on earth).

Distance (m)

The meter stick or centimeter ruler is used to measure distance in meters.
The centimeter is approximately as wide as the average pinky finger.
Centimeters are used to measure hand size things.
Kilometers are used to measure distances between cities.
Microns are used to measure microscopic size objects.
A micrometer is equal to 0.000001 meters.
2.5 centimeters are approximately equal to one inch.

Area (m²)

Area is measured in square meters by calculation: Area = length X width

Volume (l)

The graduated cylinder is used to measure liquid volume in liters.
The milliliter is approximately eight drops of water.
The volume of solid objects is measured with a centimeter ruler in cm³.
Volume is equal to length x width x height.
Volume is measured in cubic centimeters.
1 cc equals 1 ml of any liquid.

Temperature (°C)

The centigrade thermometer is used to measure temperature in degrees °C.
Room temperature is about 20 °C, human body temperature is 36.5 °C.
Do not confuse temperature with heat.
Temperature is how hot or cold something is compared to a standard.
The freezing point of pure water is 0.0 °C; boiling point is 100.0 °C (1 atm).
Centigrade refers to the 100 graduations from freezing to boiling.
This temperature scale is often called Celsius after its inventor, Andre Celsius.

Heat (cal)

A calorimeter is used to measure heat in the units calories.
A thermometer and calculations may also be used to determine heat.
Calories = mass in g X 1 cal / g-°C X change in temperature in °C.
The average junior high student needs approximately 2800 to 3000 cal/day.
Do not confuse heat with temperature.
Heat is a measure of the amount of energy available for transfer to another object (that is a measure of the kinetic energy of the molecules).

500 BC (approx.) Alcmaeon, a Greek physician from Croton in Italy dissects cadavers and notes the optic nerves, eustachian tubes and the brain.

450 BC (approx.) Empedocles a Greek in Sicily recognized the heart as the center of the system of blood vessels.

400 BC (approx.) Hippocrates of Cos becomes the "Father of Medicine" with his Hippocratic Oath which bans abortion and other acts of killing and calls on doctors to preserve life.

350 BC (approx.) Aristotle classifies 500 species of animals.

300 BC (approx.) Theophrastus a student of Aristotle describes over 550 plants.

100 BC (approx.) The Chinese idea of blood circulation is almost the same as our current idea

0 Christ is born.   **BC** = Before Christ.   **AD** = Anno Domini - "the year of our lord".

100 AD (approx.) The Chinese use dried chrysanthemums to kill insects. This is the first insecticide - pyrethrum .

300 AD (approx.) Chinese use ants to protect mandarin oranges. This is the first record of "biologic control".

541 AD Bubonic plague strikes Europe with roughly 10,000 people a day dying in Constantinople.

1250 (approx.) Albertus Magnus, from Germany advances biology by dissections.

1377 Quarantine is used to stem the new plague in Yugoslavia.

1520 Smallpox infects native Americans and Cortez (with natural immunity from childhood) conquers them.

1623 Gaspard Bauhin uses two names, one for genus and one for species (i.e. binomial nomenclature).

1628 William Harvey correctly figures out how the blood circulates.

1665 Robert Hooke views the cells in a slice of cork.

1668 Francesco Redi of Italy disproves the theory of spontaneous generation. His experiment with rotten meat is especially important because it includes a control.

1677 Anton van Leeuwenhoek a Dutch janitor discovers an invisible world full of thousands of microscopic creatures he calls "animalculae," we call them protists.

1735 Carolus Linnaeus, of Sweden publishes *Systemae Naturae*, or System of nature, in which he classifies and names thousands of plants and animals with the names we still use today.

1767 Lazzaro Spallanzani of Italy does a series of experiments to finally disprove spontanous generation and confirm Redi's results from 99 years before.

1774 Joseph Priestly, an Englishman, discovers oxygen. A German, Karl Wilhelm Scheele had discovered oxygen 2 years earlier but had not yet published his discovery.

1784 Henry Cavendish of England announces the composition of water.

1790 The Metric System is proposed in France.

1797 Edward Jenner uses cow pox as a vaccine against small pox.

1799 A mammoth is found frozen in Siberia in the USSR - perfectly preserved by the ice.

1803 Englishman John Dalton states his atomic theory.

1811 Jen Jakob Berzelius writes elements as symbols, using letters from their names.

1817 A pandemic (a big epidemic) of cholera spreads over Asia and part of Africa.

1818 Jean-Baptiste Dumas treats goiter with Iodine.

1822 William Beaumont studies digestion through a hole in a wounded man's stomach.

1827 John James Audubon begins printing his book *Birds of America*.

1831 Robert Brown discovers the nucleus of cells. There is a cholera epidemic in Europe.

1836 Theodor Schwann discovers pepsin, the first known animal enzyme.

1849 Luther Burbank develops the Burbank potato and the Shasta daisy.

1853 Pierre Roux figures out that the effects of diptheria are caused by a toxin produced by bacterium.

1856 Louis Pasteur determines that yeast causes fermentation.

1857 Gregor Mendel starts his pea plant experiments.

1864 George Washington Carver uses peanuts to restore poor soil.

1865 Joseph Lister uses a disinfectant in surgery thus saving many lives.

1866 Ernst Haeckel first uses the word ecology.

1876 Louis Pasteur explains anaerobic organisms.

1877 Robert Koch discovers the anthrax microbe and a way to grow pure cultures of bacteria.

1879 By accident, Pasteur discovers weakend bacteria do not cause cholera.

1881 Pasteur develops the first man-made vaccine.

1882 Robert Koch discovers the tuberculosis bacterium.

1883 Koch discovers <u>Cholera</u> <u>vibrio</u>, the cholera microbe, is spread by bad food and water.

1885 Pasteur makes the first rabies vaccine.

1890 Emil von Behring develops the tetanus and diptheria vaccines.
      Koch announces "a cure for tuberculosis".

1892 Tobacco mosaic disease is said to be caused by a virus, something too small to be seen under a light microscope.

1897 Ronald Ross figures out that malaria is carried by the <u>Anopheles</u> female mosquito.

1900 Walter Reed proves yellow fever is transmitted by the <u>Aedes</u> mosquito.

1902 Ivan Pavlov carries out conditioning experiments with dogs.

1909 Charles Nicolle discovers that typhus is transmitted by a body louse.

1912 Casmir Funk first uses the term vitamin.

1921 Alexander Fleming by accident discovers that lysozyme in mucus dissolves bacteria.

1922 Elmer McCollum discovers vitamin D in cod liver oil and uses it to treat rickets.

1928 Alexander Fleming discovers penicillin.

1931 Ernest Goodpasture uses eggs to grow viruses for vaccine production against polio, etc.

1932 Charles Glen King isolates vitamin C from lemons.

1933 Last Tasmania wolf dies.

1935 Gehard Domagk saves his daughter's life by using the first "drug" against infection.

1937 Hans Adolf Krebs figures out the cycle of oxidation in living cells.

1938 Tom D. Spies discovers the first antibiotics.

1943 Wilhelm Kolff makes the first artificial kidney.

1952 Polio epidemic in the United States.

1954 Jonas Salk uses his polio vaccine on millions of children.
      J. Hin Tjio and Albert Levin discover the correct number of human chromosomes is 46.

1961 Marshall Nirenberg figures out the first code of a gene on a chromosome.

1969 The first footprint of a living thing, American Neil Armstrong, is made on the moon.

An excellent reference for timetable information is:
The Timetable of Science, by Alexander Hellemans and Bryan Bunch, published by Simon and Shuster Co. New York, 1988.

APPENDIX IV LEAF KEY

This key is designed for use with **only** the 16 species on the key. The instructor must limit the samples to be keyed out to these 16 species. Small branch samples should be given with notes on bark, twigs and fruit.

READ BOTH DESCRIPTIONS AT A GIVEN STEP THEN GO TO THE NEXT STEP INDICATED.

1. A. Needle or scale like leaves _____ 2
   or
   B. Broad flat leaves _____ 6

2. A. Scale like leaves in flat branches _____ Northern white cedar.
   or
   B. Needle like leaves _____ 3

3. A. Needles bluish & sharp, pointed outward _____ Blue spruce (p.60).
   B. Needles green and/or soft to touch _____ 4

4. A. Needles over 3 cm long, in pairs; red orange bark _____ Red pine
   B. Needles short _____ 5

5. A. Twigs yellow, secondary branches point downward _____ Norway spruce
   B. Twigs brown, needles shiny green on top, 2 light lines on bottom _____ Balsam fir

6. A. Leaves compound _____ 7
   or
   B. Leaves simple _____ 10

7. A. Twigs and young stems hairy, horn shaped reddish fruit _____ Staghorn sumac
   B. Twigs and stem not hairy, fruit a nut or winged _____ 8

8. A. Leaves opposite, leaflets smooth edged, winged fruit _____ White ash
   or
   B. Leaves alternate, _____ and with finely toothed leaflets, nuts _____ 9

9. A. Leaflets feel velvety, most with a terminal leaflet, nuts longer than wide _____ Butternut
   or
   B. Leaflets not velvety, most without terminal leaflet, nuts almost round _____ Black walnut

10. A. Leaves entire _____ 11
    or
    B. Leaves lobed _____ 13
    or
    C. Some leaves entire, others lobed, edges toothed, has berries _____ White mulberry.

11. A. Long narrow leaves with fine toothed edge, orange hair on midrib of many _____ Black cherry (p.97)
    B. Leaves nearly as wide as long, no orange hair _____ 12

12 A. Leaves large, toothed, base often uneven _____ American basswood.
   or
   B. Leaves small (3-9 cm), single small round fruits _____ Hackberry (varieties).

13. A. Leaves opposite, _____ and lobes pointed _____ 14
    or
    B. Leaves alternate, lobes round _____ White oak.

14. A. Smooth between the points on the lobes _____ Sugar maple (cover).
    or
    B. Toothed between the points on the lobes _____ Red maple.

178

LIFE SCIENCE All Creatures Great And Small

Periodic Table of The Elements

In the periodic table the elements are arranged in order of increasing atomic number. Vertical columns headed by Arabic numerals are called *Groups*. A horizontal sequence of elements is called a *Period*. The most active elements are at the top right and bottom left of the table. The staggered line (Groups 13-17) roughly separates metallic from non-metallic elements.

Groups—Elements within a group have similar properties and contain the same number of electrons in their outside energy shell.
—The first group (1) includes hydrogen and the alkali metals.
—The last (18) contains the *inert gases*.
—Group 17 includes the *halogens*.
—The elements intervening between groups 2 and 13 are called *transition elements*.
—Short vertical columns without Arabic numeral headings are called *subgroups*.

Periods—in a given period the properties of the elements gradually pass from a strong metallic to a strong non-metallic nature, with the last number of a period being an inert gas.

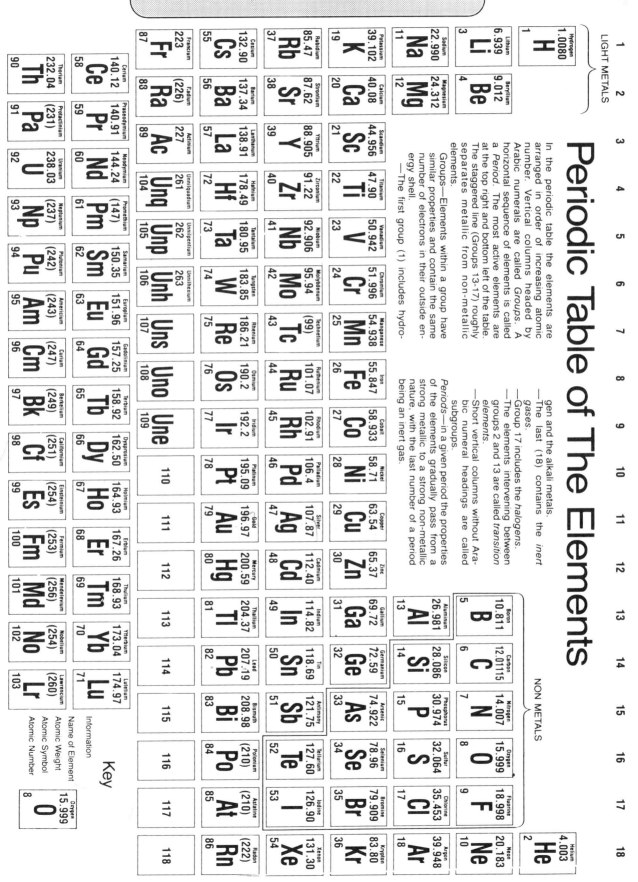

Key

Information

Name of Element — Oxygen
Atomic Weight — 15.999
Atomic Symbol — O
Atomic Number — 8

Food

Almonds
Apples
Apricots
Asparagus
Bananas
Beans
Beer
Beets
Birch beer
Blackberries
Blueberries
Bread
Cabbage
Cantalope
Carrots
Cashews
Cauliflower
Cassava
Celery
Cereals
Cherries
Cider
Cocoa
Coconut
Coffee
Corn
Crackers
Cucumbers
Dates
Doughnuts
Eggplant
Figs
Garlic
Grapefruit
Grapes
Honeydew melon
Jams
Lemons
Lettuce
Macaroni
Nectarine
Noodles

Oats
Olives
Onions
Oranges
Peaches
Peanuts
Pears
Peas
Pecans
Pepper
Peppers
Pie crust
Pineapple
Pistachio
Plums
Potato
Potato, Sweet
Prunes
Pumpkin
Raisin
Raspberries
Rhubarb
Rice
Rolls
Root beer
Rye
Sassafras
Soybean
Spaghetti
Spinach
Squash
Strawberries
Sugar beet
Sugar cane
Syrup
Tobacco
Tea
Tomatoes
Turnips
Vanilla
Walnuts
Watermelon
Wheat
Wine

Fiber

Cotton
Cotton balls
Pants
Shirts
Socks
Towels
Underwear
Flax (linen)
Paper
Books
Boxes
Cups
Dollars
Looseleaf
Napkins
Newspapers
Plates
Toilet paper
Wallpaper
Plastics
Boats
Car parts
Coats
Furniture
Gloves
Pens
Rayon
Skateboards
Surfboards
Toys
Helmets
Motorcycle parts

Wood

Baseball bats
Baskets
Beds
Boats
Cabinets
Chairs
Cutting boards

Decks
Desks
Doors
Houses
Lumber
Paneling
Pencils
Picture frames
Plywood
Skis
Straw
Tables
Wooden spoons

Other

Acetic acid
Acetone
Coal
Cork
Decorations
Ethanol
Firewood
Flowers
Formaldehyde
Gasoline
Glues
Gum
Natural gas
Oil
Oxygen
Propane
Rubber
Balls
Boots
Raincoats
Rubberbands
Sneaker soles
Tar
Tires
Tubing
Turpentine
Shade
Varnish

Science experiments are designed to solve a problem, to show relationships, or gather data for future research. The hypothesis is a suggested explanation for something that was observed. The hypothesis must be tested by a controlled experiment before it is accepted, rejected or modified.

A **controlled experiment** is made so that most variables are controlled, that is, kept the same. Variables are anything that varies, or change, and then cause a change in what is being studied. In a controlled experiment one variable is changed, this is called the **independent variable**. The variable that is being studied, and will change because the independent variable is changed, is the **dependent variable**. The dependent variable depends on what happens to the independent variable. Finally there must be a **control** where no variables are allowed to change.

For example, suppose we suspect that the starch in a cracker begins changing into simple sugars because we chew it up. Our hypothesis is that the teeth break the large starch molecules into the smaller sugar molecules. To control our experiment we will want to use the same sized test tubes cleaned with the same soap solution. We should use equal sized pieces of the same kind of crackers. All those variables must be controlled. The dependent variable will be the presence of simple sugars. We could test a chewed cracker for sugar as described in chapter 14. The test would be positive, that is simple sugar would be present. But we are not done! Maybe the test solution changes color whenever you heat it, with or without crackers. Our control would be to heat the solution without any crackers. That test would be negative.

Now can we conclude that the teeth break big starch molecules into smaller sugar molecules? Is there more to chewing than just the teeth? How about the saliva? We should chop up a cracker without saliva and test it for simple sugars. If that test is positive then our hypothesis appears correct. If the chopped up cracker without saliva is negative for simple sugar then the "teeth breaking up starch into sugar" hypothesis is incorrect.

Careful planning and plenty of thought are required for completion of successful experiments. Organization also helps. The format for writing up an experiment will ensure that your laboratory experiment reports are organized.

Laboratory Reports

Use the following eight part format to write up each experiment that you are required to carry out. In some instances not every part will be included. Always put a complete heading on the first page. All other pages should have your name and a page number. They should be arranged numerically and stapled together.

I. Title - a word or phrase about the topic.

II. Purpose - explains why the experiment is performed.

III. Materials - anything used up.

IV. Apparatus - equipment needed.

V. Procedure - step by step instructions.

VI. Data - charts, graphs, calculations, diagrams, etc.

VII. Questions - full sentences explaining ideas in the lab.

VIII. Conclusion - a brief statement that clearly indicates that the purpose of the experiment has been completed.

Graphing

Graphs are a way of showing data in a type of picture. When you draw a graph follow these steps:

1. Draw the horizontal axis about 2 cm up from the bottom edge of your graph paper. Horzontal means from side to side (———), like the horizon!

2. Draw the vertical axis about 2 cm from the left edge of your graph paper. Vertical means up and down (|).

3. Label the axes with numbers according to your data. For example: there are 25 spaces on the horizontal axis. The smallest piece of data is 3 and the biggest is 10. Divide the number of spaces by the largest piece of data: 25 / 10 = 2.5 spaces per unit of data. Use a number of spaces equal to or less than your answer to represent one unit of data. For the example, I would use two spaces for each number. Repeat for the vertical axis. Label both axes with a title and the units.

4. Plot the data with small Xs so that the center of the X is at the correct point on the graph.

5. Connect the points with a smooth curve of best fit.

6. Put a title on the graph. Put your name, date, subject and the page number or assignment on the heading.

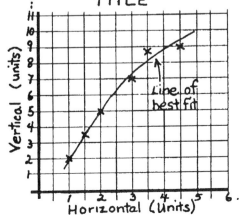

Day 1

You began when the sperm cell from your father met and united with the ovum (egg) cell from your mother. During fertilization, the two cells became a single cell. You are completely unique, not entirely like either of your parents or your ancestors. When conceived you were smaller than the period at the end of this sentence.

Week 1

The fertilized egg , you, journeys down the mother's fallopian tubes to enter the uterus (sometimes called the womb). By the end of seven days, the fertilized egg, which has grown at a rapid rate, is a cluster of cells and sinks into the spongy lining of the womb and implants itself, receiving nourishment from tiny blood vessels.

Week 2

Now you are firmly situated in the supplying goodness of your mother's womb, at about ten days you begin to send her signals that you are there. You begin to affect nearly all of your Mom's organs and tissues even though you and the balloon-like sac of waters which protects you are still smaller than the seed of an apple.

Week 3

Your heart began beating at three weeks. Your brain, backbone, spinal column, and nervous system are forming and the foundation for all the systems is carefully being established. Simple kidneys, a liver and the digestive tract are taking shape. The rapid growth of the backbone is what causes your tiny body to "curve" .

Week 4

By the end of four weeks, the month old embryo is ten thousand times larger than the fertilized egg, about the size of an apple seed. On your twenty-fourth day you had no arms or legs, but just two days later, tiny buds appeared for your arms and then your legs budded only two days after that! In just four weeks, you looked every bit like a tiny baby and even began to react and respond like one.

Month 2

The head of the embryo is now almost half its total size. Brain waves can be detected and recorded at forty days. Facial features including the nose, ears, lips, and tongue are forming. Near the end of this month the skeleton begins to change from cartilage to true bone. The jaws also form complete with milk teeth buds in the gums. Developing muscles work with the nervous system, and your body responds to touch, though your Mom won't feel movements till the fourth or fifth month. A miniature infant has now developed and grown to an inch in length. By eight weeks, all is formed and until adulthood the changes in body will be primarily in size.

Month 3

In your third month of life you grew to be more than two inches in length. You became more energetic, very graceful, like an astronaut floating and enjoying his gravity free space capsule. By the tenth week your fingers and toes were completely formed, complete with fingerprints and footprints which would never change except for size. Your entire body, except for nonfacial portions of the head, is sensitive to touch. You can feel pain from the sixth week on. Finger and toenails appear, and the genitals show a clear differentiation and already contain primitive egg or sperm cells. The vocal chords are completed and you would cry if you could at this age.

Month 4

This month is marked by rapid growth as you grow to ten inches in length and can weigh one-half pound or more. Your face takes on facial expressions similar to your parents, fine hair grows on the head and eyebrows and eyelashes appear. Some babies even start sucking their thumbs at this age!

Months 5 and 6

Now you, the unborn baby, had a wonderful experience! You heard and recognized your mothers voice! You are now very coordinated and sounds provoke energy reactions. You could survive with adequate care, if you were born now. Your lungs are well-developed and ready to preform.

Months 7-8-9

During the last three months before birth you tripled in weight to more than seven pounds and grew to twenty inches. You began to find your quarters very cramped. You developed a layer of fat beneath your skin, which began to look polished. You also developed antibodies which would protect you from disease. Your heart is now pumping three hundred gallons of blood a day! You are now ready to change your residence as you continue the life which began nine months ago, moving through childhood, adolescence, maturity, and old age.

APPENDIX IX Dendrology Handout For Students

See Chapter 3 for more info.

When collecting leaves, use this form. You will then have recorded the data needed to identify your samples. Simply circle the correct note for each characteristic, on copies of this page:

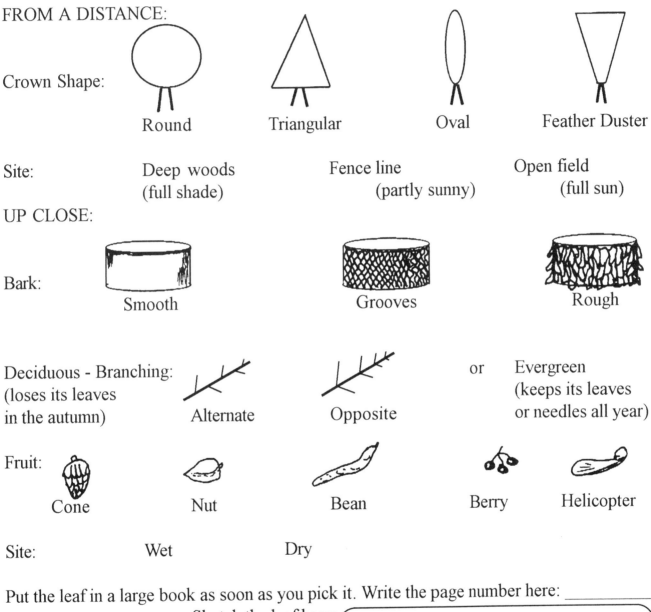

FROM A DISTANCE:

Crown Shape: Round   Triangular   Oval   Feather Duster

Site: Deep woods (full shade)   Fence line (partly sunny)   Open field (full sun)

UP CLOSE:

Bark: Smooth   Grooves   Rough

Deciduous - Branching: (loses its leaves in the autumn)   Alternate   Opposite   or   Evergreen (keeps its leaves or needles all year)

Fruit: Cone   Nut   Bean   Berry   Helicopter

Site: Wet   Dry

Put the leaf in a large book as soon as you pick it. Write the page number here: _____

Sketch the leaf here:

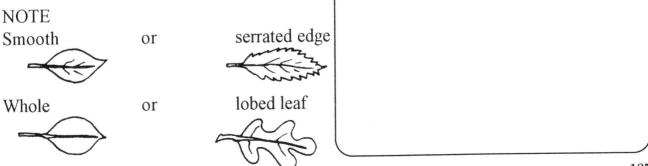

NOTE
Smooth   or   serrated edge

Whole   or   lobed leaf

Students of any age may benefit by collecting and studying insects. The following suggestions may help in making entomology a part of your activities.

NOTES:

1.   Jars and containers used for collecting insects should be plastic.

2.   Make your own insect cases from 1/2" styrofoam insulation board (from the local lumber yard) and food containers (the kind with a transparent top) from a take home salad bar, Chinese restaurant or deli.

3.   Make your own pinning blocks from 3 styrofoam coffee cups cut to the heights shown:

1.6 cm   2.2 cm   2.8 cm

4.   Soak a cotton ball with methyl acetate (or nail polisher remover) for use in the killing jar (clearly label the jar as a killing jar, even though methyl acetate is not considered highly toxic for humans). The killing jar should be glass and it should stay put in one place.

5.   Order size 3 insect pins (see sources listed below).

6.   To avoid pins with very young students, specimens may be glued. Glued collections are not the best, and the value of the specimens is reduced when they are glued instead of pinned.

7.   Labels should be as shown: 1.3 cm [ ] 2.5 cm   Top label: Town, State / Date / Collector
Lower label Family and/or Name of the insect / Identifier's name

8.   Problems to avoid:
     a. Regular straight pins rust and break off.
     b. Dermestid larvae, also known as Carpet beetle worms (Family Dermestidae) can ruin a beautiful collection. Keep the collection sealed tightly. Fumigate once or twice a year with a general household insecticide.
     c. As stated above, **do not use glass jars for collecting.**

Entomology materials may be purchased from many supply houses including:

Science Kit	Ward's	Frey
777 East Park Dr.	P.O. Box 92912	P.O. Box 8101
Tonawanda, NY, 14150-6782	Rochester, NY, 14692-9012	Mansfield, OH, 44901-8101
1-800-828-7777	1-800-962-2660	1-800-225-FREY

Resources for identification of insects include :

1. *Insects* and *Butterflies and Moths* (picture book) Golden Nature Guide, Golden Press
2. *The Insects* (for junior high) H. E. Jaques, Wm. C. Brown Co., Dubuque, Iowa
3. *A textbook of Entomology* (serious student) Herbert Ross, John Wiley & Sons, NY
4. *Eastern Forest Insects* (technical) USDA - Forest Service Misc. publication #1175

APPENDIX X A simplified key to Class Insecta

Many insects are not included in this key. After making a preliminary identification of the order for your specimen, you must use another reference to verify your conclusion. Some of the orders that have been omitted are: Strepsiptera, Trichoptera (caddis flies), Thysanoptera (thrips), Mecoptera (scorpion flies), Corrodentia (book lice), Mallophaga (bird lice), Anoplura (sucking lice), Siphonaptera (fleas), Thysanura (bristletails), Collembola (springtails) and others.

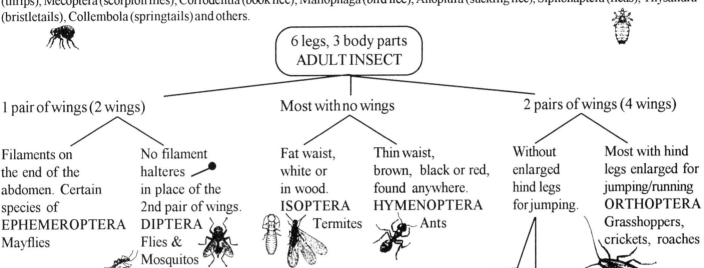

**6 legs, 3 body parts
ADULT INSECT**

1 pair of wings (2 wings)

Filaments on the end of the abdomen. Certain species of **EPHEMEROPTERA** Mayflies

No filament halteres in place of the 2nd pair of wings. **DIPTERA** Flies & Mosquitos

Most with no wings

Fat waist, white or in wood. **ISOPTERA** Termites

Thin waist, brown, black or red, found anywhere. **HYMENOPTERA** Ants

2 pairs of wings (4 wings)

Without enlarged hind legs for jumping.

Most with hind legs enlarged for jumping/running **ORTHOPTERA** Grasshoppers, crickets, roaches

---

Front wings hardened into wing covers (elytra)

With pincers on the abdomen **DERMAPTERA** Earwigs

Without pincers on the abdomen **COLEOPTERA** Beetles

Half of front wings leathery, triangular region (sclerite) on the back **HEMIPTERA**, the True bugs Back swimmer

Front and hind wings with similar texture

Wings mostly transparent

Wings usually large and covered with "scales" **LEPIDOPTERA** Butterflies and moths

Without the distinctive triangular region on the back

Developing from aquatic larvae
Adults usually near water

Antennae not apparent, wings membranous, abdomen without filaments **ODONATA** Dragonflies & damselflies

Antennae obvious, wings very delicate with or without filaments on the abdomen

2 or 3 long filaments on the abdomen **EPHEMEROPTERA** Mayflies

2 short filaments on the abdomen **PLECOPTERA** Stoneflies

No filaments on the abdomen **NEUROPTERA** Lacewings

Not developing from aquatic larvae
Adults often far from water

Usually thin waisted, most with stingers **HYMENOPTERA** Bees and wasps

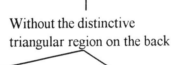

Thick waisted, wings at rest pitched like a roof **HOMOPTERA** Aphids, leafhoppers and cicadas

APPENDIX X continued: Build - A - Bug

See Chapter 3 for more information
Make a copy of this page to fill in the blanks.

In this project you will demonstrate that you are knowledgeable of the basic characteristics of insects. Technically, a "Bug" is only a small group of insects called Order Hemiptera. In colloquial jargon, however, bug means any insect.

Class Arachnida (spiders) is **not** part of Class Insecta. Spiders have more legs, but less body parts than insects. Fill in the chart below before you *Build - a - Bug:*

	INSECTA	*ARACHNIDA*
Number of body parts:	_____	_____
Number of legs:	_____	_____
Often have wings:	_____	_____
Many undergo complete metamorphosis.	_____	_____

To complete this project use items that are being discarded as trash, or are going to be recycled. You may also use pipe cleaners or string , glue, tape and paper.

Include a diagram of your *Build - a - Bug* labelled with a scientific name. Your *Build - a - Bug* may be a model of a real insect or a fictitious creature. Include your own name and the date on your diagram.

Awards may be given for: Big Bug (Biggest)
Beautiful Bug (Most artistically done)
Best Bug (Most like a real insect)
Bright Bug (Most colorful and eye catching)
Bitty Bug (Smallest)

Ask for references at the library to get ideas for your *Build - a - Bug.*

GLOSSARY

abiotic — nonliving.

absorption — the process of passing through the wall of the intestine, or through a cell membrane.

adipose cells — cells of connective tissue that contain large amounts of fat.

adrenal glands — endocrine glands located at the top of the kidneys that produce adrenalin and cortisone.

adrenalin — a hormone produced by the adrenal medulla that prepares the body for emergencies.

aerobic — using oxygen gas from the air.

Agnatha — the class of jawless fish in the Phylum Chordata.

AIDS — acquired immune deficiency syndrome - a lethal, infectious disease that destroys the body's ability to fight off other diseases.

allergy — a condition in which the immune system over reacts to a substance.

alveoli — clusters of air sacs.

amino acid — a nitrogen containing acid in proteins.

Amphibia — the class of gilled then lunged vertebrates in Phylum Chordata.

amylase — an enzyme that begins digestion of starches.

anaerobic — not using oxygen gas from the air.

Angiospermae — "hidden seed"; a class of the phylum Tracheophyta with seeds inside a fruit; Ex. flowering plants.

Animalia — the kingdom of multicellular, heterotrophic creatures without cell walls.

Annelida — the phylum of segmented worms in the Kingdom Animalia.

annulus — the ring on the stipe of some mushrooms (root word see Appendix I).

anterior — front end.

antibiotic — chemicals from molds and bacteria that can kill microbes.

antibodies — any protein produced by an organism against invading pathogens.

antiseptic — a substance that stops or prohibits infection.

anus	the opening in the digestive tract through which wastes are excreted.
aorta	the main artery of the body that exits the left ventricle.
area	a measure, in square units, of the surface of a solid; area = length times width; abbreviated A.
arm	the "C" shaped part of a microscope that hold the body tube.
or	one of the two upper limbs on a primate.
artery	thick muscular blood vessels that carry blood away from the heart.
Arthropoda	the phylum of jointed legged animals with exoskeletons.
ascus	a sac like structure containing spores in some fungi; plural = asci.
asexual reproduction	the process of making a new organism from one parent.
assimilation	the process of taking in predigested materials.
associative neuron	a nerve cell located between other neurons that puts together impulses.
atom	the smallest part of an element with all the properties of the element.
ATP	adenosine triphosphate; a high energy molecule in cells.
atrium	either of the two thin walled upper chambers of the heart that receive blood from the veins.
auditory nerve	the nerve that connects the ear to the brain.
autotroph	"self feeder"; any organism capable of making its own food.
auxins	plant hormones.
Aves	the class of warmblooded, feathered animals in Phylum Chordata.
axon	the long thin part of a nerve cell.
bacterium	unicellular heterotroph without a nuclear membrane in the Kingdom Monera, Phylum Schizomycetes.
bark	thick layer of dead cork cells on the outside of woody stems.
basidia	club shaped structures on which spores form in some fungi; singular = basidium.
beef tapeworm	a parasitic member of phylum Platyhelminthes that infects humans, found in beef.
benedict's solution	a blue solution used to test for simple sugars.
bicuspid	a type of tooth with two points (cusps), for grinding food.

190

bilateral symmetry	may be cut into two similar parts.
bile	a digestive juice produced in the liver that emulsifies fats.
binary fission	a type of asexual reproduction in which a cell splits into two equal parts.
binomial nomenclature	a system of labelling using two names for each object; (root word see Appendix I).
biology	the study of living things; root see Appendix I.
biome	a very large ecosystem resulting from climatic factors.
biotic	living.
blindness	a condition in which a person cannot see.
blue green algae	unicellular autotroph without a nuclear membrane in the Kingdom Monera, Phylum Cyanophyta.
bone	cells of connective tissue containing hard calcium salts that support the body.
bronchial tubes	the branching air passages inside each lung.
bronchus	one of the two main branches that connect the trachea to the lungs.
Bryophyta	a phylum of the kingdom Plantae containing land plants with no vascular system.
budding	a form of asexual reproduction in which DNA is duplicated but only a tiny amount of cytoplasm is given to the daughter cell.
bulb	an underground stem with enlarged leaf bases; Ex. onion.
calorie	a basic metric unit equal to the amount of heat needed to raise one gram of water one degree Centigrade.
calorimeter	an instrument used to measure heat energy in calories.
cambium	a layer of cells between xylem and phloem that divide to make new cells.
cap	the umbrella shaped top of a mushroom.
capillary	microscopic blood vessels that connect the arteries to the veins.
carbohydrate	any carbon, oxygen and hydrogen compound with two hydrogen atoms for each oxygen atom.
cardiac	referring to the heart.
carnivore	meat eater.

cartilage	a rubber like connective tissue that acts like a shock absorber.
cell	the basic unit of structure and function of living things.
cell membrane	the thin, dense film of protoplasm that surrounds the cell; also called plasma membrane.
cellular respiration	the combining of oxygen and glucose in a cell to release energy with carbon dioxide and water as waste products.
cell wall	a stiff box of nonliving material that surrounds plant cells.
centi	the metric prefix meaning 1/100 th of the basic unit; abbreviated c; (root word see Appendix I).
centigrade	the degrees on a temperature scale with fixed points at 0 C and 100 C; also called Celsius degrees; (root word see Appendix I).
centrioles	a pair of spherical structures in the cytoplasm near the nucleus that function in cell division.
cerebrum	the largest part of the brain, it controls thinking.
cerebellum	the part of the brain that controls coordination and balance.
chemical digestion	the process of changing foods into smaller pieces of different chemicals.
chemotropism	a plant response to chemicals.
chitin	an insoluble chemical forming the cell walls of many fungi; the chemical in the exoskelton of arthropods.
chlorophyll	the green pigment (coloring) that captures sunlight in plants.
chloroplast	a plastid (bubble) in plant cells that contains chlorophyll.
Chondricthyes	the class of cartilagenous fish in the Phylum Chordata.
chromosome	a double strand of DNA, consisting of many genes, with the information to operate a cell.
cilia	tiny hair-like structures used for movement by some protists.
classes	subdivisions of a phylum.
cochlea	the snail shaped part of the inner ear that changes vibrations into impulses.
Coelenterata	the phylum of animals with bag like-bodies called jellyfish.
cold-blooded	any organism that cannot maintain its body temperature independent of the environment.
colony	a mass of bacteria large enough to see without a microscope.

compound	two or more elements chemically joined in a definite ratio.
conditioned reflex	a simple quick response in which the brain takes part.
cone cells	light receptors in the eye that are sensitive to color.
conifer	"cone bearer"; any plant that has cones.
conjugation	a type of sexual reproduction in which nuclear material is exchanged.
contractile vacuole	an organelle used for excretion in protists; the contractile vacuole has a star like appearance under the microscope.
convex lens	a lens that is thicker in the middle than at the edges.
convolutions	the bumps on the surface of the cerebrum.
cornea	the clear covering on the front of the eye.
corolla	all the petals of a flower together.
cortisone	a hormone produced by the adrenal cortex that regulates the body's use of sugar and the amount of cartilage at the joints.
cotyledon	a seed leaf.
cross pollination	the process of pollen from a different flower landing on the stigma.
cuspid	a type of tooth with one point (cusp), also called a canine tooth, for ripping meats.
cuticle	a waxy transparent layer on a leaf used for protection.
cyclosis	a circular movement of the cytoplasm in a cell.
cyton	the cell body of a neuron.
cytoplasm	the protoplasm outside of the nucleus.
deafness	a condition in which a person cannot hear.
deci	the metric prefix meaning 1/10 th of the basic unit; abbreviated d; (root see Appendix I).
deka	the metric prefix meaning 10 times the basic unit; abbreviated da.
dendrites	the branch like extensions on cytons.
dermis	the living layer of skin containing capillaries, glands and nerve cells.
diabetes	a disease caused by too much sugar in the blood since the body does not produce enough insulin.

193

dialysis	the separation of solutions by diffusion from higher to lower concentration.
diaphragm	the part of a microscope that controls the amount of light reaching the slide.
or	a dome shaped sheet of muscle separating the chest from the abdomen which is important in breathing.
dicot	any plant having two cotyledons in its seeds.
diffusion	movement of material from high to low concentration.
digestion	the process in which complex foods are changed into smaller, simple foods; See chemical digestion or mechanical digestion; (root of di- see Appendix I).
direct contact	disease transmission by touching a sick person or animal.
disaccharide	a complex sugar made of two sugar rings.
disease	any condition in which an organism cannot carry out one of the life functions properly.
DNA	deoxyribonucleic acid; the chemical instructions in the nuclei of cells.
dorsal	top or back.
droplets	tiny drops of liquid.
Echinodermata	the phylum of spiny skinned animals.
ecology	the study of the relationships between biotic and abiotic factors.
ecosystem	a community of organisms and all the abiotic factors needed to continue its existence.
effectors	muscles or glands that put nerve messages into effect.
egg	a large, nonmotile cell that has only one half the normal number of chromosomes; the female gamete.
electron	the negative part of an atom spinning in the energy shell, with almost no mass.
element	a simple substance that cannot be broken down by ordinary means.
endocrine system	a system of ductless glands that produce hormones.
endoplasmic reticulum	tube-like membranes that divide a cell's cytoplasm and provide a surface for chemical reactions.
energy shell	region around the nucleus of an atom where electrons may be found.
epidermis	the outer layer of skin.

epiglottis	a flap of tissue that covers the trachea during swallowing.
equation	a chemical sentence using symbols to represent the reactants and products in a chemical change.
esophagus	the smooth muscle tube that connects the pharynx to the stomach.
estivate	to become dormant in hot weather.
eustachian tube	a tube that connects the throat to the inner ear.
excretion	the life function of eliminating waste products; (root of ex- see Appendix I).
exhale	to breathe out.
expiration	the process of breathing out.
eyepiece	the lens on a microscope near the eye; also called - occular.
eyespot	a light sensitive organelle in Euglena sp.
families	subdivisions of an order.
far-sightedness	a condition in which a person can see only distant objects clearly.
fat	one of the nutrient groups also called lipids, which are giant, high energy molecules of carbon, hydrogen and oxygen with many more hydrogen atoms than oxygen atoms.
fertilization	the process of an egg and a sperm nuclei fusing together.
fibrinogen	a protein in the blood that forms fibers when platelets initiate a clot.
fibrous root	a root system made of many small roots nearly equal in size.
Filicineae	a class of the phylum Tracheophyta containing plants that do not produce seeds; Ex. ferns.
filtrate	the liquid that passes through a filter.
flagellum	a whip like protein fiber used for locomotion.
food chain	a simplified energy relationship from producers through consumers to decomposers.
food web	energy relationships involving many interlinked food chains.
frond	the fan like leaf of a fern.
Fungi	the kingdom containing hetertrophic organisms with chitinous cell walls.
gall bladder	a balloon like organ that stores bile.

gametes	sex cells, either sperm or egg.
gas	the highest energy phase of matter, with no definite shape and no definite volume. Ex. steam.
genera	subdivisions of a family; the first half of a scientific name; singular = genus.
genetics	the study of how genes transmit traits to the next generation.
geotropism	a plant response to gravity.
germination	the process of a plant beginning to grow.
gill	thin flaps on the underside of a mushroom's cap where spores are produced. or a feathery organ, full of capillaries, used by fish and immature forms of amphibians and some insects to exchange gases under water.
glomerulus	the knot of capillaries in the capsule of a nephron where filtration occurs.
glucagon	a hormone produced in the pancreas that controls the discharge of glucose from the liver.
glucose	a simple sugar, $C_6H_{12}O_6$, also called blood sugar.
glycogen	a starch made of many glucose molecules fastened together.
golgi body	the part of a cell that makes, stores and secretes mucus in animals and cellulose in plants.
graduation	carefully inscribed markings on a measuring instrument.
gram	the basic unit of mass in the metric system (S.I.); abbreviated g.
growth	the process in which cells increase in size or number.
Gymnospermae	"naked seed"; a class of the phylum tracheophyta characterized by plants with seeds not inside a fruit; Ex. conifers.
habitat	the special place where an organism lives.
heat	the amount of energy available for transfer.
heart	the muscular organ in the chest cavity that pumps the blood.
hecto	the metric prefix meaning 100 times the basic unit; abbreviated h.
hemoglobin	a protein in the blood that carries the oxygen in the red blood cells.
hemophilia	a noninfectious genetic disease in which the blood does not clot properly.
herbaceous stem	the nonwoody, green stem of annuals and biennials.
herbivore	plant eater.

heterotrophic	other feeder; any organism that cannot make its own food.
hibernate	to become dormant in cold weather.
hiccups	spasms of the diaphragm that force short bursts of air out of the lungs.
hormones	chemical messengers that regulate body activity.
host	an organism that is attacked by a parasite or pathogen.
humus	dark, decayed organic matter in topsoil.
hybrid	an organism with two different genes for the same trait.
hydrotropism	a plants response to water.
hyphae	a thread like filament of fungal cells.
immunity	the ability of the body to resist disease.
impulse	an electrical nerve message.
incisor	a type of tooth shaped liked a chisel for cutting off herbaceous foods.
indirect contact	disease transmission by use of articles used by a sick person.
infectious	able to be transmitted from one to another.
inferior vena cava	the major vein from the lower part of the body.
ingestion	the process of taking in food that is already manufactured; (root word in- see Appendix I).
inhale	to breathe in.
insectivore	insect eater.
inspiration	the process of breathing in.
instinct	a built in series of actions directed toward a specific end result.
insulin	a hormone made in the Islands of Langerhans that regulates the use of glucose in the cells.
involuntary	not able to be controlled by the conscious mind.
IPMAT	an acronym for remembering the stages of mitosis; interphase, prophase, metaphase, anaphase, and telophase.
iris	the "colored" part of the eye that adjusts the size of the pupil.

irritability	the ability to respond to stimuli; also referred to as sensitivity.
Islands of Langerhans	patches of tissue in the pancreas that produce insulin.
joint	the point where two bones meet; immovable, ball and socket, hinge or gliding.
kilo	the metric prefix meaning 1000 times the basic unit; abbreviated k.
kingdoms	the 5 largest taxons in our modern system of classification.
lacteal	a small lymph vessel inside a villus that absorbs fatty acids and glycerol.
large intestine	a short thick section of the digestive tract where water is absorbed.
larva	an immature form in many kinds of animals; larval insects are also called caterpillers.
larynx	the voice box, made of cartilage, that contains vocal cords.
learning	the process of using experiences to determine future responses to stimuli.
lenticel	a small opening in the bark of young stems for gas exchange.
ligament	a fibrous connective tissue that holds bone to bone.
liquid	the phase of matter with no definite shape but with a definite volume. Ex. water.
liter	the basic unit of liquid volume in the S.I.; abbreviated l.
liver	the largest organ of the body that produces bile and takes part in other metabolic activities.
lugol's solution	a brown solution used to test for starch.
lung	a sack like organ, rich in capillaries used by mammals, birds reptiles and mature amphibians to exchange gases in the air.
lung cancer	a noninfectious, environmental disease caused by smoking.
lysosome	small bubble like parts in a cell that contain digestive enzymes and may help in defense against disease.
macronucleus	a large nucleus in paramecium that controls cell metabolism.
malaria	an infectious disease transmitted by an animal vector, the female Anopheles mosquito.
Mammalia	the class of warm blooded, milk producing animals that are covered with hair.

198

marrow	the soft center of the long bones where red and white blood cells are made.
mass	the amount of matter in an object.
mechanical digestion	the process of breaking food down into smaller pieces of the same material.
medulla	the part of the brain that controls involuntary actions.
mega	the metric prefix meaning 1 000 000 times the basic unit; abbreviated **M**.
meiosis	special cell division in the gonads that reduces the number of chromosomes by one half.
meniscus	the curved surface of a liquid in a small container.
metabolism	the sum total of all life functions.
metamorphosis	the process of changing shape.
meter	the basic unit of length in the S.I.; abbreviated m; (root see Appendix I).
meter stick	an instrument used to measure length that is graduated into 10, 100, and 1000 divisions of the meter.
metric system	the common name for the Systemae International (S.I.), a decimal system of measurement.
micro	the metric prefix meaning 1/1 000 000 th of the basic unit; abbreviated u; (root word see Appendix I).
micron	a unit of length equal to .001 mm; also called a micrometer; abbreviated um (root word see Appendix I).
micronucleus	a small nucleus in paramecium that takes part in sexual reproduction (conjugation).
micro-organism	an organism too small to be seen without a microscope.
milli	the metric prefix meaning 1/1000 th of the basic unit; abbreviated m; (root word see Appendix I).
mineral	an element needed by a living system in small amounts.
mitochondrion	a cell organelle containing a folded membrane where energy in the form of ATP is made available to the cell (pl. mitochondria).
mitosis	regular cell division in which two new cells are formed, both with a complete set of chromosomes.
mixture	two or more substances together in any ratio, each keeping its own characteristics.
molar	a type of large, broad, flat tooth for crushing food.

199

molecule	the smallest part of a compound with all the properties of the compound.
Mollusca	the phylum of soft bodied animals, most with a hard shell.
Monera	the kingdom containing organisms without nuclear membranes and without organelles.
monocot	any plant having one cotyledon in its seed.
monosaccharide	a simple sugar made of one ring.
motor neuron	a nerve cell that sends impulses out to muscles or glands.
mucus	a sticky secretion that lines much of the respiratory, reproductive and digestive tracts.
multicellular	many celled.
mushroom	some members of the Kingdom Fungi, Phylum Basidiomycota.
muteness	a condition in which a person cannot speak.
mutualism	a symbiotic relationship which benefits both organisms; represented as (+,+).
mycelium	a mass of fungal hyphae.
mycologist	a person who studies fungi.
nearsightedness	a condition in which a person can see only nearby objects clearly.
Nematoda	the phylum of round worms in the Kingdom Animalia.
nephron tubules	the long thin part of a nephron where reabsorption occurs.
nephrons	a part of the kidney with capsules containing capillaries and tubules that filter blood.
neuron	a nerve cell.
neurotransmitter	a chemical that carries a nerve message across a synapse.
neutron	the neutral part of an atom in the nucleus, with a mass of 1 amu.
niche	the occupation of an organism in a community.
nodule	a small bump on the root of a legume containing nitrogen fixing bacteria.
noninfectious	not able to be transmitted from one to another.
nosepiece	the part of a microscope that holds the objective lenses.
nostrils	the openings in the nose.

nuclear membrane	the thin film that controls what enters or leaves the nucleus.
nucleus	the dense center region of an atom.
or	the dense round structure in a cell that controls cell activity.
nutrient	any substance needed by a living thing.
nutrition	the process of getting and using food.
nymph	an immature form of an animal that undergoes incomplete metamorphosis.
objective	the lense on a microscope that is near the object.
olfactory nerve	the nerve that connects the nose to the brain.
omnivore	an animal that eats all kinds of food.
optic nerve	the nerve that connects the eye to the brain.
orders	subdivisions of a class.
organ	a group of tissues working together to do a single function.
organism	any living thing.
osmosis	the diffusion of water through a membrane.
Osteichthyes	the class of bony fish in the Phylum Chordata.
ovaries	the female gonads that produce egg cells.
oxidation	the process of oxygen combining with another substance.
palisade layer	a layer of tall cells in a leaf where most photosynthesis takes place.
pancreas	a glandular organ that secretes pancreatic juice, insulin and glucagon.
parasitism	a symbiotic relationship that benefits one organism and harms the other; represented as (+,-).
pasteurization	the process of heating milk or another liquid to kill bacteria.
pathogens	any disease causing organisms.
pellicle	a stiff cell membrane that gives shape to paramecium and euglena.
pepsin	an enzyme in gastric juice that begins the chemical digestion of protein.
periosteum	literally "near the bone"; the lining that surrounds and nourishes a bone.
peristalsis	rhythmic, wave like contractions of the digestive tract.
phagocytes	white blood cells that ingest pathogens.

pharynx	the region at the back of the nose and mouth above the esophagus.
phloem	tube like cells that transport food in a plant.
photosynthesis	the process in which plants use light to make food; (root see Appendix I).
phototropism	a plant response to light.
phyla	subdivisions of a kingdom; singular = phylum.
pigment	any coloring substance.
pinworm	a parasite member of Phylum Nematoda that infects humans causing uncomfortable itching.
pistil	all the female parts of a flower.
pith	storage cells in the center of a stem.
pituitary gland	a tiny gland at the base of the brain that is called the master gland.
placenta	a capillary rich organ formed by mammalian embryos to allow diffusion of food and wastes to and from the unborn and its mother.
Plantae	the kingdom containing autotrophic organisms with cellulose cell walls.
plasma	the liquid part of the blood.
platelet	a colorless partial cell in the blood that begins the clotting process.
Platyhelminthes	the phylum of flat worms in the Kingdom Animalia.
pollination	the process of pollen being transferred from the anther to the stigma.
polysaccharide	many sugar molecules fastened into a long chain to form a starch molecule.
pore	a small opening.
Porifera	the phylum of pore bearing animals called sponges.
posterior	rear end.
precipitate	a solid that forms and falls to the bottom of a test tube when two liquids react.
primary consumer	organisms that eat producers.
producers	green plants.
protein	one of the nutrient groups; long chains of amino acids.
Protista	the kingdom containing unicellular, or very simple, organisms with nuclear membranes and organelles.

proton	the positive part of an atom in the nucleus, with a mass of 1 amu.
protoplasm	living matter.
pseudopod	a projection of the cytoplasm of ameboid protists used for locomotion; root see Appendix I.
pulmonary artery	either of the arteries that carry oxygen poor blood from the heart to the lungs.
pulmonary circulation	the path of blood vessels from the heart to the lungs and back to the heart.
pulmonary vein	any of the veins that carry oxygen rich blood back to the heart from the lungs.
puncture	a small but very deep wound.
pupa	an immature, resting stage of an organism that undergoes complete metamorphosis.
pure	an organism with the same genes for a given trait.
pylorus	a ring like muscle that closes the lower end of the stomach.
pyrenoid	a starch storage area in algae.
radial symmetry	may be cut along the radii of a circle into similar parts.
reasoning	the process of using learning to solve new problems.
receptors	the parts of a sensory organ that receive input from the environment.
rectum	the storage area for solid waste at the end of the large intestine.
red cell	disk shaped cells in the blood, containing hemoglobin for carrying oxygen.
regeneration	the process of growing again a missing part of the body.
reproduction	the life process necessary for the species in which living things produce more of their own kind.
Reptilia	the class of scaly skinned animals with lungs.
residue	the solid caught in a filter.
respiration	external - the taking in of oxygen and release of carbon dioxide; also called breathing.
or	internal - the process of getting energy by linking oxygen with food; also called oxidation.
response	the movement of a muscle or gland due to an impulse from a motor neuron.

retina	the photosensitive tissue that lines the inside, back of the eye.
rhizoid	thin root like structure on fungi, mosses and ferns.
rhizome	an underground, horizontal stem that can produce a new plant.
ribosome	a small dot-like organelle on the endoplasmic reticulum where proteins are made.
ringworm	an infectious fungus that produces a ring like depression in the skin.
RNA	ribonucleic acid; a chemical in the cytoplasm that has part of the instructions from the DNA.
rod cells	light receptors in the eye for black and white vision.
root cap	specialized cells that protect the tip of a root.
root hairs	elongated epidermal root cells used for absorption.
saliva	a secretion from the glands in the walls of the mouth containing amylase.
saprophytism	a relationship in which an organism uses dead organisms as a food source.
scurvy	a noninfectious disease caused by lack of vitamin C.
secondary consumers	organisms that eat primary consumers.
seed dispersal	the scattering of seeds.
self pollination	the process of pollen from the same flower landing on the stigma.
semicircular canals	three fluid filled loops inside each ear that send impulses to the cerebellum for balance.
semipermeable	able to be penetrated by some molecules but not by others.
sensory neuron	a nerve cell that sends impulses into the brain.
septum	the wall of cardiac muscle that separates the left and right sides of the heart.
sessile	attached by the base.
sexual reproduction	the process of making a new individual from two parents.
simple goiter	a swelling of the thyroid gland.
small intestine	the longest organ of the body in which digestion is completed and absorption occurs.
solid	the lowest energy phase of matter with a definite shape and a definite volume. Ex. ice.

soluble	able to dissolve.
solute	the substance that dissolves, usually the smaller amount.
solvent	the substance that does the dissolving, usually water.
sori	clusters of sporangia on the undersides of fronds; singular - sorus.
species	the smallest taxons, divisions of a genus; second half of a scientific name; one kind of organism.
sperm	a small motile cell that has only one half the normal number of chromosomes; the male gamete.
spongy layer	a loosely packed layer of cells in a leaf where gas exchange takes place.
sporangia	structures in which spores are made.
spore	a tiny thick walled structure of a bacterium formed when environmental conditions become unfavorable. or an asexual reproductive cell that can produce a new fungus, moss or fern.
sporulation	a method of asexual reproduction in which a spore produces a new organism.
stage	the flat part of a microscope on which the slide is placed.
stamen	all the male parts of a flower.
stimulus	anything that causes a sensory neuron to send an impulse.
stipe	the stem like part of a mushroom.
stolon	a thin, often fan shaped, sheet of fungal hyphae.
stomach	an organ that holds food for two to five hours and mixes it with gastric juice.
stomate	an opening in the lower epidermis of a leaf.
stool	the solid matter excreted from the rectum.
striations	bands or lines.
superior vena cava	the major vein from the upper part of the body that enters the right atrium.
sweat glands	tiny coiled tubes in the skin that form perspiration for excretion through pores.
synapse	the microscopic space between a dendrite and another nerve cell.
synthesis	the process of making useful chemicals in an organism.
system	a group of organs working together to do the same function.

systemic circulation	the path of blood vessels from the heart to all systems of the body and back to the heart.
tap root	a root system with one very large central root.
taste buds	bumps on the tongue and sides of the mouth that contain nerve cells sensitive to sweet, sour, salt and bitter.
taxon	group.
taxonomy	the science of naming an organism's taxons; (see Appendix I).
temperature	how hot or cold compared to a standard.
tendon	a fibrous connective tissue that connects bone to muscle or muscle to muscle.
tentacle	a long soft appendage of the invertebrates, sometimes with nematocysts or suction cups.
tetanus	an anaerobic infectious disease called lockjaw that is spread by puncture wounds.
tethelin	the growth hormone produced by the pituitary.
thigmotropism	a plant response to touch.
thyroid gland	an endocrine gland located on each side of the windpipe that secretes thyroxin.
thyroxin	the hormone produced by the thyroid gland that regulates metabolism.
tongue	a thick muscular organ in the mouth.
trachea	the wind pipe, a cartilage reinforced tube from the pharynx to the bronchi.
Tracheophyta	a phylum of the kingdom Plantae containing plants with a vascular system.
translucent	anything that allows light to pass through but cannot be seen through clearly.
transpiration	the process of water evaporating from a plant.
transport	the life function that includes the absorption and distribution of materials sometimes called circulation.
testes	the male gonads that produce sperm cells.
trichocysts	barbed projections used by a paramecium for defense.
tropism	a general term for plant responses.
tuber	a short, enlarged, underground stem specialized for storage; Ex. potato.

unconditioned reflex	a simple quick response that does not require the brain, a simple reflex.
unicellular	one celled.
unit	the label part of a measurement that specifies the quantity being measured.
urea	a colorless nitrogen compound eliminated by the kidneys as waste.
ureters	the two ducts that lead from each kidney to the urinary bladder.
urethra	the one duct that leads from the urinary bladder to the outside of the body.
urinary bladder	a balloon like organ in the lower abdomen that stores urine.
urinary tract	all the parts of the body that form and eliminate urine.
urine	a mixture of water, nitrogen wastes and other soluble compounds formed in the kidneys for elimination.
vaccine	any substance used to give immunity from specific diseases when injected.
vacuoles	bubble like parts of a cell that may contain air or food.
vascular system	the fibers and xylem and phloem tissues of a plant which form a system for transport of liquids.
vector	an organism that carries a pathogen from one host to another.
vegetative propagation	a method of asexual reproduction in which a part of one plant is used to produce another plant.
vein	thin walled blood vessels with valves that carry blood back to the heart.
ventral	underside or bottom.
ventricle	either of the two lower, muscular chambers of the heart that pumps blood into the arteries.
Vertebrata	a subphylum of Phylum Chordata containing all organisms with vertebrae forming a backbone.
villus	a finger like projection of the lining of the small intestine that absorbs digested nutrients.
vitamin	an organic compound needed by a living system in small amounts.
virus	a DNA or RNA particle, usually with a protein coat, able to take over a host cell's metabolism.
vocal cords	two thin membranes in the larynx that cause sound when vibrated.
volume	a measure in cubic units of the amount of space an object takes up; volume = length times width times height; abbreviated V.

207

88, 95, 125,

27,

132

voluntary	able to be controlled by the conscious mind.
volva	a cup like structure at the base of a mushroom's stipe.
warm blooded	any organism that maintains a steady body temperature regardless of environmental temperatures (within limits).
water	a low energy chemical made of two hydrogen atoms and one oxygen atom; also called hydrogen oxide.
white cell	ameboid cells in the blood that engulf and destroy pathogens.
woody stem	dead xylem and fibers surrounded by the xylem and phloem of a perennial.
xylem	straw like cells that carry water and minerals upward in vascular plants.
zygote	the new, individual produced by fusion of a sperm cell and an egg cell.

Pink Ladyslipper is one of the species of rare and protected plants of New York State.

INDEX

Crossword Puzzle Answers
The crossword puzzles are located at the beginning of each chapter.

Chapter 5 - Life Science
All Creatures Great and Small

Chapter 2 - Life Science
All Creatures Great and Small

Chapter 1 - Life Science
All Creatures Great and Small

Chapter 6 - Life Science
All Creatures Great and Small

Chapter 4 - Life Science
All Creatures Great and Small

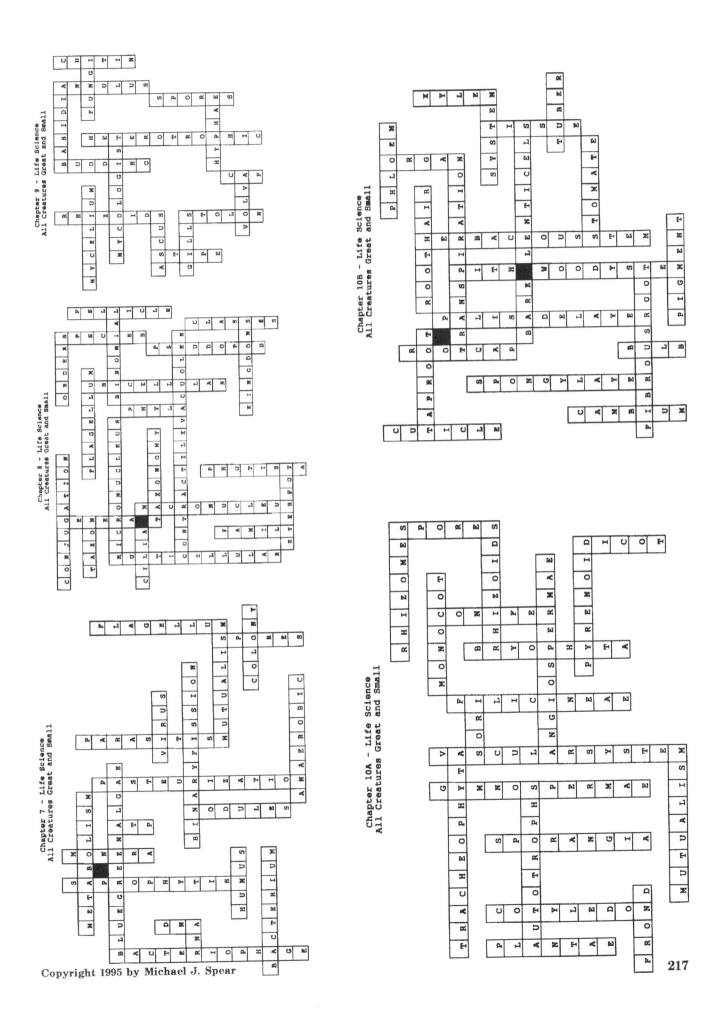

Chapter 7 - Life Science
All Creatures Great and Small

Chapter 8 - Life Science
All Creatures Great and Small

Chapter 9 - Life Science
All Creatures Great and Small

Chapter 10A - Life Science
All Creatures Great and Small

Chapter 10B - Life Science
All Creatures Great and Small

217

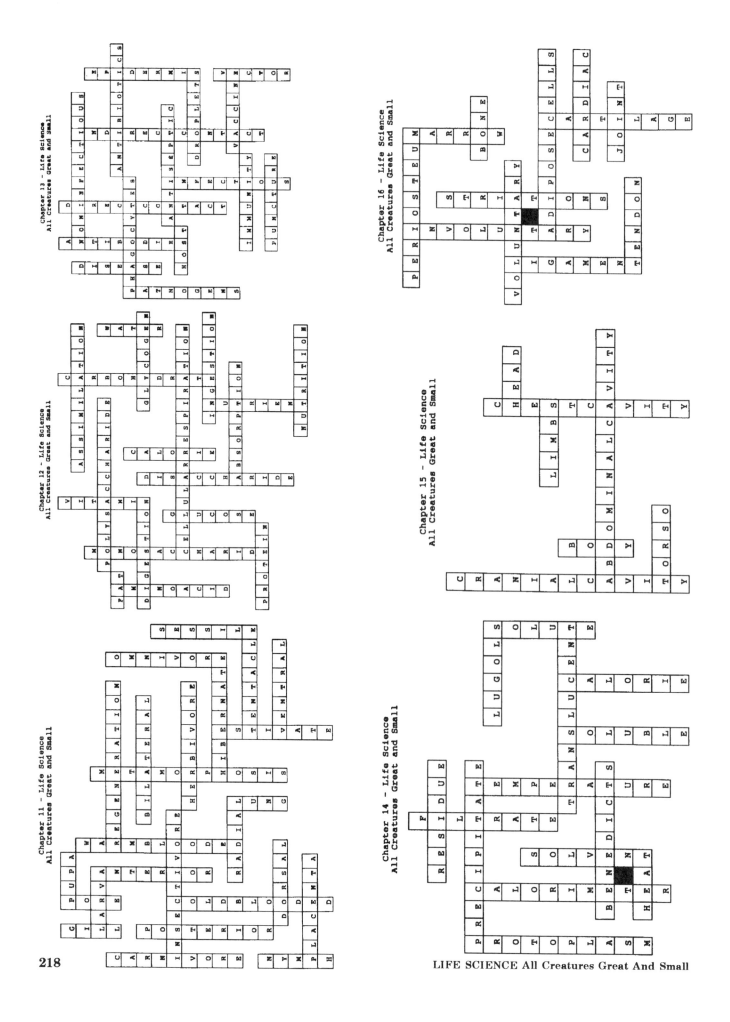

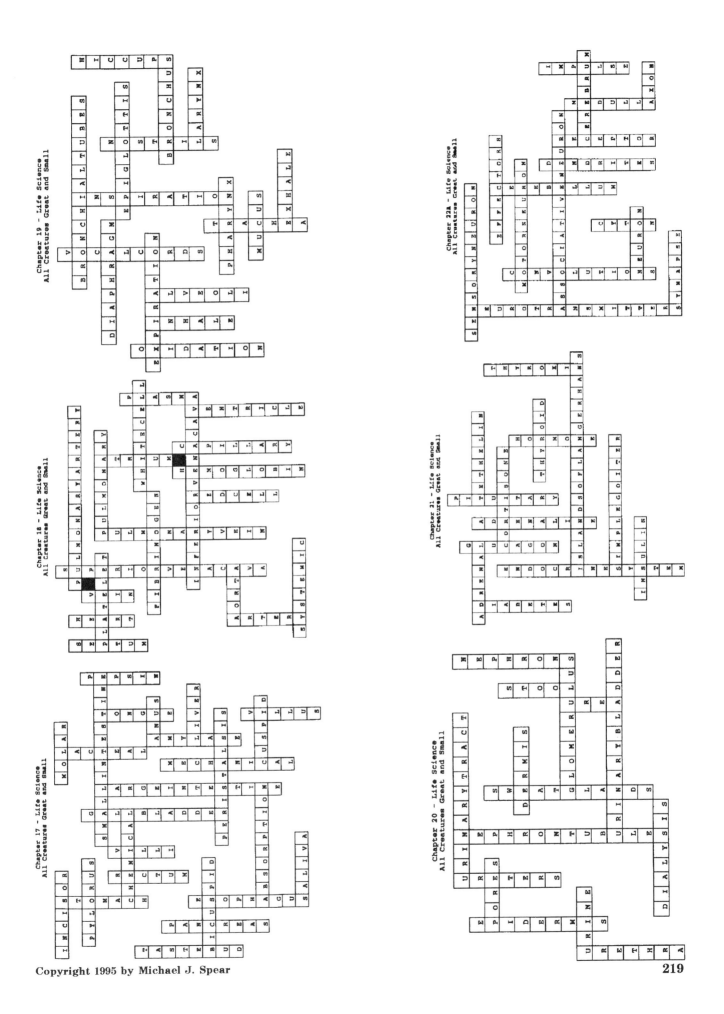

Chapter 17 - Life Science
All Creatures Great and Small

Chapter 18 - Life Science
All Creatures Great and Small

Chapter 19 - Life Science
All Creatures Great and Small

Chapter 20 - Life Science
All Creatures Great and Small

Chapter 21 - Life Science
All Creatures Great and Small

Chapter 22A - Life Science
All Creatures Great and Small

Chapter 22 contains so much information that it is divided into two parts, A and B. The puzzle for part A appears at the beginning of the chapter, here is the B puzzle.

DOWN

2. The nerve from the ear to the brain.
3. A snail shaped part of the ear.
6. A tube connecting the ear to the pharynx.
7. The nerve from the eye to the brain.
10. A condition in which only far objects are seen clearly.
12. The clear covering of the eye.
13. Color receptors in the eye.
14. The inability to speak.

LIFE – depends on each one of us!

ACROSS

1. The eye focuses too near the lens.
4. Cells for black and white vision.
5. Unable to hear.
8. Nerve from the nose to the brain.
9. Light sensitive area in the eye.
11. Three loops inside each ear.
15. The inability to see.
16. A lens that is thicker in the middle than at the edges.
17. The colored part of the eye.

LIFE SCIENCE All Creatures Great And Small

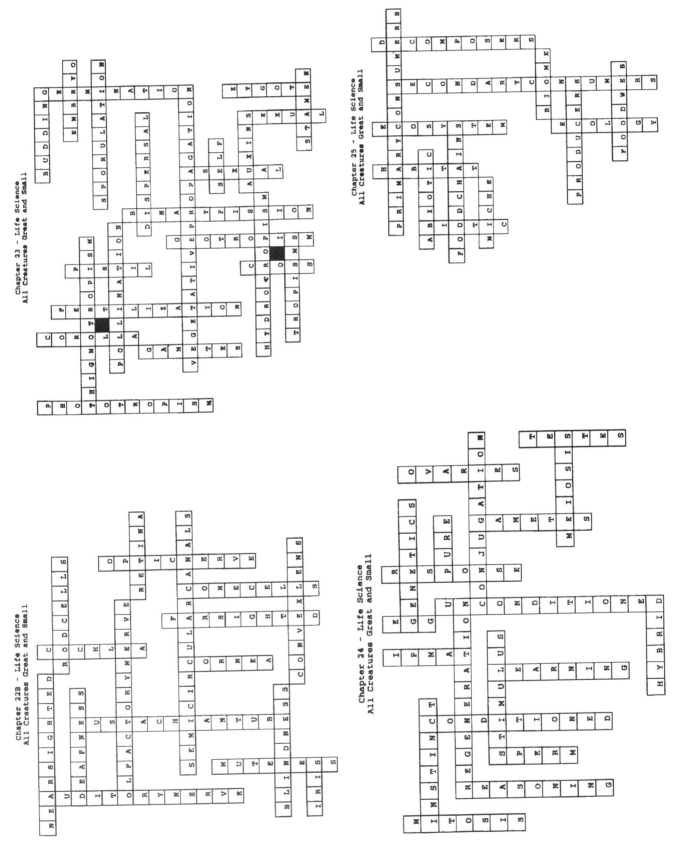

Chapter 23 - Life Science
All Creatures Great and Small

Chapter 22B - Life Science
All Creatures Great and Small

Chapter 25 - Life Science
All Creatures Great and Small

Chapter 24 - Life Science
All Creatures Great and Small

221

BALD EAGLE
(Haliaeetus leucocephalus)

HOW BIG IS IT? Length—to 3½ feet (1.1 m); Weight—to 14 lbs. (6.4 kg); Wingspan—to 8 feet (2.4 m).

WHAT DOES IT EAT? Mostly fish such as salmon, eels, lake trout, and carp. Also small mammals and birds, including rabbits, grebes, and injured waterfowl.

WHERE DOES IT LIVE? Only in North America, with a large concentration in Alaska. Also found in most of the lower 48 states and in Canada, nesting close to lakes, rivers, and marshes in wild, remote areas.

DID YOU KNOW? The bald eagle is not really bald at all! The word bald comes from the Old English word "balde" which means white and refers to the white feathers covering the head of the mature bald eagle.

BALD EAGLE—EAGLET
(Haliaeetus leucocephalus)

WHAT TYPE OF NEST? Bald eagles nest close to lakes and rivers, building nests (aeries), usually in tall trees, out of large sticks. The nest is lined with grasses and usually contains several fresh green sprigs.

WHAT KIND OF EGG? The female lays one to three white, rough-shelled eggs averaging 2.7 in. (6.9 cm) by 2.1 in. (5.3 cm).

HOW LONG IS ITS INCUBATION PERIOD? 34 to 35 days.

DID YOU KNOW? A famous eagle nest in Vermilion, Ohio, was built 81 feet (24 m) from the ground and had been occupied by a pair of eagles every year for thirty-six years. The nest was 12 feet (3.6 m) tall, 8½ feet (2.6 m) in diameter, and weighed two tons (1.8 metric tons) before it was blown down in a violent storm.

SOCKEYE SALMON
(Oncorhynchus nerka)

HOW BIG IS IT? Length—to 33 in. (84 cm); Weight—averages 5 lbs. (2.3 kg).

WHAT DOES IT EAT? Plankton, shrimp, and other small forms of aquatic and marine life.

WHERE DOES IT LIVE? Along the coasts of the Aleutian Islands, to Los Angeles Harbor, California. Rather abundant, especially in British Columbia and Washington State. In salt water around islands, stream entrances, and swift currents.

DID YOU KNOW? From the time salmon leave the sea to return to the river of their birth for spawning (laying and fertilizing eggs) they stop eating—completely—even if food is abundant. They live on energy stored in their body tissues and off of their body fat. They may go for months without eating.

CONIFEROUS FOREST

WHAT IS IT? A forest with vegetation consisting primarily of cone-bearing, needle-leaved or scale-leaved evergreen trees found in regions of the world that have long, very cold winters and high annual precipitation.

WHAT LIVES THERE? In the U.S., trees such as aspens, alders, spruces, firs, larches, hemlocks and other northern-growing trees. A variety of animals including moose, elk, black-tailed deer, weasel, squirrels, jays, crossbills and grosbeaks.

WHERE IS IT? Mainly in the cold northern lands known as the Boreal Zone (from the Greek word "Boreas," meaning north wind) and on the cool slopes of mountains in warmer areas.

DID YOU KNOW? The leaves of coniferous trees such as the black spruce stay green year-round and are specially adapted to withstand the cold weather, ice, and snow. The leaves' tough tissues and low water content keep them from freezing.

GOLDEN EAGLE
(Aquila chrysaetos)

HOW BIG IS IT? Length—to 3 feet (.9 m); Weight—to 16 lbs. (7.3 kg); Wingspan—to 7 feet (2.1 m).

WHAT DOES IT EAT? Small mammals, birds, snakes, and fish. Also eats a large amount of carrion when live prey is scarce.

WHERE DOES IT LIVE? In North America from northern Alaska and Canada, south to North Carolina and Tennessee, Texas, and Mexico. From northern Scandanavia and Siberia, south to Spain and northern Africa.

DID YOU KNOW? The golden eagle is the only "booted eagle" in the New World. It is called booted because it has short, light brown feathers all the way down to its toes.

GOLDEN EAGLE—EAGLET
(Aquila chrysaetos)

WHAT TYPE OF NEST? The golden eagle's nest is built on inaccessible crags and cliff faces and occasionally in trees. It is made of sticks, twigs, brush, roots, and even bits of trash, with a lining of grasses, leaves, soft mosses, and lichens.

WHAT KIND OF EGG? The female lays one to three white, thick-shelled eggs spotted red, gray, and brown. Eggs average 3 in. (7.6 cm) by 2.3 in. (5.8 cm).

HOW LONG IS THE INCUBATION PERIOD? 28 to 35 days.

DID YOU KNOW? Indians of the southwest United States valued the golden eagle's feathers. They would take a golden eagle from its nest, raise it in captivity, and collect the feathers whenever the eagle molted (shed its feathers).

BLACK-TAILED JACK RABBIT
(Lepus californicus)

HOW BIG IS IT? Length—to 21 in. (53 cm); Weight—to 7 lbs. (3.2 kg).

WHAT DOES IT EAT? Mainly grass, and plants such as sagebrush, snakeweed, and sometimes cactus and mesquite.

WHERE DOES IT LIVE? In arid country from Oregon to Mexico, and eastward to Texas.

DID YOU KNOW? The jack rabbit's long ears function like the radiator of an automobile. Its body cools off by releasing heat through the many blood vessels close to the surface of its ears.

SNAKE RIVER CANYON, IDAHO

WHAT IS IT? A canyon formed during the past two million years by the Snake River cutting through layers of rock to depths of 800 feet (244 m). The environment of the river-canyon is generally very dry or arid.

WHAT LIVES THERE? Deep soils, shrub-grass vegetation and the river support more than 250 species of animals including mule deer, a variety of raptors (birds of prey), coyotes, badgers, skunks, rabbits, ground squirrels, snakes, lizards, toads, and fish.

WHERE IS IT? In southwestern Idaho, in the Snake River Birds of Prey Natural Area.

DID YOU KNOW? The mix of geographic location, geology, climate, soils, and the plant and animal populations in this area create an ideal nesting area for birds of prey. Approximately 600 pairs of raptors nest within an 81 mile reach of the canyon.

Reprinted from the 1981 National Wildlife Week poster from the National Wildlife Federation, Washington, D.C.

BATELEUR EAGLE
(Terathopius ecaudatus)

HOW BIG IS IT? Length—to 2 feet (.6 m); Weight—to 6½ lbs. (3 kg); Wingspan—to 6 feet (1.8 m).

WHAT DOES IT EAT? Mainly snakes, also small mammals and birds, reptiles, and carrion (dead animals).

WHERE DOES IT LIVE? In Africa, throughout open forest and savanna.

DID YOU KNOW? Some African tribes believe the bateleur never comes to the ground. Bateleurs fly for many hours a day, about 200 to 400 feet (61 to 122 m) above ground, at a speed of 35 to 50 miles per hour (56 to 80 km). It has been estimated that they fly 200 to 300 miles (322 to 483 km) daily.

BATELEUR EAGLE—EAGLET
(Terathopius ecaudatus)

WHAT TYPE OF NEST? This eagle builds its nest in acacias and other broad-topped trees, often near footpaths or elephant trails. The nest is composed of coarse sticks, and lined with grasses.

WHAT KIND OF EGG? The female lays one large, rough-shelled egg, generally all white, but occasionally marked with red or purple. Eggs average 3 in. (7.6 cm) by 2.4 in. (6.1 cm).

HOW LONG IS ITS INCUBATION PERIOD? 43 to 55 days.

DID YOU KNOW? Bateleur means "tumbler" or "tightrope walker." This eagle received its name because it performs siderolls, somersaults, and other acrobatics as it flies.

PUFF ADDER
(Bitis arietans)

HOW BIG IS IT? Length—to 5 feet (1.5 m); Girth—to 9 in. (23 cm).

WHAT DOES IT EAT? Rats, mice, and cold-blooded prey such as frogs.

WHERE DOES IT LIVE? Throughout Africa, except on the northern coast. Also found on the Arabian peninsula. Prefers savanna or semi-desert environment.

DID YOU KNOW? The puff adder is a very poisonous snake that gets its name from its habit of inflating itself and hissing violently when it is alarmed.

SAVANNA

WHAT IS IT? A grass covered plain with widely spaced trees, found in many areas of the tropics where annual rainy seasons alternate with periods of drought.

WHAT LIVES THERE? Grass outproduces all other plant life; small shrubs, fig trees, baobab trees, camel foot trees, acacias, and cork trees also grow there. Animals include baboons, buffalo, zebras, gazelles, leopards, puff adders and other snakes, hawks, swallows, and hornbills.

WHERE IS IT? In Africa between the extremes of rain forest and desert.

DID YOU KNOW? A tree called the "upside down" tree grows on the savanna and is one of the tallest trees there. The tree's actual name is baobab tree, but it gets its nickname because its gnarled, often leafless branches resemble dry roots projecting out of the ground.

PHILIPPINE EAGLE
(Pithecophaga jefferyi)

HOW BIG IS IT? Length—to 3½ feet (1.1 m); Weight—to 16 lbs. (7.3 kg); Wingspan—to 7 feet (2.1 m).

WHAT DOES IT EAT? Mainly flying lemurs, palm civets, hornbills, monkeys, and squirrels.

WHERE DOES IT LIVE? In the subtropical rain forests of the Eastern Philippine Islands of Mindanao, Luzon, Leyte, and Samar.

DID YOU KNOW? The Philippine eagle is the national symbol of the Philippines and until recently was known as the monkey-eating eagle. After a recent scientific study noted that this large bird of prey rarely eats monkeys, President Marcos decreed the name change for his nation's symbol.

PHILIPPINE EAGLE—EAGLET
(Pithecophaga jefferyi)

WHAT TYPE OF NEST? The Philippine eagle builds its nest in the canopy (uppermost spreading branchy layer) of the rain forest, in tall trees such as the giant kapok. Its nest is a huge platform of sticks, lined with leaves, which may be occupied year after year.

WHAT KIND OF EGG? The female lays one white egg every two years. No published information on the size of this eagle's egg is available.

HOW LONG IS ITS INCUBATION PERIOD? Approximately 60 days.

DID YOU KNOW? The Philippine eagle, only discovered in 1896, is one of the most threatened of all the world's eagles. Recent research estimates that only 300 to 500 of these eagles remain in the wild. Destruction of forest habitat and collection by trophy seekers, zoos, and museums are the main causes for this raptor's (bird of prey) decline.

COMMON PALM CIVET
(Paradoxurus hermaphroditus)

HOW BIG IS IT? Length—to 21 in. (53 cm); Weight—to 10 lbs. (4.5 kg).

WHAT DOES IT EAT? Birds, small mammals, reptiles, locusts, worms, bird eggs, and fruits.

WHERE DOES IT LIVE? In Africa and southern Asia in a wide variety of habitats ranging from wilderness to human settlements.

DID YOU KNOW? Like the skunk, the palm civet lets out a strong, offensive odor from glands at the back of its body when it is threatened by a predator.

PHILIPPINE RAIN FOREST

WHAT IS IT? A dense evergreen forest in the Philippines characterized by broad-leaved trees. The climate is usually humid with abundant rainfall of more than 100 in. (254 cm) annually.

WHAT LIVES THERE? Small ferns, orchids and other epiphytes (plants that grow on other plants), kapok trees, eucalyptus, Philippine mahogany, and other broadleaf evergreen trees, and animals including flying lemurs, flying squirrels, several species of bats, and palm civets.

WHERE IS IT? Major islands of the Philippines, including Luzon, Samar, Mindanao, and Leyte.

DID YOU KNOW? Most of the leaves in rain forests have pointed ends that look like arrowheads. These are called "drip tips" and they allow the heavy rains to run off the surface of the leaves.